Families in Rehabilitation Counseling

Michael J. Millington, PhD, CRC, is currently the course director and senior lecturer in the rehabilitation counseling discipline at the University of Sydney, Sydney, Australia. He collaborates in family and community projects in the Asia/Oceania region through the university and within its association with the Centre for Disability Research and Policy. His 25-year career in the rehabilitation counseling field has been a balance of advocacy, practice, management, research, and education. Dr. Millington is a certified rehabilitation counselor. He has published more than 50 journal articles and book chapters.

Irmo Marini, PhD, DSc, CRC, CLCP, is currently a professor in the department of rehabilitation at the University of Texas–Pan American. He earned his master's in clinical psychology from Lakehead University in Thunder Bay, Canada, and his PhD in rehabilitation from Auburn University in Alabama. Over his 22-year academic career, Dr. Marini earned two outstanding faculty research awards at Arkansas State, three more faculty research awards at Pan American, two outstanding teaching awards at Pan American, and one service award. On a national level, he was the recipient of the 2009 Distinguished Career in Rehabilitation Education award by the National Council on Rehabilitation Education, and a year later received the 2010 James F. Garrett Distinguished Career award in rehabilitation research from the American Rehabilitation Counseling Association. He was also voted the National Council on Rehabilitation Education's 2013 recipient of the Rehabilitation Educator of the Year award. In 2012, Dr. Marini received an honorary doctorate in science from his alma mater, Lakehead University. To date, he has published more than 75 peer-reviewed journal publications and 26 book chapters, and coauthored and coedited 3 books on counseling and rehabilitation counseling psychology–related topics. He is former president of the American Rehabilitation Counseling Association and former chair of the Commission on Rehabilitation Counselor Certification.

Families in Rehabilitation Counseling

A Community-Based Rehabilitation Approach

Michael J. Millington, PhD, CRC
Irmo Marini, PhD, DSc, CRC, CLCP

Editors

SPRINGER PUBLISHING COMPANY
NEW YORK

Springer Publishing Company, LLC
11 West 42nd Street
New York, NY 10036
www.springerpub.com

Acquisitions Editor: Sheri W. Sussman
Production Editor: Shelby Peak
Composition: S4Carlisle

ISBN: 978-0-8261-9875-4
e-book ISBN: 978-0-8261-9876-1
Instructor's Manual ISBN: 978-0-8261-9631-6

Instructor's Manual: Instructors may request supplements by emailing textbook@springerpub.com

14 15 16 17 / 5 4 3 2 1

The author and the publisher of this Work have made every effort to use sources believed to be reliable to provide information that is accurate and compatible with the standards generally accepted at the time of publication. The author and publisher shall not be liable for any special, consequential, or exemplary damages resulting, in whole or in part, from the readers' use of, or reliance on, the information contained in this book. The publisher has no responsibility for the persistence or accuracy of URLs for external or third-party Internet websites referred to in this publication and does not guarantee that any content on such websites is, or will remain, accurate or appropriate.

Library of Congress Cataloging-in-Publication Data

Families in rehabilitation counseling : a community-based rehabilitation approach / Michael J. Millington, PhD, Irmo Marini, PhD, DSc, CRC, CLCP, editors.
    pages cm
  Includes bibliographical references and index.
  ISBN 978-0-8261-9875-4—ISBN 0-8261-9875-9—ISBN 978-0-8261-9876-1 (ebook) 1. Rehabilitation counseling. 2. Family counseling. 3. People with disabilities—Rehabilitation. 4. People with disabilities—Family relationships. 5. People with mental disabilities—Family relationships. I. Millington, Michael Jay. II. Marini, Irmo.
  HD7255.5.F36 2014
  361'.06—dc23
                                                                            2014024111

Special discounts on bulk quantities of our books are available to corporations, professional associations, pharmaceutical companies, health care organizations, and other qualifying groups. If you are interested in a custom book, including chapters from more than one of our titles, we can provide that service as well.

For details, please contact:
Special Sales Department, Springer Publishing Company, LLC
11 West 42nd Street, 15th Floor, New York, NY 10036-8002
Phone: 877-687-7476 or 212-431-4370; Fax: 212-941-7842
E-mail: sales@springerpub.com

Printed in the United States of America by Gasch Printing.

This book is dedicated to my family. You know who you are. You know what you mean to me. In this constellation, there is one who shines for me. Thank you for the light, Dori Ashton. Thank you for us.

MJM

What an appropriate topic for me to have the opportunity to dedicate to my family and the wonderful community of people inside my and Darlene's life space at some point over our lives. To my parents Cecile and Oresto, who I know would be pleased that things didn't turn out so bad for me after all. To the love and support of my sisters Diane, Carole, Connie, and Darlene—it was mostly good but sometimes bad being the only Italian boy in the family. Thank you for the pleasant memories of extended family, being blessed with four brothers-in-law, nine nieces, and now great nieces and nephews. To godparents, aunts and uncles, lifelong friends—too many to be named but for sure Dave Krasnichuck and Jamie Coady, who helped my parents after I no longer could. And to the rest of you, like Dave Shannon, who know what you did for us before and after my injury. To Darlene's parents, four sisters and brothers-in-law, seven nieces and nephews, and her extended family, thank you all for your unconditional caring, love, and support. It is difficult living 2,000 miles away from you all but we are comforted knowing you are there. Then, in no particular order, for their unconditional kindness, to our American community support system: Love and thanks to Karen and Preston McGill, Karen Pell, the Auburn Randy and Nancy McDaniel and the Jonesboro Bobby and Tonya McDaniel, Mark and Bonnie Stebnicki, John and Gina Slate, Marty and Claudia Diebold, Lynn Howerton, Paula and Bill Kimball, Martin and Lisa Furtado, Noel Ysasi, Noreen Glover-Graf, and apologetically to the many more I am not naming, but who touched us and helped us along the way. This book is for and about you, and it is my way of saying thank you for a life fully lived. Finally, to my wife Darlene: I can find no words in any dictionary that can express my love and gratitude for you seeing something in me so long ago that convinced you to want to spend your life with me. We have lived life large because of you, and I have millions of happy pictures in my mind that make me smile when I look at them.

IM

Contents

PART I. A COMMUNITY-BASED APPROACH

PART II. FAMILY EXPERIENCE OF DISABILITY AND REHABILITATION

PART III. SELECTED ISSUES FOR COMMUNITY-BASED REHABILITATION COUNSELING

Contributors

Malachy Bishop, PhD, CRC
Professor
Rehabilitation Counseling
University of Kentucky
Lexington, Kentucky

Alicia D. Brown, PhD, LPC-A, LCAS-A
Assistant Professor
Department of Rehabilitation Counseling
California State University, Fresno
Fresno, California

R. Rocco Cottone, PhD
Professor
Department of Counseling and Family
    Therapy
University of Missouri–St. Louis
Columbia, Missouri

Charles Edmund Degeneffe, PhD, CRC, ACSW
Professor and Coordinator
Rehabilitation Counseling Program
San Diego State University
San Diego, California

Marianne Farkas, ScD
Clinical Professor
Center for Psychiatric Rehabilitation
Boston University
Boston, Massachusetts

Judy Frain, PhD, RN
Assistant Professor
Goldfarb School of Nursing
    at Barnes-Jewish College
St. Louis, Missouri

Julianne Frain, PhD, CRC
Vocational Expert Consultant
Rehab Pro Assessment & Consultation
West Palm Beach, Florida

Michael Frain, PhD, CRC
Associate Professor
Department of Counselor Education
Florida Atlantic University
Boca Raton, Florida

Joan M. Griffin, PhD
Associate Professor
Center for Chronic Disease Outcomes
    Research
Minneapolis VA Health Care System
University of Minnesota Medical School
Minneapolis, Minnesota

Cheryl Hanley-Maxwell, PhD
Professor and Associate Dean
School of Education
University of Wisconsin–Madison
Madison, Wisconsin

Zakia S. Hossain, PhD
Senior Lecturer, Faculty of Health Sciences
University of Sydney
Sydney, New South Wales, Australia

Benjamin C. Jenkins, CRC
Doctoral Candidate
Department of Rehabilitation Counseling
University of Texas–Pan American
Edinburg, Texas

Gloria K. Lee, PhD, CRC
Associate Professor and Director of
  Rehabilitation Counseling MA Program
Office of Rehabilitation and Disability
  Studies
Department of Counseling, Educational
  Psychology and Special Education
College of Education
Michigan State University
East Lansing, Michigan

Lisa Lopez Levers, PhD
Professor
Counselor Education and Supervision
University of Duquesne
Pittsburgh, Pennsylvania

Terri Lewis, PhD, CRC
Assistant Professor
Rehabilitation Counseling
National Changhua University
  of Education
Changhua, Taiwan

Sue Lukersmith, MErg, OT
Researcher
Centre for Disability Research and Policy
University of Sydney
Sydney, New South Wales, Australia

Rosamond H. Madden, MSc, AM
Senior Research Fellow
Centre for Disability Research and Policy
University of Sydney
Sydney, New South Wales, Australia

Irmo Marini, PhD, DSc, CRC, CLCP
Professor
Department of Rehabilitation
University of Texas–Pan American
Edinburg, Texas

Lynda R. Matthews, PhD
Associate Professor
Ageing, Work and Health Research Unit
University of Sydney
Sydney, New South Wales, Australia

Kristin Maxwell, MS
Doctoral Candidate
Rehabilitation Psychology
University of Wisconsin–Madison
Madison, Wisconsin

Michelle Medway, MHSc, MSc
Psychologist
RNS Community Health Centre
Royal North Shore Hospital, St. Leonard's
Sydney, New South Wales, Australia

Michael J. Millington, PhD, CRC
Senior Lecturer and Course Director
Faculty of Health Sciences
University of Sydney
Sydney, New South Wales, Australia

Nancy Molfenter, MS
Doctoral Candidate
Special Education
University of Wisconsin–Madison
Madison, Wisconsin

Elias Mpofu, PhD, CRC
Professor and Head of Discipline
Faculty of Health Sciences
University of Sydney
Sydney, New South Wales, Australia

Kumbirai Mpofu, BEd, MA
Graduate Student
Health Education
University of Western Sydney
Sydney, New South Wales, Australia

Charlotte Scarf, PhD
Lecturer
Faculty of Health Sciences
University of Sydney
Sydney, New South Wales, Australia

Tim Tansey, PhD, CRC
Assistant Professor
Rehabilitation Psychology
University of Wisconsin–Madison
Madison, Wisconsin

Philomena Tanui, BEd, MEd
Graduate Student
Rehabilitation
University of Arkansas at Fayetteville
Fayetteville, Arkansas

Natalie Taylor, BHSc
Graduate Student
Rehabilitation Counseling
Griffith University
Brisbane, Queensland, Australia

Molly K. Tschopp, PhD, CRC
Associate Professor and Program Director
Rehabilitation Counseling
Ball State University
Muncie, Indiana

Mark Tucker, PhD, CRC
Assistant Professor
Rehabilitation Counseling Program
San Diego State University
San Diego, California

Foreword

I was both honored and pleased that Drs. Millington and Marini asked me to write the Foreword for this important area of study that continues to be an integral part of the ongoing dialog in health and human care with a focus on rehabilitation counseling. My interest in the family began on a personal level, similar to the experiences of the authors. As a child, I experienced the peaks and valleys of living and growing up in a family that, like most others, had its share of illness and disability-related defeats and victories. These early and ongoing personal family experiences most certainly created my sensitivity to the impact of the human challenges on all family members when disability occurs.

Families are complex, emerging as well as evolving systems. They live in a world with an environmental atmosphere composed of past, present, and future fears, hopes, dreams, and aspirations. Under the most ideal circumstances, even the most resourceful and resilient families can be tested and challenged by the demands and uncertainties of the life and living experience. Factor in the enormity of illness, disability, loss, and change, and there is now a potentially toxic environment that can challenge and overwhelm most families. In fact, given what many families have to deal with, it is amazing that as many manage as well as they do!

It is with the understanding of the family from a theoretical, practical, systemic, and personal perspective that the authors have conceptualized and written this most timely and important book. The authors have set a stage on which the family can be presented, appreciated, and understood to be better served by a health and human care system that is often limited not only by resources but also by lack of vision and creativity.

Often, it takes personal experiences to create the conditions for insightful learning and meaningful action. This point was driven home by a mother who was working with me in my rehabilitation counselor years to develop services, meaningful interventions, and supports for her young adult daughter who was living with a brain injury. After several visits, I had prepared what I thought was the most appropriate plan and presented it to this mother, who followed through with all the listed tasks and expectations. When I received a call that she wanted a follow-up meeting, I was anticipating some positive news regarding the gains being made related to the rehabilitation plan. To my surprise, this mother told me that many of the facilities and programs I had suggested were not relevant to the current and emerging needs of her daughter. She further stated that she would do something about the resources that existed and that she would change the system. This was in 1979 when the treatment and rehabilitation options for people and families living with brain injury were very limited. The mother was Marilyn Price Spivack, cofounder of the Brain Injury Association, an international organization that today has a major impact on policy and service delivery for people and families living with not only brain injury, but other life-altering conditions as well. While I did the best I could with the resources that were available, as a professional I did not have the educational preparation, vision, and perhaps the desperation that this mother and countless other parents and families have when their needs are not met or even understood or appreciated by the systems or personnel that provide support and care.

As an academic, I worked with Bob Marinelli on our series of psychosocial books. We began to realize the need to expand the vista of improved quality services to include the family. This work began with the research of Dr. Paul Power, who was working with families of veterans living with Huntington's disease. After many discussions of the need for family involvement and the ongoing issues and challenges not only for veterans and their families but others as well, Paul suggested that we offer a course on the family and rehabilitation as well as write a book. This was in 1975. The course, at Boston University, was the first step in organizing and preparing the material that took shape in our first family book, *The Role of the Family*, in 1980. This book was the foundation for our ongoing work with the family that occurred in the classroom and our clinical work. With the publication of additional books and presentations, we began to expand our understanding of the family and its ongoing developmental needs and issues.

A major force in our journey was the support and input from many in the consumer movement who were on the front line of the battle and were the true voice for the family, and the realistic dreamers of what could and should be in meaningful and relevant treatment and rehabilitation services. Millington and Marini have further focused on how an effective and efficient community-based approach inclusive of families should work, while concomitantly addressing the realities of where policies, services, and support fall short.

Before reviewing their book, I had realized that while my colleagues and I were expanding our understanding of the family back then, we were not fully attending to the more complex evolving issues that families were facing in navigating their environment, the quagmire of gaps in medical services, and the need for better policies and more resources. Many of these issues are addressed in this book, which presents the family in a comprehensive and emerging context. Key to this work is addressing the critical issues families live with on a daily basis in a dynamically changing world.

A major concern for all is that while the needs and concerns of the family will be better understood, there may not be adequate traditional resources to meet the growing and ongoing needs of families. A major premise of the Millington and Marini book is their recognition of the need for a community-based approach where the family is a central player in establishing, advocating, and securing the best of care for its loved one with a disability.

There are many similar stories and situations that reflect how consumers of health care and rehabilitation services have made the effort to become partners in their treatment and care while supporting the ongoing development of meaningful, competent, and caring services for them and their family members. Millington, Marini, and associates cover a gamut of disabling conditions in this book by providing actual case stories that discuss the families' lived experience of caring for a loved one with a disability and the reciprocal relationship families face with community-based resources. Regardless of whether community resources are abundant or scarce, families are the first line of support. While it may be somewhat easier to identify the ongoing problems faced by families engaged in treatment and rehabilitation while living with the reality of illness and/or disability, it is often a much greater challenge to conceptualize and implement those policies and interventions that help families to stabilize and survive the loneliness, isolation, abandonment, heartache, and disappointment that is often the norm of their day-to-day lives.

A critical factor in the process to maximize benefits to families is the realization and appreciation that families are distinct and unique in some dimensions of their life experiences, financial resources, values, and cultural norms, to name a few. However, they are very similar in their desire to have meaningful health care and rehabilitation services and a realistic hope for what is possible and what is not. Too often families and providers have the expectation that if we have and provide the very best care and the most expensive resources, the family member or they themselves will improve or return the person to his or her preinjury state of functioning. The very harsh and often unacceptable reality for too many families is that many human conditions are not treatable, preventable, or improvable. Sometimes things will deteriorate and just get worse. Consequently, some families are faced with a situation in which no matter what they do or how hard they try, their goals may not be achieved. This does not imply that families or their members cannot have a meaningful or improved quality of life.

I admire Drs. Millington and Marini for taking on the task of trying to synthesize and present the multitude of issues—past, present, and future—that are the foundation of a comprehensive and emerging system of community-based care for a very diverse group of people from very different backgrounds and unique life experiences, and with very different options. It is important to mention that many families are not functioning with adequate resources. Often they enter the health care and rehabilitation system in a state of emotional, financial, and spiritual bankruptcy. Consequently, the authors address the concepts of family identity, power, and capital. The resilience of families at all levels of status is explored, noting the particular adversities of those who are oppressed and discriminated against.

This book is a creative and practical attempt to not only connect the dots but also add the dots that provide the connections to a clearer understanding and relevant responses to the current and emerging needs, as well as the reality families live with and within. It also challenges health and human care systems, those who are responsible for them, and those who are served by them to look beyond what is and reach for what could and should be. The ongoing challenge addressed by the authors is not only to explore the needs of the present, but also to anticipate the emerging needs of the future. While this may seem to be a most difficult task, just compare the role of the family and the health care and rehabilitation process 50 years ago with what it is today. The present and the future welfare of families and their loved ones with a disability requires rehabilitation counselors to have a complete understanding of their holistic needs and to provide community-based rehabilitation services in the least restrictive ways feasible. It also requires rehabilitation professionals to become advocates for and with families.

Drs. Millington and Marini and I have all lived disability experiences with our families in addition to working with other families who have experienced health-altering conditions. We have also had the opportunity to witness the resilience and gratitude of families who are well supported by community-based resources, and conversely become equally as frustrated and angered by the lack of resources that often leaves families to fend for themselves. Ensuring family inclusion and effective community services is the intergenerational legacy that we all share and must continue to aspire toward. What we may also share are those mentors, friends, clients, and strangers who have been role models on how to live with and in spite of extraordinary life challenges. Thankfully, many of these people have become the leaders and advocates for other people and their families by challenging and improving community-based systems designed to help and not hinder the rehabilitation process. Congratulations to Millington and Marini for their dedication and expertise in addressing this critical topic of family inclusion about which we continue to have much to learn.

Arthur Dell Orto, PhD

Preface

My brother and I sit alone in a crowded mental health clinic waiting room. The plastic chairs are bolted to a metal rail in an immovable semicircle with all eyes trained on the nurse behind the bulletproof glass. There is a magazine rack full of old *Golf Digest*s and *Condé Nast Traveler*s that no one ever reads because no one golfs or has vacations. The waiting room rules are simple: (1) arrive on time, (2) wait, and (3) do not disrupt the system. If you are late, your appointment will be canceled. If you cannot wait, you can leave—this will be noted in your records. Disruption will not be tolerated. The waiting room is full. No one talks. The psychiatrist arrives late through a private entrance and takes her post behind the barricade. The billing commences as the names are called. "MILLER," calls the nurse behind the glass. She sits at eye level in her elevated post and commands a clear view of the room. Every 30 minutes the buzz-click of the security lock opens the door to therapy. A patient enters on the right and a person exits on the left and the circle is complete. "JAMES." Buzz-click. . . . "VALIANT." Buzz-click. . . . Suddenly, the numbing routine is interrupted by a frantic interlude. A woman darts breathlessly to the desk. She is here for her husband. Yes, she is aware that she is 10 minutes late. Yes, she knows he's supposed to come, but he is too sick, and he's out of medication. She apologizes repeatedly and pleads her case again. The families in the room can all hear her desperation and you can literally watch it wash over them. We all know how this ends. For her, tonight will involve the police and more traumas for the kids. Now on the verge of tears, she wails, "I don't know why y'all treat us this way. We just need a little help is all." Jeannie is her name. Her husband is Ray. They are just names in a chart that goes back on the shelf. The nurse stands up, now towering over the woman, now turning her back to signal the end of negotiations. Jeannie dares not continue, lest the nurse call security (on speed dial), but instead turns to leave. She is defeated and looking very small. The room is full of families, in twos and threes. You could feel them rise slightly when the woman spoke, and then shrink back down in their chairs when she left. But the worst part was how casually the nurse turned back to the routine, how quickly she turned to share a small jest with the file clerk, apparently at the patient's expense.

This book was written because my brother and I were there, a family of our own, taking care of the caring business that families do so well. Later that night, while Jeannie dealt with the crisis in her life, we worked on an ethics chapter called, "What is Required of Us? Rethinking Ethical Conduct in the Practice and Profession of Vocational Rehabilitation." It was in recalling this room of victimized families and our inability to formulate a meaningful response to the shame and humiliation we observed that David and I first proposed a lived philosophy for rehabilitation counseling: "We must actively work against isolation, alienation, and disenfranchisement of those we serve. In doing so, we must actively fight the non-beneficence and lack of cooperation, the maleficence and deprivation of autonomy, the betrayal and injustice present in the community that excludes them" (Miller & Millington, 2002, pp. 291–292).

For better and worse, I have tried to live that philosophy ever since, and I have tried to turn that philosophy into rehabilitation counseling practice and real social justice outcomes. The pieces have come together slowly. I found the family–community connection in the aftermath of Hurricane Katrina. I saw how communities respond to tragedy by opening their homes, how the great diaspora of the poor atomized families, and how the search for family brought people back together again. I sat with colleagues in a makeshift command center in a blown-out library in Metairie. I found some sense of family among them as we shared our refugee stories. I saw the repercussions of generations of oppression gathered with armed guards at the Superdome. I heard stories of people with disabilities abandoned by attendants and drowning in their homes and people with psychiatric disabilities being turned away from the shelter and care of the Red Cross tents. Thank God, I also saw the redeeming grace of people and professionals pulling together to save whom they could.

I found the professional–community connection in the communities of practice that we established in the National Clearinghouse of Rehabilitation Training Materials. This connection to family was obscure at first. I found the power of social networks and social identities rising out of the shared aspiration and collaborative work of a small group of committed professionals. They started the Summit Group, which grew from a knot of true believers to a professional movement toward quality assurance and excellence in management strategy. If you look at the model they profess, you will find the consumer and the family at the center of their outcome measures.

But the synthesis of theory and practice did not begin until I confronted the conundrum of family counseling in the profession through my contribution to Marini, Glover-Graf, and Millington (2012). The chapter on family counseling ended with the question: How do we, as rehabilitation counselors, address the profound influence that families have on process and outcomes when we are not family counselors? This book is my first attempt to synthesize my experiences and provide an answer to that question.

The dialog established with Irmo as coeditor and author became the process for working through this existential issue. My vision was philosophical. I sought to establish a reasoned basis for practice that grew out of our values and moved from values to models to theory and practice. Irmo's vision was grounded in the practical. He established the family stories as experiential scaffolding for the book. Irmo brought the "insider perspective" to the dialog, reconciling my idealistic yin with his visceral yang. He insisted on the importance of anchoring aspirations and theory to the lives of people with disabilities and to remember "never about us, without us." Irmo and I developed a relationship through this dialog and over the shared work it produced. In the trade of our small community of practice (expanding with contributing authors) we learned to trust. In trust, we took chances. The rough ideas I had going in were transformed and the vision of the book is fully shared. We made integration across chapters a priority. Thus each chapter contribution has informed the model and each author shares ownership of the larger proposition.

The answer that the book posits is that the reason family has been so poorly served by rehabilitation counseling is due to structural, fundamental flaws in the way the profession conceives of itself in relationship to its client, and the way it perceives the client in relationship to the environment. The implication of this explanation is that practice is not likely to advance until these problems are addressed.

Part I—"A Community-Based Approach"—makes the case from philosophy to praxis for an alternative to current rehabilitation counseling paradigms. Nothing of our current practice is lost, but much is gained in its translation into a social model that places community at the center of a client-centered practice. This approach creates the appropriate space to bring rehabilitation counseling and the family together. Read in synthesis, the first five chapters present the framework for a community-based approach to rehabilitation counseling beyond the family.

Part II—"Family Experience of Disability and Rehabilitation"—recounts the family disability experience across disability contexts. Each chapter provides a unique profile that maps the current relationship between rehabilitation counseling and the family experience. These chapters can be read alone as the state of practice and a guide to current rehabilitation counseling interventions. They can also be read in light of the community-based approach that is insinuated in chapter structures and that resonates in the case study narratives. Obviously, the community approach thus framed has not been intentionally implemented at this point in history, but by framing the chapters in the family experience, we can see the features of community that have been there all along. Themes emerge across these chapters that await the reader's discovery.

Part III—"Selected Issues for Community-Based Rehabilitation Counseling"— considers a sampling of the professional implications and considerations of moving forward with a community-based model. The culture chapter is adapted from Marini, Glover-Graf, and Millington (2012) but it takes on new meanings in light of the revealed strength of our advocacy roots (see Chapter 3). Assessment and management chapters focus on what we measure in our profession and how we use this information from organizational and service perspectives. The final chapter reaffirms the discursive nature of the family theme of the book. It is written as a conversation between Irmo and me, reflecting on the practice and science of rehabilitation counseling at the threshold of community.

An Instructor's Manual is also available to supplement the text. **To obtain an electronic copy of the Instructor's Manual, faculty should contact Springer Publishing Company at textbook@springerpub.com.**

This book is written for anyone who wishes to bridge family practice and rehabilitation counseling. It is written primarily for graduate-level studies. The argument for a community-based model would be excellent fodder for debate in seminar—on its merits or in its implementation. The book stands as a primary text in disability studies on the family and a supporting text in applications with rehabilitation counseling. The emphasis on community opens its value to practitioners, managers, and policy advocates. This book is an approach, not a model. It is the humble, if insightful, beginning of a public conversation on the future of the family in rehabilitation counseling and, by extension, the future of the profession itself. It does not assume to have the answers, but sets the stage to pursue them. If it fills its purpose, it will bring people together to have this conversation and a community will form around the proceedings. In the middle of this community, dictating the next edition and leading the discussion, will be the families and the persons with disabilities who live within them. In the end, this is the fundamental target audience.

Michael J. Millington, PhD, CRC

REFERENCES

Marini, I., Glover-Graf, N. M., & Millington, M. J. (Eds.). (2012). *Psychosocial aspects of disability: Insider perspectives and counseling strategies.* New York, NY: Springer.

Miller, D., & Millington, M. (2002). What is required of us? Rethinking ethical conduct in the practice and profession of vocational rehabilitation. In J. D. Andrew & C. W. Faubion (Eds.), *Rehabilitation services: An introduction for the human services professional* (pp. 278–295). Osage Beach, MO: Aspen.

Acknowledgments

We would like to acknowledge Sheri W. Sussman, Executive Editor, Springer Publishing Company for her talent, wisdom, and support in shepherding this project to completion. Sheri realized the significance of family from our previous book and approached us with the offer of a stand-alone book. We are sincerely grateful for her guidance. We would also like to thank Dr. Art Dell Orto for his time and expertise in writing the Foreword. Dr. Dell Orto's numerous books set the standard for quality and the foundation for practice in disability and the family. We are grateful for his work. Dr. Dell Orto realized more than 30 years ago that the family was being left out of the conversation and began leading the way in helping rehabilitation educators and counselors understand the true significance and importance of family inclusion. His work has been pivotal in the development of this book. We are honored to have his approval. We would also like to acknowledge every contributor to every chapter. This was a challenging project and your patience and hard work have made all the difference.

CHAPTER 1

Finding the Family in Rehabilitation Counseling

MICHAEL J. MILLINGTON, BENJAMIN C. JENKINS, AND R. ROCCO COTTONE

The family is the natural and fundamental group unit of society and is entitled to protection by society and the State, and that persons with disabilities and their family members should receive the necessary protection and assistance to enable families to contribute towards the full and equal enjoyment of the rights of persons with disabilities.
—Preamble, UN Convention on the Rights of Persons with Disabilities (United Nations, 2006)

Defining the family presence in rehabilitation counseling has been a perennial issue—often engaged, but never fully resolved. Family members have been recognized for their influence on rehabilitation process and outcomes (Sutton, 1985; Westin & Reiss, 1979). Academics have argued the potential role of family therapy models within rehabilitation counseling (Millington, 2012; Power & Dell Orto, 2004). Family experience with service has been explored from a systems perspective (Cottone, 2012). Ecological models have been employed to justify families as partners in service and as service recipients (Kelley & Lambert, 1992; Power, Hershenson, & Fabian, 1991). The specialized knowledge of family counseling has become part of the qualified rehabilitation counselor identity (Leahy, 2012). Despite these advances, the family discourse has not translated into a sustained movement in research (Bryan, 2009), practice (Frain, Berven, Chan, & Tschopp, 2008; Freedman & Fesko, 1996), training (Riemer-Reiss & Morrissette, 2002), or policy (Kneipp & Bender, 1981).

What accounts for this gap between intent and achievement? The premise of this book is that rehabilitation counseling's failing with the family is a problem of models. Originally shaped by the values and epistemology of a psychomedical model, rehabilitation counseling struggles with the residual effect of a worldview that it has ostensibly left behind. A new social construction is required to make sense of the proper relationship between service and family. The social movement has provided one on a global stage. Rights-based advocacy, as part of the movement, changed the meaning of disability and reoriented the relationship between family and care at an international level. Rehabilitation counseling has embraced this movement in principle, but has not addressed the conceptual work of constructing a new model for the family around movement values.

This chapter chronicles the emergence of the family ethos in rehabilitation counseling from values, to theory, to its model implications. Rehabilitation counseling for families is cast as community counseling, with family as first community. The discipline's identity in this new context is explored through the applied values of the fundamental mission. An argument is made that rehabilitation counseling in the family has three distinct transactional expressions in identity, power, and capital.

FAMILY ETHOS IN REHABILITATION COUNSELING

Finding the family ethos in rehabilitation counseling begins with an understanding of community values. John Dewey, an American educational philosopher and contemporary of the psychologist William James, argued that ethical behavior is a social and humanistic pursuit. For the individual, it is the pursuit of a satisfying life within social institutions, that is, in community. For society, it is the pursuit of policy that provides a satisfying community life for its citizens. We pursue the good life through the moral behavior of the individual and the collective. The path is always a challenge. There is no simple concordance of the good, the right, and the virtuous; no imperative rule or immutable truth that precludes thinking (Field, 2005). Directed at living an ethical life or building an ethical profession, the path to moral behavior is always a social process of discovery. The ethos that emerges from experience is a rational, value-laden extension of our epistemology (see Tarvydas, 2012). Our professional identities are driven by our values and shaped by reflective praxis.

The special identity of rehabilitation counseling (Maki & Tarvydas, 2012) is negotiated in the lived community experience of disability. It is unique among counseling specialties in that it exists in the space of society's ethical failure in this specific regard. The profession was legislated into being to address the exclusion of people with disabilities from society. Rehabilitation counseling is society's ethical policy response to that injustice. Rehabilitation counselors are agents of social justice (see Marini, 2012), advancing an applied theory and practice of community values.

Miller and Millington (2002) described the ethos of the profession (the moral character of the profession as it is expressed through action) in terms of the historical democratic ideals of equality, liberty, and fraternity. These values guide professional practice, infusing both process and outcome with meaning:

- *Equality* is a reciprocal respect and regard for the unique nature of the individual and a valued recognition for his or her distinctive contribution to the whole, without consideration of physical or mental function. Accordingly, all are valued equally. Due respect and regard are expressed through the equitable allotment of resources. Each person is provided what he or she needs and receives it such that he or she is able to utilize it in the expression and development of his or her potential—whatever that potential may be.

- *Liberty* is the space created by this transaction in equity that allows for the expression and development of individual potential. Liberty is the freedom to choose one's path through one's intentional and unencumbered actions. Through the expression and development of the individual's potential, each person makes a distinctive contribution to the whole. Because it is only through cooperation that this becomes possible, both the individual and the community come to appreciate and desire that cooperation.

- *Fraternity* is that shared space beyond liberty where people are free to choose their associations, free to align their work with the cooperative of community. Fraternity directs our actions because what we seek to achieve together is viewed as worth achieving by each participant. It produces in us a desire to continue to work together in order to sustain what we have achieved. Disability legislation is an expression of these values writ large. To realize a democracy, however, legislation must find expression through the good work of local community action (Dewey, 1916). Rehabilitation counselors as agents of the democratic ideal on behalf of people with disabilities are citizen professionals (see Doherty, Mendenhall, & Berge, 2010) and the instruments of that good work. Rehabilitation counseling philosophy (Maki & Murray, 1995) is derived from these community values and this ethos. Rehabilitation counseling is a value-driven profession (Tarvydas, 2012) anchored in community by a fundamental mission of full community inclusion (Szymanski, 1985).

Family Voice in Community

The fundamental mission links rehabilitation counseling with an evolving, global social movement. The history of democracy in the United States is told in the narratives of marginalized and disenfranchised peoples who united in common cause to resist oppression; negotiate their identities; trade in the marketplace; and claim their share of liberty, equality, and fraternity. People with disabilities have been engaged in this political struggle for decades and family has figured prominently in their action. As rehabilitation counseling has been a party to the movement, it is within this advocacy frame that the emerging family voice is most clearly heard.

Advocacy Roots for Rehabilitation Counseling

Counseling has its roots in the social reform movements of the 19th century (Sales, 2012) and the programmatic governmental response in the early 20th century (Elliott & Lueng, 2005). Vocational counseling was created to meet an urgent public need to facilitate the rapid shift of the population from rural/agriculture to urban/industrial life and work (Savickas & Baker, 2005). Rehabilitation counseling was an early offshoot of vocational counseling conceived in spirit as a government-sponsored alternative to charity for veterans with disabilities following World War I. It was established in principle under the Vocational Rehabilitation Act of 1920. A detailed account of vocational rehabilitation (VR) counseling in legislation is beyond the scope of this chapter. However, the political subtext of the profession's evolution is clear: Community advocacy defines and advances rehabilitation counseling through the promise of inclusion.

Medical Model Obfuscates Family Role

The family connection to VR counseling was strained by the residual paternalism of the charity movement, the epistemological constraints of the psychomedical model (Cottone & Emener, 1990) that gave them legitimacy, and the subtle social oppression of a society that was designed to exclude. The language, structures, and functions of rehabilitation were forged in a medical model, and rehabilitation counseling was a party to the process. In the medical model, disability was pathology within the person that required a diagnoses and a "cure." Assessment focused on a statistical approximation of normality to which the client, by definition, fell short. Strategies were arranged by experts. Treatment was meant to resolve shortcomings. Failure only proved the model's assumptions of client inadequacy. Services in such a climate tended to institutionalize and segregate (Nosek, 2012) people with disabilities. Vocational evaluation often culled out those who required the most support for being "too disabled" (Cottone & Cottone, 1986). Sheltered workshops promised competitive employment, usually without success. People were warehoused in nursing homes and hospitals far from family and any sense of community. All of this was expertly done for the good of the client. Typically, neither the client nor the family was asked to define what "good" meant.

The medical model has no active role for the family. When disability is in the body, its impact on significant others is a tragedy that falls outside of service. When experts control the language, the client has no voice. When the science is reductive, the social network is invisible and the issues of family are not recognized. For all the good intent, the medical model falls short for all rehabilitation professions, but particularly for rehabilitation counseling, which had democratic values in its theoretical bones (Wright, 1983).

Social Movement, Social Model

The social model arose as a rejection of the medical model (Stubbins, 1984). Disability was redefined as a social construction (Oliver, 1983) imposed on people as "systematic patterns of exclusion that were—quite literally—built into the social fabric" (Hughes & Patterson, 1997, p. 328). The social model reinterprets psychological wellness in terms of the relationship between impairment and the disabling effects of the environment. It focuses on the political, the importance of personal resistance, and group advocacy in claiming an identity within the community.

The initial social model was complete in its rejection of medical hegemony (Oliver, 1990). The confluence of interests across disability groups aligned in the rejection. A political community of practice arose with the movement; it was the shared vision, history, and emerging language of a true disability community based on civil rights. Rejecting the medical model was the beginning of the normalization of disability. Disability was embraced in the social model as an authentic part of the human experience, to be accepted on its own terms, and celebrated for what it contributes to community (Remley, 2012). The full meaning of disability, its value and its challenges, came from a complex of social relationships (Llewellyn & Hogan, 2000), not from the person in isolation. The medical perspective was eventually rehabilitated back into the social model's worldview (Shakespeare, 2006), but without the power to ascribe meaning beyond the physical structure and function of impairment.

The Family Voice Emerges

The sociopolitical perspective recognized the importance of family and provided a platform and a voice. Family became a central theme in the disability studies literature. Family experiences across cultures, disabilities, and roles opened up the dialog to consider the impact of disability within the family and on the relationship between the family and the larger community. Families figured prominently in the collective response of the recovery movement in substance abuse (White & Savage, 2005) and mental health, giving rise to unprecedented family engagement in advocacy, treatment, and community-based peer support (Howe & Howe, 1987).

Family activism within the disability movement influenced the course of legislation. The Individuals with Disabilities Education Act and the Americans with Disabilities Act recognized the family support role in preserving the rights of the family member. Title 1 of the 1998 Amendments to the Rehabilitation Act identifies families as direct recipients of support services and training designed to empower them as informed consumers within the VR system (Section 103(a) [17]). Family access to services is contingent on instrumental impact on client employment

(34 CFA 361.5(b) [23]), but offers extensive support and liberally inclusive family criteria. Compensable services include interpreters, support groups, information resources, peer networks, counseling (referrals to therapy beyond the scope of VR), day care, respite, financial management, and education. Family is defined as any person with a substantial interest in the client's welfare who lives within the home.

The empowering family trend has continued. The Family Medical Leave Act advanced employment protections to families coping with emergency care. President Obama included family leadership in policy development around the "year of community living" initiative (ca. 2009–2010). Family efforts were key in advocating for improved access to information, one-on-one counseling, and streamlined services for home-based care (Perez, 2012).

Rehabilitation Counseling Responds to the Family Voice

Rehabilitation counseling has attempted to move in concert with policy trends. What should have been the watershed moment for systems change, the 26th Institute on Rehabilitation Issues (IRI, 2000) addressed the emerging family ethos in VR counseling and proposed a way forward to more family-integrated and family-responsive service. Families were to be supported in their caring roles. VR's propensity for poor communication with family and the resulting unwarranted lowering of family expectations of VR service delivery were identified as systemic barriers to client success. The IRI recognized that client-centered service was not defined by the client in isolation, but the client embedded in family. The client had a right to choose who "family" was and to direct family roles in VR service partnership. As bona fide stakeholders in the VR process, family members had rights to informed choice and autonomy. Family was not simply to be recognized; it was to be understood. The family was to be respected in its diversity with sensitivity to its changing needs and accommodated accordingly. The family offered specialized knowledge, skills, connections, and resources that were essential for long-term successful employment outcomes. And with that, the family moved from the periphery to the core of rehabilitation counseling practice—at least in (emerging) theory.

Proclamation was the easy part. The 26th IRI was literally a summation of what was already expressed in legislation. Its recommendations were merely guidelines describing what the family in rehabilitation counseling should look like. What the recommendations did not include was any strategy for implementing family inclusion in VR practice. This shortcoming was recognized within the IRI and it foreshadowed the historic lack of progress made since:

> Yet, even when we understand the value of and need for family involvement, even when we are empowered to act, we remain hesitant. Perhaps our hesitancy arises, in part, from confusion over the role and function of the rehabilitation counselor. Our profession continues to struggle with the limitations of the medical model, which focuses on disease and deficits. When such pathology dominates our thinking we continue to look for evidence of disease, deficiency, or malfunctioning when we should shift our primary focus

to family strengths. We should assess those strengths and work with the family rather than working around the family or standing in opposition to the family. As vocational rehabilitation enters the 21st century, our challenge must be to create a new model that creates a true partnership between people with disabilities, families and rehabilitation professionals. (IRI, 2000, p. 44)

FAMILY, THEORY, AND REHABILITATION COUNSELING

Rehabilitation counseling's science and practice is predicated on the values of human rights. Rehabilitation counseling transacts specifically in the gap between society's egalitarian aspirations for its citizenry and society's failure in achieving these just ends. Defined as it is by these community transactions, rehabilitation counseling's identity is differentially expressed across settings, developmental across time, and always in the context of the gap. Rehabilitation counseling is embedded in a social movement and defined by the search. It is a transitional profession (Miller & Millington, 2002) with a dynamic identity that requires constant challenge and revision.

The family conundrum at the center of this identity issue is not a feature of rehabilitation counseling; it is a passing symptom of professional growth. Rehabilitation counseling evolves in its role and function, albeit unevenly, in response to societal change because rehabilitation counseling science is not simply a description of the world as it is, but the investigation of what makes a more humane world. Rehabilitation counseling is a science of social construction where empirical observation is charged with meaning. The social construction of rehabilitation counseling requires a social psychology that embraces liberation.

Social Construction of Disability and the Family

Lewin (1935) is known in rehabilitation counseling for the ubiquitous citations of his conceptualization of behavior as a function of the person and the environment. The gestalt of Lewin's work reveals the deep connections of theory to rehabilitation counseling values, to the pursuit of systems change, and to the irreducible nature of family and community. Lewin's understanding of the social nature of psychology is a proper framework for engaging the family in rehabilitation counseling.

Lewin's theoretical work was unified by his dedication to applied social science in the service of advocacy. He was concerned with the issue of power and its ability to eclipse social justice for the disenfranchised (Burnes, 2004). The origins of social psychology are inseparable from the values of democracy in Lewin's strongly held belief; society's complete commitment to democratic values was its only protection from the worst extremes of social conflict (Burnes, 2004). Gordon Allport went as far as to aver that Lewin's corpus of theory was the epistemological complement to Dewey's educational philosophy. "Without knowledge of, and obedience to, the laws of human nature in group settings, democracy cannot succeed. And without freedom for research and theory as provided only in a democratic environment, social science will surely fail" (Allport, 1948, p. xi). Lewin sought to improve the circumstances of the individual through planned change in the group and saw his theoretical themes of field theory, group dynamics, change theory, and action research as interdependent components of planned change at the individual, group, and societal levels.

Field Theory

Lewin's famous $B = f(P, E)$ equation addresses the interdependent physical, psychological, and sociological characteristics of lived experience. The function establishes the inseparability of the individual and the "life spaces" he or she navigates (Hall & Lindzey, 1978). Behavior is enmeshed in a complex network of proximal and distal influences; that is, vector forces that push and pull on self-expression. We shape, and are shaped by, our environments through unceasing reflexive transactions.

Group Dynamics

The evolving social identity that binds individual to group manifests through group dynamics. Through "interdependence of fate and task," individual behaviors coalesce in fraternal collaboration. A complex and reciprocal social system arises where identity is negotiated group-to-individual and individual-to-group (Smith, 2001).

Change Theory

Continuity of group behavior creates a social equilibrium not easily changed by individual action. Group change is best effected through collective action. Intentional change is initiated by a disruption of the status quo, a shared desire for transition to a new state, and a consensus that the effort to change is worth the risk (Schein, 1996). Change is accomplished as new models of behavior become engrained in habit; new structures and traditions crystalize around social transactions; equilibrium returns; and a new identity emerges for group and individual (Burnes, 2004).

Action Research

The means to direct intentional change in constructive ways is accomplished through action research. Action research was meant to empower (minority) groups to address and resolve local problems and to identify general laws of group life through the application of basic social research. Group members collaborate through a cyclical process of planning overall goal and incremental steps, implementing change, and evaluating outcomes. Outcomes have three purposes, to evaluate the action against the goal, provide an opportunity to learn from the experience, and inform the next iteration (Lewin, 1946).

Lewin interpreted Dewey's educational philosophy into an applied science of advocacy for oppressed groups. The practice that followed would facilitate democratic social change toward fuller participation in a more democratic society (Smith, 2001). Lewin and Dewey shared the social constructionist view, later professed of the disability rights movement, that planned change is not authoritarian but egalitarian in a process that combines research, education, and management to community-enhancing ends (Hatch, 1997).

Extension in Rehabilitation Psychology

Lewin's social psychology provided a systems alternative to the clinical appraisal of psychomedical tradition. Wright's seminal work (1983) in the somatopsychological and psychosocial dynamics of physical disability was a turning point. She conceived a value-laden set of principles that recast disability as a complex phenomenon embedded in a social system (World Health Organization [WHO], 2002) and set the precepts for the nascent field of rehabilitation psychology.

Impact of the Social Context

Human beings are by nature social creatures that fail to thrive without care (Bowlby, 1969) and for whom isolation is the ultimate punishment. We seek out social attachment and negotiate who we are through social learning. We are constantly engaged in proximal social processes (Bronfenbrenner & Morris, 2006) with the people, things, and information that populate our environment. Through this sustained activity, we develop habits of behavior, thinking, and feeling that define our social identity (Sluzki, 2010). Our social identities are contextually dependent and constantly in flux. As we move from role to role, we find that social identities are the compromise between what we believe ourselves to be and what society will allow. We flourish where we are accepted, and we struggle to adapt where we are not.

People with disabilities find themselves assigned to an identity (Goffman, 1963) not of their choosing (Barker, Wright, Meyerson, & Gonick, 1953), historically one of stigma and devaluation (Dembo, 1982). The social lessons taught and learned are embedded in the disabling context, for example, the attitudes of others (Shontz, 1977), inaccessible physical environments, policies that create dependency, and language that denies respect. To these insults, add the pervasive professional negative bias (Dunn & Elliot, 2005) of a disability industry that reifies its assumptions of deviance in the population it purports to serve (see Cottone & Cottone, 1986; Tremain, 2005). These contextual barriers, often invisible to those who do not live the experience, are a far greater threat to positive adjustment than the functional aspects of impairment (Shontz, 1977).

Impact of Advocacy

Early researchers drew parallels between the struggle of people with disabilities and the marginalization and disenfranchisement of other minority groups (Barker et al., 1953). The minority meme resonated with people with disabilities and their families (Meyerson, 1988). It made empirical and intuitive sense and, for the first time, provided for an activist response to one's position as outsider (Fine & Asch, 1988). This collective activist response is the impetus for action in Lewin's action research. The disability rights movement moved special education into the mainstream, sheltered employment into competitive employment (with supports), and institutionalization into independent living. Research did not lead these movements, but responded to them as part of a larger system of change.

The disability rights movement has encouraged an epistemological shift from interindividual traits to intraindividual relationships; from psychological states to ecological processes; from individual counseling to counseling in systems. Theoretical constructs have evolved accordingly. Families are recognized as the most proximal of many nested and networked social systems (Bronfenbrenner, 1977) in which the person with a disability interfaces. They are constituted of a complex of *social-emotional bonds* (Dembo, Leviton, & Wright, 1975) interacting in dyadic (parents), tryadic (parents and child), and higher order exchanges (e.g., female members of the extended family) that provide the scaffold for group and individual identity and the tools for adapting to change (see Bateson, 1972; Minuchin, 1985).

Evolving Constructs

Systems thinking redefines disability in the social sphere. Impairment is a personal experience, but disability resides in the relationships that connect people. Disability happens to a family as well as an individual, and the response to it can be registered at both levels. For example, rehabilitation psychology was predicated on the psychosocial framework of coping with disability (Wright, 1983)—a construct with both inter- and intraindividual interpretations. An individual's response to environmental stressors is dependent on cognitive appraisal (Lazarus, 1993) of the situation, the consequent perception of self-efficacy, and the choice and implementation of coping strategies. Each impacts the next in succession. Generalized practice of effective coping strategies across contexts and time (Maddux, 1995) creates psychologically resilient individuals. Self-appraisal of a supportive social network raises an individual's perceived self-efficacy in problem solving and thereby encourages self-directed change-making in his or her world, and stress reduction (Bandura, 1997). Similarly, groups are collectively more effective when their members are confident in their abilities to overcome obstacles (Bandura, 1998). The concept of coping has expanded to strategies of social support (Pierce, Sarason, & Sarason, 1996). The perception of strong social support provides a degree of affective coping simply by its presence. Supportive relationships lead to more positive and accurate assessment of self and support network efficacy. Support within specific dyadic relationships, especially spousal support, has been found to be effective in rehabilitation settings (Revenson & Majerovitz, 1990). Networks of supports, most notably families, enhance individual coping with challenges in the rehabilitation process (Porrit, 1979).

Resilience, once reserved to describe individual's ability to "bounce back" following personal loss, has now taken on an additional systemic application in describing families (Walsh, 2003). Resilience is recognized in the synergistic relationship between the individual and the group. The person is simultaneously an extension of the family and feature of its resilience, and a recipient of family support and the resilience it affords. This is particularly poignant for people with disabilities and their families. The key to coping with the stressors around disability, foremost among these being community exclusion, is to find strength in the family and purpose in the community (Li & Moore, 1998).

Systems in Rehabilitation Counseling

Cottone's (1987) systemic theory of VR represents the first steps taken in building a rehabilitation counseling framework that bridges family and service structure (Cottone, Handelsman, & Walters, 1986). The theory posited that the degree of "fit" between the service systems governing rehabilitation practice and the family systems governing client participation was an influential arbiter of rehabilitation success, perhaps more important that the person × environment fit that the system itself espoused. Cottone and Cottone (1986) proposed that VR actually functioned as a complex system for screening social deviance before it functioned in its formal capacity. In their critique of vocational evaluation, they suggested that vocational evaluation recommendations were heavily influenced by counselor expectations and agenda, making it more of a tool for preserving the organization than a resource for advancing the client's goals (Cottone & Cottone, 1986).

Preliminary research suggested that social relationships were more influential in determining employability determinations than psychological evidence (Cottone, Grelle, & Wilson, 1988), specifically in regard to clients with nonphysical disabilities. It was Cottone's contention that family-oriented rehabilitation counseling would provide a more effective point of client engagement in a self-serving service system. The professional community's response to this call was underwhelming, despite the ethical questions raised for state VR and the implied need for organized family advocacy.

In 2012, Cottone renewed his call for systems applications in rehabilitation counseling in further explorations of the role of families. For Cottone, the inclusion of family in rehabilitation process requires a rejection of the psychomedical model and its Newtonian trait/factor worldview for the Lewinian-inspired relational worldview of field theory. Cottone saw systems theory leading to a true paradigmatic change for the profession, then and now. But paradigmatic change comes slowly and unevenly.

Today, systems theory has a broader appeal and a more receptive audience in rehabilitation counseling. With family in the vanguard, we have both an impetus and a framework for progress.

Sense of Community: A System of Inclusion

Moving to a systems model creates a language that includes the family in the social discourse of disability, but to what end? What is the relationship between the family experience of disability and the fundamental mission of full community inclusion? How is rehabilitation counseling supposed to engage this relationship on behalf of its client? Coming out of a quasipsychomedical worldview, these questions were difficult to even ask. Rehabilitation has adopted a biopsychosocial model to expand its explanatory power, but the activities and participation of the ICF (WHO, 2002) give us only the mechanics of inclusion. These advancements in construct do not yet capture the dynamics of the relationships through which community is actually expressed. Community is like music in this sense. It is expressed only in the moment of exchange between players. It is a subjective experience that lives in the collected and collective memory of those moments.

McMillan's "sense of community" (2005) provides a vocabulary upon which we may build a "sense of family." Sense of community reflects the basic human need for affiliation, group cohesion, psychological attachment, and personal bonding. Sense of community is an empirical theory rather than a normative one. Sense of community describes the phenomenon of people coming together. McMillan (1996) conceptualized the affective "sense" of community in psychosocial terms, revealing both its human nature and the demands humans place on it. Sense of community arises from lived experience of community inclusion, framed by four community transactions (McMillan, 1996; McMillan & Chavis, 1986): (a) membership/spirit, (b) influence/trust, (c) need fulfillment/trade, and (d) shared emotional connection/art.

Membership/Spirit

The first sense of community, or perhaps the deepest, is the sense of belonging to something larger than oneself. It is a primal drive (gemeinschaft), evident in every social gathering. Individuals derive their identity and a concordant sense of well-being from the safety and welcoming acceptance afforded by membership. Members share symbols and rituals that bind them in affiliation and mark them as insiders. Membership is the spirit in esprit de corps, and the allegiance to the corps can run very deep.

Spirit grows in finding common ground. The novice shares increasingly personal and sensitive information about him- or herself within the space of the community.

The community members share similar stories and secrets in turn. McMillan and Chavis (1986) referred to this as "freedom from shame." Such sharing is a risk taken through a call and response. The individual reveals, "Here I am." The community responds, "One of us." The danger is when the community does not respond or rejects the call outright. Shame and humiliation are the death of community and the denial of identity. The more we risk in self-revelation, the higher the emotional stakes, the deeper the meaning of membership.

Influence/Trust

Communities exist to serve the membership. Structures and processes form around these intents as strategies and plans, rules and regulations, roles and functions. Structure and habit allow for specialization and more effective pursuit of community goals and impart a comfortable predictability and trust among members. People are drawn to order. It creates a framework for identity and makes relationships among members clear.

Order requires a subjugation of individual freedoms to the common good. It is part of the dues of membership and part of the assumed social identity. Order and community cohesion are sustained through the negotiation of authority and responsibility among members. Individuals are attracted to groups that can leverage their collective influence (e.g., labor unions, advocacy groups) in areas of individual interest. Members are more willing to acquiesce to authority when they believe they have input into its exercise. Community is most successful when authority is responsive to and works in service of the membership (McMillan & Chavis, 1986). Trust evolves from the perceived benefit of compliance, equity of power relationships, and the predictability of consequences. An individual's sense of community is enhanced if he or she has a say in what the community does, sees the community as working in his or her interest, and believes that he or she is being treated fairly within it.

Integration of Fulfillment of Needs/Trade

Having established a sense of belonging and an orderly environment within which to act, the economic work of community may commence. Trade is the engine of community. It is the essence of *Gesellschaft*, that is, membership as personal benefit. Community action is shaped around the collective leveraging of individual resources.

Individuals exchange economic, social, psychological, and political capital in the internal community marketplace, which advances both community cohesion and individual prosperity in all dimensions. Cohesiveness comes from a proper matching of needs to resources. Sense of community is advanced when the individual's contribution is valued, he or she can fulfill his or her needs, and he or she is free to trade in equity.

Shared Emotional Connection (1986)/Art (1996)

Community is a process reified by its history and the artifacts it creates. Community histories are replete with origin stories, recollections of pivotal moments in history, the journeys of heroes, and cautionary tales of members gone wrong. Buildings and monuments are testament to the history. Celebration and ceremony mark the milestones of life, honor membership, and instill faith in the constancy and relevance of the group.

This is the fruition of the sense of community, the celebration of one's part in the whole. In the sense of transaction, it circles back to the first sense, membership and spirit. But now the novice is the master. He or she transacts in wisdom as one who listens to the initiate's story and responds with the group's secret mythology to include the novice as "one of us."

Family as First Community: Implications for Rehabilitation Counseling

Synomorphy describes the natural systems "fit" that occurs between standing patterns of group behavior (e.g., shopping) and the features of the nonbehavioral environments in which they occur (e.g., business hours, malls, advertisements, public transportation; Barker, 1968). Fit in this sense is a self-organizing process, where form follows function and function follows form. It is possible to deduce one knowing the other and to find them paired wherever either is found. Lewin (1951) used this concept to study measures of economic interdependence and demonstrated that synomorphy could be explored at multiple levels (e.g., the economic interdependence of city, neighborhood, or family). The same can be said for Dewey's conceptualization of big "D" democracy's dependence on small "d" participation of local communities, and the origins of democracy in the education of the individual within a democratic system. McMillan similarly bridged sense of community theory to couples (McMillan, 1997) and the families they evoke. Thus the thread of community runs unbroken from the broadest contexts of philosophy, to society and its problems, through professional praxis and its solutions, down to the family and its lived experience with disability. Family is the first synomorphic instance of community and thus the most immediate experience of inclusion available to the client or counselor. If community inclusion is the fundamental mission of rehabilitation counseling, the most sensible strategy for pursuing it would be to start with its function in the family and work outward.

Strengthening Community in the Family

The sense of family arises out of collaborative participation in instrumental tasks that achieve goals that are collectively valued (Verdonschott, de Witte, Reichraft, Buntinx, & Curfs, 2009). The degree and character of a family member's active inclusion in the business of the family provide social learning content about his or her role and efficacy in the world. A client-centered approach to community inclusion begins with an evaluation of the familial relationships. How does the individual express her- or himself in family rituals of membership? How does the individual negotiate the authorities and obligations of his or her role within the family structure? How does the individual contribute to and draw from the collective family resources? For each of these issues add, ". . . and how does the family respond?" Unlike the questions and contexts that opened this chapter, these are questions that can now be entertained.

Each member of the family will experience the phenomenon of disability differently, but it is a shared experience that contributes to group identity. Deepening the sense of family requires sharing these personal experiences (in culturally appropriate ways), reflecting upon them, and responding to them in intentional and inclusive ways. A strong sense of family shared by all members is the optimal foundation for advancing the goals of rehabilitation counseling in the community at large.

Strengthening Family in the Community

Individual family members draw strength from their trade with multiple communities beyond the family. These may be communities of practice that revolve around work, school, or other shared interests. They may be geographically bound or virtual. These communities may be an individual pursuit of one family member, the family as a whole, or a subset. In every permutation, the experience of disability follows the individuals into other memberships, as it is a part of their identity. It is part of the stories they tell. When they negotiate their role in the organization, they negotiate within the experience of disability. When they trade in resources, the experience of disability contributes in some fashion for good, ill, or otherwise.

Families are nested and networked in a community of their own making. The groups they join, they join because it serves a family need. Peer and advocacy groups may trade in disability specific knowledge, support, and connections designed for individuals or families. Cooperatives may serve a broader mission (e.g., fair trade products, culture and the arts) that builds inclusion into service. Even strictly social groups (e.g., work-sponsored bowling teams) potentially provide linkages between the family and desired resources that may serve the client (e.g., job openings). Rehabilitation counseling in the community engages family efforts in marshaling existing community resources and expanding their social network to strategic advantage.

Family and the Rehabilitation Counseling Ethos

An unbroken thread runs from the values that unite the profession, community, and family, to the models that make sense of the disability experience, to the practice of rehabilitation counseling. Community values resonate through the relationship with the family. At the point of transaction, they take on the look of action research. The client invites the family and the counselor to collaborate on problems of mutual concern. Employment is often the proximal reason for the gathering, but the family's perspective is complex and extends over the course of years. They see employment as the first step in a career. They see the career as part of a social life beyond work and home. They see the arc of a social life into old age. And each family member sees him- or herself in the family narrative . . . or he or she sees none of this, and that is the problem. The client and his or her family set about the task of visioning an objective and planning the steps required. They share, negotiate, and settle on something worth doing. They proceed, succeed or fail, and then share their perspectives in review. Then they repeat the process. Along the way, they acquire knowledge and learn new skills. This is what families do.

The rehabilitation counselor engages the family process as a resource designed to facilitate the work of families through three community-based transactions:

- Identity provides the working alliance and space for psychosocial support as persons with disability and their families negotiate life challenges. Identity is rooted in the democratic ideal of liberty. It asks, "Who am I (who are we) in the face of change?" It is realized in the exchange of the personal with the collective in search of belonging—the spirit of family and community.
- Power provides a voice for the family seeking social justice, alone and in the collective. Power is rooted in the democratic ideal of equality. It asks, "What do I (we) direct and what directs me (us)?" It is realized in the exchange of authority and responsibility in search of an empowered sense of justice—the sense of structure, stability, and trust.
- Capital provides networks and networked resources for the development, implementation, and evaluation of planned action. Value is rooted in the democratic ideal of fraternity. It asks, "What do I (we) have to offer and what is proffered in return?" It is realized in the exchange of capital, real and social, in search of sense of enrichment and quality of life.

We can recognize the familiar in these transactions as they track closely to traditional counseling, advocacy, and case management roles. Here the roles are unified in community values. Dealing with the family requires all three orchestrated in delivery. As we attend to each in the coming chapters, it will become apparent that they are facets of a single irreducible whole, much like the fundamental mission that drives them.

REFERENCES

Allport, G. W. (1948). Foreword. In G. W. Lewin (Ed.), *Resolving social conflict* (pp. vii–xiv). London, England: Harper & Row.

Bandura, A. (1997). *Self-efficacy: The exercise of control.* New York, NY: Freeman.

Bandura, A. (1998). Personal and collective efficacy in human adaptation and change. In J. G. Adair & K. L. Dion (Eds.), *Advances in psychological science, Volume 1: Personal, social, and cultural aspects* (pp. 51–71). Hove, England: Psychology Press.

Barker, R. G. (1968). Behavior settings: Defining attributes and varying properties. In *Ecological psychology: Concepts and methods for studying the environment of human behavior* (pp. 18–34). Stanford, CA: Stanford University Press.

Barker, R. G., Wright, B. A., Meyerson, L., & Gonick, M. R. (1953). *Adjustment to physical handicap and illness: A survey of the social psychology of physique and disability* (2nd ed.). New York, NY: Social Science Research Council.

Bateson, G. (1972). *Steps to an ecology of mind.* New York, NY: Ballantine.

Bowlby, J. (1969). *Attachment: Attachment and loss: Vol. 1. Loss.* New York, NY: Basic Books.

Bronfenbrenner, U. (1977). Lewinian space and ecological substance. *Journal of Social Issues, 33,* 199–212.

Bronfenbrenner, U., & Morris, P. A. (2006). The bioecological model of human development. In W. Damon & R. M. Lerner (Eds.), *Handbook of child psychology* (vol. 1, 6th ed., pp. 793–828). New York, NY: Wiley.

Bryan, J. (2009). Engaging clients, families, and communities as partners in mental health. *Journal of Counseling & Development, 87,* 507–511.

Burnes, B. (2004). Kurt Lewin and the planned approach to change: A re-appraisal. *Journal of Management Studies, 41,* 977–1002.

Cottone, R. R. (1987) A systemic theory of vocational rehabilitation. *Rehabilitation Counseling Bulletin, 30,* 167–176.

Cottone, R. R. (2012). Family and relationship issues. In D. Maki & V. M. Tarvydas (Eds.), *The professional practice of rehabilitation counseling* (pp. 131–146). New York, NY: Springer.

Cottone, R. R., & Cottone, L. P. (1986). A systemic analysis of vocational evaluation in the state-federal rehabilitation system. *Vocational Evaluation and Work Adjustment Bulletin, 19,* 47–54.

Cottone, R. R., & Emener, W. G. (1990). The psychomedical paradigm of vocational rehabilitation and its alternatives. *Rehabilitation Counseling Bulletin, 34,* 91–102.

Cottone, R. R., Grelle, M., & Wilson, W. C. (1988). The accuracy of systemic versus psychological evidence in judging vocational evaluator recommendations: A preliminary test of a systemic theory of vocational rehabilitation. *Journal of Rehabilitation, 54,* 45–52.

Cottone, R. R., Handelsman, M. M., & Walters, N. (1986). Understanding the influence of family systems on the rehabilitation process. *Journal of Applied Rehabilitation Counseling, 17,* 37–40.

Dembo, T. (1982). Some problems in rehabilitation as seen by a Lewinian. *Journal of Social Issues, 38*(1), 131–139.

Dembo, T., Leviton, G., & Wright, B. (1975). Adjustment to misfortune: A problem of social psychological rehabilitation. *Rehabilitation Psychology, 22,* 1–100.

Dewey, J. (1916). *Democracy and education: An introduction to the philosophy of Education.* New York, NY: MacMillan.

Doherty, W. J., Mendenhall, T., & Berge, J. M. (2010). The families and democracy and citizen health care project. *Journal of Marital and Family Therapy, 36,* 389–402.

Dunn, D. S., & Elliott, T. R. (2005). Revisiting a constructive classic: Wright's physical disability: A psychosocial approach. *Rehabilitation Psychology, 50*(2), 183–189.

Elliott, T. R., & Leung, P. (2005). Vocational rehabilitation: History and practice. In W. B. Walsh & M. Savickas, M. (Eds.), *Handbook of vocational psychology: Theory, research, & practice* (3rd ed., pp. 318–343). Mahwah, NJ: Lawrence Erlbaum.

Field, R. (2005). John Dewey (1859–1952). *Internet encyclopedia of philosophy.* Retrieved from http://www.iep.utm.edu/dewey/#H4

Fine, M., & Asch, A. (1988). Disability beyond stigma: Social interaction, discrimination, and activism. *Journal of Social Issues, 44*(1), 3–21.

Frain, M. P., Berven, N. L., Chan, F., & Tschopp, M. K. (2008). Family resilience, uncertainty, optimism, and the quality of life of individuals with HIV/AIDS. *Rehabilitation Counseling Bulletin, 52*, 16–27.

Freedman, R. I., & Fesko, S. L. (1996). The meaning of work in the lives of people with significant disabilities: Consumer and family perspectives. *Journal of Rehabilitation, 62*(3), 49–55.

Goffman, E. (1963). *Stigma: Notes on the management of spoiled identity.* Englewood Cliffs, NJ: Prentice-Hall.

Hall, C. S., & Lindzey, G. (1978). *Theories of personality* (3rd ed.). New York, NY: John Wiley.

Hatch, M. J. (1997). *Organization theory: Modern, symbolic and postmodern perspectives.* Oxford, England: Oxford University Press.

Howe, C. W., & Howe, J. W. (1987). The national alliance for the mentally ill: History and ideology. *New Directions for Mental Health Services, 34*, 23–33.

Hughes, B., & Paterson, K. (1997). The social model of disability and the disappearing body: Towards a sociology of impairment. *Disability & Society, 12*(3), 325–340.

Institute on Rehabilitation Issues. (2000). The family as a critical partner in the achievement of a successful employment outcome. *26th Institute on Rehabilitation Issues.* Retrieved from http://iriforum.org/download/26IRI_family.pdf

Kelley, S. D., & Lambert, S. S. (1992). Family support in rehabilitation: A review of research, 1980–1990. *Rehabilitation Counseling Bulletin, 36*, 98–119.

Kneipp, S., & Bender, F. (1981). Services to family members by state vocational rehabilitation agencies. *Journal of Applied Rehabilitation Counseling, 12*(3), 30–134.

Lazarus, R. S. (1993). From psychological stress to the emotions: A history of hanging outlooks. *Annual Review of Psychology, 44*, 1–21.

Leahy, M. (2012). Qualified providers of rehabilitation counseling services. In D. R. Maki & V. M. Tarvydas (Eds.), *The professional practice of rehabilitation counseling* (pp. 193–211). New York, NY: Springer.

Lewin, K. (1946). Action research and minority problems. *Journal of Social Issues, 2*(4), 34–46.

Lewin, K. (1951). *Field theory in social science; selected theoretical papers* (D. Cartwright, Ed.). New York, NY: Harper & Row.

Lewin, K. A. (Ed.). (1935). *A dynamic theory of personality.* New York, NY: McGraw-Hill.

Li, L., & Moore, D. (1998). Acceptance of disability and its correlates. *Journal of Social psychology, 138*(1), 13–25.

Llewellyn, G., & Hogan, K. (2000). The use and abuse of models of disability. *Disability & Society, 15*(1), 157–165.

Maddux, J. E. (1995). *Self-efficacy, adaptation, and adjustment: Theory, research and application.* New York, NY: Plenum.

Maki, D. R., & Murray, G. (1995). Philosophy of rehabilitation. In A. Dell Orto & R. Marinelli (Eds.), *Encyclopedia of disability and rehabilitation* (pp. 555–561). New York, NY: MacMillan.

Maki, D. R., & Tarvydas, V. M. (2012). Rehabilitation counseling: A specialty practice of the counseling profession. In D. R. Maki & V. M. Tarvydas (Eds.), *The professional practice of rehabilitation counseling* (pp. 3–13). New York, NY: Springer.

Marini, I. (2012). What we counsel, teach, and research regarding the needs of persons with disabilities: What have we been missing? In I. Marini, N. M. Glover-Graf, & M. J. Millington (Eds.), *Psychosocial aspects of disability: Insider perspectives and counseling strategies* (pp. 481–498). New York, NY: Springer.

McMillan, D. W. (1996). Sense of community. *Journal of Community Psychology, 24*(4), 315–325.

McMillan, D. W. (1997). *Create your own love story.* Hillsboro, OR: Beyond Words.

McMillan, D. W. (2005). *Emotion rituals.* New York, NY: Routledge, Taylor & Francis.

McMillan, D. W., & Chavis, D. M. (1986). Sense of community: A definition and theory. *Journal of Community Psychology, 14*(1), 6–23.

Meyerson, L. (1988). The social psychology of physical disability: 1948 and 1988. *Journal of Social Issues, 44*(1), 173–188.

Miller, D. J., & Millington, M. J. (2002). What is required of us? Rethinking ethical conduct in the practice and profession of vocational rehabilitation. In J. D. Andrew & C. W. Faubion (Eds.), *Rehabilitation services: An introduction for the human services professional* (pp. 278–295). Osage Beach, MO: Aspen Professional Services.

Millington, M. J. (2012). Counseling families. In I. Marini, N. M. Glover-Graf, & M. J. Millington (Eds.), *Psychosocial aspects of disability: Insider perspectives and counseling strategies* (pp. 399–431). New York, NY: Springer.

Minuchin, P. (1985). Families and individual development: Provocations from the field of family therapy. *Child Development, 56,* 289–302.

Nosek, M. A. (2012). The person with a disability. In D. R. Maki & V. M. Tarvydas (Eds.), *The professional practice of rehabilitation* counseling (pp. 111–130). New York, NY: Springer.

Oliver, M. (1983). *Social work with disabled people.* Basingstoke, England: MacMillan.

Oliver, M. (1990). *The politics of disablement.* Basingstoke, England: Macmillan.

Perez, T. E. (2012). *Olmstead enforcement update: Using the ADA to promote community integration.* Testimony before the Senate Committee on Health, Education, Labor & Pensions, United States Senate. Retrieved from http://www.help.senate.gov/imo/media/doc/Perez3.pdf

Pierce, G. R., Sarason, I. G., & Sarason, B. R. (1996). Coping and social support. In M. Zeidner & N. S. Endler (Eds.), *Handbook of coping: Theory, research, applications* (pp. 434–451). New York, NY: John Wiley.

Porrit, D. (1979). Social support in crisis: Quantity or quality? *Social Science and Medicine, 124,* 715–721.

Power, P. W., & Del Orto, A. E. (2004). *Families living with chronic illness and disability: Interventions, challenges, and opportunities.* New York, NY: Springer.

Power, P. W., Hershenson, D. B., & Fabian, E. S. (1991). Meeting the documented needs of clients' families: An opportunity for rehabilitation counselors. *Journal of Rehabilitation, 57*(3), 11–16.

Remley, T. (2012). Evolution of counseling and its specializations. In D. R. Maki & V. M. Tarvydas (Eds.), *The professional practice of rehabilitation counseling* (pp. 17–38). New York, NY: Springer.

Revenson, T. A., & Majerovitz, D. (1990). Spouses' support provision to chronically ill patients. *Journal of Social and Personal Relationships, 7,* 575–586.

Riemer-Reiss, M., & Morrissette, P. J. (2002). Family counseling in vocational rehabilitation education. *Rehabilitation Education, 16,* 277–281.

Sales, A. (2012). History of rehabilitation counseling. In D. R. Maki & V. M. Tarvydas (Eds.), *The professional practice of rehabilitation counseling* (pp. 39–60). New York, NY: Springer.

Savickas, M. L., & Baker, D. B. (2005). The history of vocational psychology: Antecedents, origin, and early development. In W. B. Walsh & M. L. Savickas (Eds.), *Handbook of vocational psychology: Theory, research, & practice* (3rd ed., pp. 15–50). Mahwah, NJ: Lawrence Erlbaum.

Schein, E. H. (1996). Kurt Lewin's change theory in the field and in the classroom: Notes towards a model of management learning. *Systems Practice, 9*(1), 27–47.

Shakespeare, T. (2006). *Disability rights and wrongs.* New York, NY: Routledge.

Shontz, F. C. (1977). Six principles relating disability and psychological adjustment. *Rehabilitation Psychology, 24,* 207–210.

Sluzki, C. E. (2010). Personal social networks and health: Conceptual and clinical implications of their reciprocal impact. *Families, Systems, & Health, 28*(1), 1–18.

Smith, M. K. (2001). Kurt Lewin, groups, experiential learning and action research. In *Encyclopedia of informal education.* Retrieved from http://www.infed.org/thinkers/et-lewin.htm

Stubbins, J. (1984). Vocational rehabilitation as social science. *Rehabilitation Literature, 45,* 375–380.

Sutton, J. (1985). The need for family involvement in client rehabilitation. *Journal of Applied Rehabilitation, 16,* 42–45.

Szymanksi, E. M. (1985). Rehabilitation counseling: A profession with a vision, an identity, and a future. *Rehabilitation Counseling Bulletin, 29*(1), 2–5.

Tarvydas, V. (2012). Ethics and ethics decision making. In D. R. Maki & V. M. Tarvydas, (Eds.), *The professional practice of rehabilitation counseling* (pp. 339–370). New York, NY: Springer.

Tremain, S. (2005). Foucault, governmentality, and critical disability theory: An introduction. In S. Tremain (Ed.), *Foucault and the government of disability* (pp. 1–24). Ann Arbor: University of Michigan Press.

United Nations. (2006). *Convention on the rights of persons with disabilities (CRPD).* Geneva, Switzerland: Author. Retrieved from http://www.un.org/disabilities/default.asp?id=260

Verdonschot, M. M., de Witte, L. P., Reichraft, E., Buntinx, W. H., & Curfs, L. M. (2009). Community participation of people with intellectual disability: A review of empirical findings. *Journal of Intellectual Disability Research, 53,* 303–318.

Walsh, F. (2003). Family resilience: Strengths forged through adversity. In F. Walsh (Ed.), *Normal family processes* (3rd ed., pp. 399–423). New York, NY: Guilford.

Westin, M. T., & Reiss, D. (1979). The family's role in rehabilitation: Early warning system. *Journal of Rehabilitation, 1,* 26–29.

White, W., & Savage, B. (2005). All in the family: Alcohol and other drug problems, recovery, advocacy. *Alcoholism Treatment Quarterly, 23*(4), 3–37.

World Health Organization. (2002). *Toward a common language for functioning disability and health: The international classification of function.* Geneva, Switzerland: Author. Retrieved from http://www.who.int/classifications/icf/training/icfbeginnersguide.pdf

Wright, B. A. (1983). *Physical disability: A psychosocial approach.* New York, NY: Harper & Row.

CHAPTER 2

Counseling in the Context
of Family Identity

MICHAEL J. MILLINGTON AND ROSAMOND H. MADDEN

Who am I (who are we) in the face of change?

Identity arises out of the sum of our experiences. It gives us a sense of constancy and centeredness across the sometimes-turbulent change that comes with living. This is our sense of self. It is tied closely to our sense of community. In this chapter, we trace the developmental concept of identity through its manifestations at different levels of community, revealing a complex and systemic context for rehabilitation counseling. Each level of identity (personal, social, and collective) denotes a potential point of counseling exchange with the family.

To properly frame what these counseling exchanges with the family might entail, we describe how the experience of disability challenges the family system and how that experience is inculcated at each level of identity for each participating member. The family field on which all rehabilitation counseling acts becomes more than a backdrop for client service at this point. Family context, relations, and transactions create meaning in the shared disability experience. Family changes in response to the experience and becomes an agent of change in its own right as it moves in the collective on behalf of the person with a disability. Rehabilitation counseling becomes a party to this meaning making and a partner in family efforts to redefine itself in its wake. It is important for a family-inclusive profession to contemplate the meaning of rehabilitation counseling in the context of family identity. Counseling beyond the individual is a novel frame for rehabilitation. The essential presence of the family requires a reconsideration of the applied psychological counseling constructs that undergird current practice.

Families in rehabilitation counseling are peers and partners in a person-centered initiative to advance full community inclusion for their loved one. They enter into the relationship voluntarily and at the request of the client. They are the foremost experts in the lived experience of caring for the client and are strategically situated to facilitate or sabotage any plan devised. They are the first community that includes the client and advocates on her or his behalf. Rehabilitation counseling in this context is social strategy. The working alliance between the counselor and the family eschews the clinical for an intentional community of purpose that emerges from a joint common cause: full community inclusion for the person with a disability, and support for the participating family. We join the family in a shared space of community and counsel in the context of identity because we need to know, and become part of, the network that surrounds and supports the client.

FINDING IDENTITY IN THE FAMILY

Within the flickering inconsequential acts of separate selves dwells a sense of the whole which claims and dignifies them. In its presence we put off mortality and live in the universal. The life of the community in which we live and have our being is the fit symbol of this relationship. The acts in which we express our perception of the ties which bind us to others are its only rites and ceremonies. (Dewey, 1922, pp. 331–332)

The "rites and ceremonies" of our social relationships are the conduit through which we discover and create our world. It is the field of Lewin's life space (1936), where our sense of self is given form in the interaction between the person and his or her unique construction of a subjective world. Translating Lewin's formula to its identity equivalent, we are a function of the environment we create ($P = f[B, E]$).

Meaning and Identity

To understand identity, we must first understand meaning and how it is made. Meaning is value given form in the objects and events of lived experience (Pearlin, 1991). We make meaning with every intentional act. We orient our lives to the act of making meaning and then impose our meanings on all phenomena we encounter. In making meaning, we conceptualize our world, our identities, and ultimately our sense of self.

Meaning is predicated on core beliefs and value-laden goals (Park & Folkman, 1997). Beliefs are an encyclopedic and personal epistemology that informs the individual's worldview and frames behavior. Personal beliefs in regard to locus of control, self-worth, and optimism are important prerequisites for initiating and sustaining action. Beliefs function at the collective level to direct group action. Families that engage in collective problem solving do so with a collective belief in an orderly and responsive universe. Conversely, families that see themselves as a cohesive group are more likely to collaborate in problem solving than one that espouses a strong belief in rugged individualism (Oliveri & Reiss, 1982). Beliefs about the social environment are part of group and individual identity, played out in the problem-solving tasks of life (Oliveri & Reiss, 1981). We act and react according to our individual and shared beliefs, whether or not they are an accurate reflection of reality.

Goals turn meaning into intent. They provide the impetus and direction of our participations. There is a goal behind every intentional act, and so they are as numerous as our beliefs. They differ widely in importance, commitment, and centrality to our lives. They are hierarchical and complex in their interactions. We take on proximal goals to serve more distal ones. We invest time and energy into goals in proportion to our motivation to achieve them. Beliefs and goals provide the character of our community participation and together they make meaning in our lives.

Our self-concept is the global meaning we derive from putting these beliefs and goals to work (Schwartz, 2001). Self-concept grows and changes with experience, but comes with a bias toward stability. A stable self-concept is a secured one and we jealously guard it. Presented with a challenge to our self-concept, we are more likely to change the interpretation of the data behind the challenge than our comfortable worldview. We seek out environments that reinforce our standing beliefs. We see ourselves in a more optimistic and complimentary light than facts would support. We value concrete personal relevance over abstract ideals. We have an investment in our present identity. Actual change, even positive change, comes at a cost, that is, stress (Park & Folkman, 1997). This rather ambivalent relationship to change is what Lewin called, "quasi-stationary equilibrium" (Burnes, 2004, p. 981); the status quo tends to be well secured by environmental conditions and a kind of social inertia. Meaning crystallizes through our habits and rituals (see Costa, 2013), into a perceived (if sometimes illusory) stable and unified identity.

Personal Identity

Personal identity develops with one's cognitive abilities (Erikson, 1968) and evolves through community participation. As we grow into and out of developmental roles, our beliefs are challenged and our goals change in normative and expected ways. We experiment with identity alternatives across domains (e.g., occupation, politics; Schwartz, 2001), evaluate their fit in our lives, and make an eventual commitment to an identity, its values, and its worldview. The process of identification moves along axes of exploration and commitment (Marcia, 1966). A person's first contact with a role is usually characterized as one of diffusion. He or she has neither explored nor committed to this identity in any meaningful way and so has no deep investment in it. Having explored the role, one may reserve commitment (moratorium) until meaning is internalized (achievement). Others may take on new roles in a leap in faith and commit without exploring (foreclosure). Their challenge comes when the role does not live up to faith-based expectations.

It follows that a personal history of evolving identities leads to the present concept of self. It is a path of challenge and self-discovery. Our motivations along the way are not always conscious (Schwartz, 2001). The forces influencing our decisions are not always clear. The impact of intense experience is not easily interpretable in the traumatic moment (Pals, 2006) or its immediate aftermath, which is why telling the creation story of our identities is a powerful act of meaning making (King & Hicks, 2006) advanced in the narrative approach to identity development (McLean & Pasupathi, 2012).

In the theory of narrative identity, individuals construct a personal mythology out of their life experiences. They repurpose memories, interpret current events through the new narrative, and project their future in its image. Story construction gives one a sense of meaning in the present and reinforces the sense of continuity in the unfolding saga over time (McAdams, 2001). More than personal reflection, the narrative story is a social process that appreciates an audience (Weeks & Pasupathi, 2010). Identity as developmental path and socially constructed history is realized on the community stage, where opportunities for roles are found and one's stories will be heard.

Community creates the opportunity to develop personal identity through the role experiences it offers the individual. In the first community, each family role is differentiated by its function in the group and its relationship to other family roles (Deaux, 2001). The mother role, for instance, implies a specialized relationship with a child with attendant tasks and routines, suggests a series of defining relationships with other proximal roles (i.e., father, grandmother, grandfather), and may be locally defined by connections with a number of distal roles in the community (e.g., social worker, teacher). Thus are family roles networked and interdependent.

Personal identity is drawn from a multitude of roles. Mothers are also sisters, aunts, and grandmothers within the family. Beyond the family, they are workers, students, and activists. Each role comes with a different set of meanings and connections (Tajfel & Turner, 1979). Each role lays claim to its own facet of one's personal story. Some roles are more salient than others. All are in flux, multifaceted, and developmental (Cox & Lyddon, 1997). Personal identity is defined by *all* of the roles one plays in community. "Who I am" is a living history of the roles that the individual has explored and inhabited in the past, in the present, and intends to pursue in a goal-directed future. The concordance of personal meaning that the individual constructs out of the totality of role experiences is his or her unique answer to the question of identity (Skaff & Pearlin, 1992). We are the stories we tell ourselves.

Social Identity

Whereas personal identity reflects meaning associated with individuation (*who I am*), social identity reflects meaning associated with affiliation (*who we are*). Social identity trades in a social field (Reicher, Spears, & Haslam, 2010) of the collective's values, norms, and worldview. Herein, the individual shapes, and is shaped by, a shared identity. Social identity is not secondary to personal identity or dependent on it. Social identity springs from a primal drive to belong to a social order that has its own values and meanings.

Social identity is comparative in nature. The in-group differentiates itself by comparisons to an out-group. The family is defined as much by what it stands for, as what it stands against. The distinction between in-group membership and out-group status is one of boundaries. Boundaries are the social skin of identity, and value keeps it in place. Membership must be seen as added value to attract and keep members in. Values must also be in place to justify keeping others out. Outsiders must be different in some meaningful way, and in this difference they must be unworthy of member-ship. It is human nature to discriminate along lines of affiliation. Research has shown that random assignment to groups based on arbitrary categorization is enough to induce discrimination against out-group members (Tajfel & Turner, 1986). As the salience of categorization increases, so does one's commitment to the social identity. Strong boundaries make strong identities and acts of both inclusion and exclusion are at work in group dynamics.

The psychological attraction of community inclusion is very strong. Inclusion requires members to see the world through a collective lens (Turner, 1982). In this social communion, individuals draw upon the self-efficacy of the group (Bandura, 1998) and upon its resources (Iyer, Jetten, Tsivrikos, Postmes, & Haslam, 2011). A group characterized by strong social identification is more cohesive, more effec-tive in collaborative effort, and less prone to internal conflict (Putnam, 2000). Individual members of such a group respond to stress and threats with more resolve (Haslam & Reicher, 2006), feel more empowered in their action (Camp, Finlay, & Lyons, 2002), and sustain mental health through trauma and crises bet-ter when social identity brings meaning to suffering (Kallezi, Reicher, & Cassidy, 2009). Social identity is an essential component of self-concept (Hogg & Abrams, 1988). It is fortified by the confidence that comes from external validation and support (Stets & Burke, 2000).

Community exclusion, as social identity theory suggests, is an active force that also motivates membership and assimilation into a shared social identity. McMillan and Chavis (1986) identified "freedom from shame" as part of the socializing process and added value of established membership. In it, the candidate engages in a sharing of personal and sensitive information, or otherwise opens him- or herself to the poten-tial for rejection by the group. It is the group prerogative at that point to share secrets or turn its collective back. Becoming vulnerable is risk taken and the cost of membership. The psychological value of membership is tied to the depth of the potential for shame. Shame pushes people out, but it does so with the consent of the individual. Shame is to be found wanting in some aspect of social identity and for the shamed person to accept this shortcoming as a legitimate claim. For the candidate, it is an agreed on and deserved end to community. Humiliation, on the more sinister hand, does not require cooperation from the stigmatized individual (Klein, 1991). It is the forced and public rejection of the person regardless of his or her claims to membership. If shame is the death of community, humiliation is its murder. The fear of shame and humiliation are powerful tools for maintaining social boundaries and group prejudices.

Where one's social identity is strong and commitment is high, loss of membership is catastrophic. Insiders, threatened with expulsion, will commit heinous acts against their better nature to retain their in-group status. Humiliation is ubiquitous in group dynamics, subtly applied, and implied. Demotion is nearly as good as expulsion. Any loss of resource, position, power, or face is a tool that political animals in any group will use to better their own position at the expense of others. One tool of control is to assign labels to people you wish to diminish and thus force them into spoiled identities (Goffman, 1963) that mark them permanently as outsiders.

Klein (1991) wrote of the humiliation dynamic, its powerful influence, and the psychosocial damage left in its wake. It is familiar ground for rehabilitation counselors dealing with the stigma of disability experienced by individuals. But the traditional models of personal counseling have mostly dealt with the person's individual efforts at coping with the "disabled" role to which he or she has been relegated. Social identity theory was created to address community exclusion with a community response.

Social Identity and the Social Movement

Social identity theory (Tajfel & Turner, 1979) sought to understand the psychosocial dynamics and strategies of low-status groups in dealing with stigmatized, devalued, or otherwise marginalized identities imposed by high-status groups. Theorists wanted to know how disenfranchised individuals might effectively self-advocate by participating in the collective. They identified three sociostructural characteristics that influence how minority groups respond: permeability, stability, and legitimacy. Permeability is the ability of group members to join or leave the group freely, that is, social mobility. Stability is the degree to which group status is subject to change. Legitimacy is the perception that people have concerning whether or not the group's diminished status is a valid appraisal of their character or worth. The interplay of these three characteristics defines the strategies available to group members attempting to escape stigmatization (Verkuyten & Reijerse, 2008).

Denying one's membership in a stigmatized group is a potential strategy, especially when high stability and legitimacy limit other options. People with invisible disabilities could choose to "pass." This option is codified in the Americans with Disabilities Act (ADA) after a fashion and is commonly taught as a strategy in job seeking, that is, employers cannot ask about irrelevant characteristics in the selection process, and job seekers are conversely advised not to offer information about irrelevant physical or psychological impairments. As convenient as this strategy might be for persons not strongly committed to a disability identity, it does nothing to address the injustice that makes it necessary. In fact, "passing" supports the legitimacy of oppression and reinforces the notion of permanence by the lack of community response.

Where boundaries are impermeable and status is immoveable, options for change are limited to perspective. The stigmatized group can redefine itself in contrast to an even more stigmatized group, by accentuating what positive dimensions the dominate group might deign of value, or by redefining the meaning of membership completely. These responses are passive, but at least they maintain group cohesion.

Self-Categorization Theory and Community Building

Where group identity is salient and commitment is high, the group can organize to challenge its status under the gaze of others (Deyhle, 2009) through reinforcing, intensifying, and redefining its own social identity in terms of resistance (Latrofa, Vaes, Cadinu, & Carnaghi, 2010), actively rejecting and challenging the status quo, and advocating a new relationship in collective action (Schmitt & Branscomb, 2002). Social identity creates the possibility for a discourse with power (Clare, Rowlands, & Quin, 2008).

This advocacy-oriented approach to social identity was promulgated by self-categorization theory (Turner, Hogg, Oakes, Reicher, & Wetherell, 1987). It extends social identity theory into activism based on three insights:

1. Social identity is an adaptive process that sublimates difference within a group, accentuates differences between groups, produces collective behavior, and makes cooperation and influence among members possible.
2. Self-categorization is a reflection of the groups a person sees him- or herself aligned with and alienated from (us vs. them); salience of a particular category depends on its fit with personal values, meanings, and utility (Turner, 1999).
3. The stronger the sense of social identity, the more likely the individual is to acquiesce to group decisions, seek comity with members, give of him- or herself, and work cooperatively toward shared goals (Turner, 1991).

Self-categorization is an active process that is reinforced through community action. From the collective perspective, stronger bonds between members generate greater emotional, physical, and social resources available to the individual. The processes that create social identity and self-categorization (e.g., sharing and cooperation) are the same means by which social capital is accumulated (Haslam, O'Brien, Jetten, Vormedal, & Penna, 2005), community is built, and social change is pursued.

Finding Family Identity in Family Systems

Family as first community provides for the origins of identity at the personal, social, and collective levels. We find the family identity in the collective, beyond individuation and affiliation of the individual. Family is a corporate identity, if boundaries hold, that acts on group needs in a social field populated with other social entities

(Lewin, 1936). The plans of the collective concentrate influence and orchestrate resources in ways that support each individual and advance group meanings and goals in the marketplace. Family identity arises from these social exchanges, paralleling the processes previously described.

Family Function: McMaster Model

The McMaster model looks at family function in three family task domains (Epstein, Ryan, Bishop, Miller, & Keitner, 2003): basic, developmental, and hazardous. Basic tasks sustain the day-to-day family operations (e.g., procuring and managing food, shelter, money, transportation). Developmental tasks facilitate growth and transitions (graduation, marriage, procreation, death). Hazardous tasks respond to crisis and the unexpected (disability, job loss, bankruptcy, divorce, death). Task performance involves effective (a) problem solving, (b) communication, (c) role function, (d) affective responsiveness and involvement, and (e) behavior control.

Problem-Solving Effectiveness. The family engages a problem-solving process to address instrumental (getting things done), and affective (feelings surrounding family function) issues that become an impediment to family function. Effective and logical steps to solution include some variant of (a) problem identification, (b) communication of problem among appropriate stakeholders, (c) generating alternative action plans, (d) specific plan identification, (e) plan implementation, (f) monitoring implementation, and (g) evaluating outcomes. The everyday problems of family are many and most are resolved without consciously moving through the steps. But the greater the novelty and risk associated with the problem, the more important a strategic approach to problem solving becomes. Systemically complex life problems do not, by definition, have simple answers. Layers of problems beneath surface symptoms require a steadfast application of problem-solving skills and the ability to learn from failure and improve on partial success. Resilient families are not differentiated by the number of problems they have, but by their commitment to the problem-solving process (Epstein et al., 2003). Problems arise with the lack of skill.

Communication. There are many channels of communication in a social system, and all must be recognized for their contribution to group cohesion. Theory has focused overwhelmingly on verbal communication as the primary medium of information exchange between participants. Verbal communication of instrumental and affective content can be characterized in terms of its (a) clarity of message and (b) directness to the intended recipient. Clarity is a straightforward standard of good communication. There are no conditions where garbling the message is a positive aspect of communication, unless confusion is the intended message. Directness is more of a style issue. In some cultures (and situationally within any culture), directness is valued under some circumstances, whereas in others it is viewed as abrupt, rude, or disrespectful. Within the family, there is much more to communication than meets the ear.

A raised eyebrow, a handshake between cousins, even the silence that passes between any family dyad can speak volumes. Problems arise when communication is absent, garbled, mismatched as to style, or the content is toxic to the relationship in any medium of exchange.

Role Function. Family roles have specialized functions and relationships that provide structure and circulate resources into and through the family system. Some of the more important functions include (a) acquiring/generating resources, (b) nurturance and support, (c) sex and intimacy, (d) personal development and advancement (e.g., career support), and (e) family management. Family management includes decision making, boundary maintenance, distribution of resources, care giving, role allocation (how tasks are meted out); and role accountability (responsibility to the family and the authority within the family). Role functions are negotiated for balance within the family. Problems arise when that balance is missing.

Affective Responsiveness and Affective Involvement. Responsiveness is the ability to react with appropriate emotionality to family cues. Involvement is the degree to which individuals engage emotionally, intellectually, and physically with other members. Engagement runs a continuum from complete isolation to symbiotic loss of identity, with healthy balance usually (but not always) found in more moderate positions. The range in both depth of responsiveness and the means by which it is communicated varies widely across cultures. In the family, emotional responsiveness may vary within specific relationships, for example, compare the strength and character of the socioemotional bonds between spouses, siblings, and along gender lines. Being role dependent, the nature of these family bonds change as roles mature and when challenged by events. Crises can bring us together or drive us apart. Problems arise at the extremes when relationships are unresponsive to the need for change.

Behavior Control. Family roles are circumscribed by hierarchy, rules, and sanctions. Well-established family structure removes uncertainty about one's place in the order of things, the consequences of one's actions, and expectations for the future. Families range from autocracy to anarchy in the expression of behavioral control, with culturally mediated democratic approaches in the productive middle (Epstein et al., 2003). Entering into this compact of roles, one trades autonomy for security. The rewards are a comforting sense of predictability and constancy, and a clearly defined social identity. Problems arise when behavior control acts against the best interests of the individual.

Family Life Cycle. Family systems are constantly evolving through time (McGoldrick & Carter, 2003), cycling through developmental transitions and shifting in composition in response to external pressures and internal forces. Local expectations vary by culture and shift on socioeconomic tides, but there are some rather consistent, almost universal themes in the arc of family life (Steinglass, Bennett, Wolin, & Reiss, 1987).

Childbirth brings family members together to provide support. There is an expansion of social circles through childhood and a distancing in adolescence. Rituals mark the generational transitions from youth to adulthood, from debutante to spouse to parent, to elder, and passing on . . . ad infinitum. In this way, family identity is always becoming, changing in culturally patterned ways that provide a sense of constancy over time.

FINDING REHABILITATION COUNSELING IN THE FAMILY IDENTITY

Disability manifests in the family system (McKellin, 1995) through the same social exchanges that create personal, social, and collective identity. Roles change in response to disability (Yeates, Henwood, Gracey, & Evans, 2007). External relationships end (Feigin, 1994) and new relationships are formed. Crises come and go; life stabilizes around a new system; along the way, disability becomes part of the family identity (McKellin, 1995) at every level.

Experience of Disability

Disability is a complex phenomenon fundamentally captured in the interaction between health conditions (i.e., disorders or disease) and the contextual factors that embed the person in his or her environment.

Figure 2.1 represents the experience of disability from the first-person perspective. The diagram is adapted from the model espoused in the International Classification of Function (ICF; World Health Organization [WHO], 2013). It has been inverted here to emphasize the psychosocial point of view and adapted to show the connection with the family. The family appears as a category within the individual's environment. The exchange between the person and the family is represented by the reciprocating arrow that joins them. This exchange is similarly connected to the bodily structures and functions, the activities, and ultimately the participation of the individual in the community. To demonstrate that the experience of disability in a family system does not stop at the boundary of the individual, a second ICF diagram has been embedded in the environmental domain, representing the experience of each family member. Disability enters the experience of each family member as a feature of his or her environment and through the social identity he or she shares with the family member with a disability. The individual experiences of disability channeled through supporting family members are as systemically integrated into the ICF system as the direct personal experience of the client. All biopsychosocial aspects of family function are influenced by proximity to and interaction with disability. As family changes the disability experience, the experience changes the family.

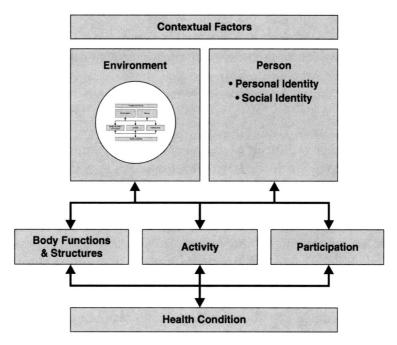

FIGURE 2.1 How disability is experienced within the family.

Health Conditions

The instrumental characteristics of the health conditions that mediate the experience for families include onset, course, outcome expectations, and predictability (Rolland, 2012). Acute onset is most often a traumatic family event, creating a distinct moment in time that demarcates identity, before and after. Disability may be introduced at birth or later in life as a disease, complication, or traumatic injury. Gradual onset provides a gray time of transition. The course of the illness dictates the tasks of adjustment. Progressive illness dictates a constant adjustment to increasing limitations; the faster the progression, the more destabilizing the effect. In extreme circumstances, the family is in a state of continual reorganization. Where progress is intermittent, the family may develop different contingency plans for relapse and remission. Where illness prompts contemplation of death or profound loss, anticipatory grief creates avoidance behaviors that may serve to protect one from the intensity of experience, but at the cost of emotional separation and social isolation. Predictability (Rolland, 2012) is a metacharacteristic affecting all of the other attributes. Unpredictable disease creates a level of ambiguity that makes planning difficult.

Functions and Structures

Changes to body functions and structures may occur, related to one or more health conditions an individual may experience. While these changes are sometimes a component of health outcomes, the relationship is not necessarily simple or linear. In the ICF, problems with body function and structure are called impairments and may relate to effects such as problems with muscle or joint functions, mental functions, loss of limbs, spinal injury, or skin damage. These are aspects of physiology and anatomy and are often seen as the domain of medical and other health professionals, in treatment and rehabilitation. While very much of the body, impairments also relate to a person's environment. The healing of muscle functions may be slow if the physical home environment is difficult to navigate or if family support of a sometimes-demanding exercise regime does not reinforce the efforts a person may need to make.

Decreasing impairment may be an end in itself. A person may consider a reduction in pain levels or a reduction in scarring and a related improvement in mental functions such as confidence as worthwhile goals. A professional may concentrate on achieving the increase in joint movement he or she considers is possible, on the basis of his or her knowledge and experience, and considers this a worthwhile goal, assuming but not investigating possible flow-on benefits.

Impairments do not necessarily have a direct causal relationship with a person's activities or participation. For example, loss of limb may not restrict mobility with the right equipment and in the right environment. Conversely, lack of mobility may relate to a range of impairments (e.g., muscle, mental, or perceptual functions). The degree of importance a person attaches to impairments of body function and structure may relate directly to the importance he or she attaches to the range of activities that require these functions. This relationship, or perceived relationship, may thereby affect motivation in rehabilitation.

Activities and Participation

The ICF distinguishes between activity (the execution of a task or act) and participation (involvement in life situations). Both take place in any lifespace, from learning, to mobility, to interpersonal relationships. The model thus recognizes that a person may be undertaking activities but may never feel involved. He or she may lack choice, control, or a sense of inclusion; he or she may wash dishes but not be truly involved in discussions of the menu. The disability experience is ultimately defined in its impact on participation as the essence of community inclusion. Participation in the domains of work, education, and independent living have been the contexts most familiar to rehabilitation counselors to date. But if community inclusion is indeed the fundamental mission, wherever participation is diminished or denied is a domain of interest.

Stress and Disability

The reason rehabilitation counseling is engaged is not the presence of health issues, structural or functional impairment of bodily systems, or alternatively problems in environmental or personal contextual factors. We engage because participation is not served and so we look to the family system for ways to facilitate. We are engaging change processes. We engage the reactive change that disability has wrought upon the family, and the proactive change that is the family response to disability in its midst. In both cases, the system is challenged and stress is the result. Stress can motivate, but with sufficient intensity or duration, it also creates systemic physical, psychological, and social challenges to rehabilitation and threats to personal and familial well-being. There are two models of stress that provide useful perspectives on the dynamics of disability in the family. Although both are psychosocial in application, they start from psychological and social roots, respectively.

The Transactional Model of Stress

The transactional model of stress posits that stress is not an objective feature of the person or the environment, but a subjective emotional response to the interaction between the two (Lazarus & Folkman, 1984). The process begins with an objective event. Perhaps mother has an accident at work, or a child is born with a congenital disability. A personal appraisal of the event follows. Mother contemplates all of the consequences of lost income and the risks and hardships that await her rehabilitation and return to work. The parents of the child deal with the initial shock of an unexpected diagnosis and grapple with understanding present needs while only vaguely grasping the enormity of change coming in the ensuing years. The primary appraisal addresses the question, "Is this situation a threat?" Perhaps in these cases, yes, there is a threat. The first appraisal establishes the motivational relevance of the event (Lazarus, 1993).

Risks that rise to the level of personal threat are met with an emotionally charged response (Perrewé & Zellars, 1999) and a second appraisal. Can I resolve this threat? Can I cope? The individual contemplates the meaning of the experience, the resources at his or her disposal, and his or her potential for response. Perhaps the worker sees a way through the experience. Rehabilitation will be a challenge, but the job is secure, the family is supportive, and the impairment can be accommodated. The woman is secure enough in her self-concept that any residual loss can be managed. Perhaps the infant's parents do not have such a positive appraisal. Specialized services and medical care are nonexistent in their rural community. The community is burdened with poverty, and alcoholism has become a generational problem. The parents are estranged and underemployed. They fear that having a child with a disability will bring shame on their families. They do not have the resources, skills, or confidence to mount response. In the absence of response, the threat and the stress remain. To the degree that stress is only partially resolved, stressors become strains (Pearlin, 1983).

The event precipitating stress can be sudden and traumatic like a heart attack, or the iconic last straw of cumulative chronic strain (Pearlin, Menaghan, Lieberman, & Mullan, 1981). In either case, the deepest threat is existential. To discover that one is not in control, not powerful, and not respected is a direct assault to self-beliefs: self-efficacy, self-esteem, and self-worth (Aneshensel, Pearlin, & Shuler, 1993). Faced with a situation that challenges one's global beliefs and negates one's cherished goals (Park &

Folkman, 1997), a person is compelled to defend his or her self-concept, create new meaning that transcends the challenge, or succumb to a spoiled identity (Wright, 1983).

The stress model that explains individual struggle is adaptable to the family system (Kelly & Steed, 2004). Caregiving demands can become primary stressors (Pearlin, Aneshensel, & LeBlanc, 1997) on the family system. The resultant strain can in turn exacerbate a litany of secondary psychosocial stressors that challenge the family identity and the roles within it (Aneshensel et al., 1993). The incremental change in spousal relationships in the context of progressive illness is a direct affront to role identity. For the individual with Alzheimer's, stress comes from feelings of loss of control and loss of meaning in the relationship. Stress for the caregiver comes from ever-increasing demands, the loss of identity in the relationship, and role engulfment (Skaff & Pearlin, 1992) with its consequent loss of social connections outside of the carer role (Aneshensel et al., 1993).

The public face of the family is also challenged. Family participation in new circles of formal care must be incorporated into present beliefs and goals. Attitudes and expectations about disability within the family's existing social network set up the potential for conflict. The micro-oppressions of a stigmatizing society are a chronic stressor on the family's emerging disability identity as well as the social identity of the person identified with the disability community (Nario-Redmond, 2010).

The transactional stress model was a major shift in psychology away from a psychomedical bias of state and trait diagnostics (Pearlin, 1983) and clinical behaviorism in favor of a psychosocial perspective of mental health that integrated cognition, affect, and social relationships (Lazarus, 1993). In defining psychological stress processes in Lewin's person × environment field, it captured the essence of identity. As Lazarus (1993) said, "Indeed, the differences between physiological and psychological stress are profound and center on an issue that psychologists have long had great difficulty dealing with, namely, *personal meaning*" (p. 4, italics added). The transactional stress model has provided a solid foundation for theoretical development and practical interpretation in individual, family, and community applications (Turner & Schieman, 2008).

Conservation of Resources Model

Hobfoll (1989, 2001) offers a community variation on the psychosocial appraisal of stress that recognizes both the family and the "tribe" beyond the family as concentric frames required to capture the whole of the social experience of stress. The conservation of resource (COR) theory posits that stress "appraisals are embedded in the social context in which individuals find themselves, and that the idiographic aspects of appraisal are secondary to biological and overlearned automatic processes, on one hand, and socio-cultural processes, on the other hand" (Hobfoll, 2001, p. 341). Hobfoll does not discount the mind in the interpretation of stress. He emphasizes the importance of more fundamental aspects of the person × environment transaction.

The central tenet of COR theory is that the basic drive of people is to acquire, preserve, protect, and cultivate resources. Families are living systems constantly consuming and pursuing resources that sustain a dynamic equilibrium. This is the drive that creates the need for community because it provides the most efficient and effective structure for satisfying the many and varied needs the family has. Resources are anything of value from food and clothing, to barter and money, to space and time, to ideas and personality characteristics. Acquiring resources is crucial to recover from harm, overcome threat, and advance in the face of challenge (Lazarus, 1993). COR theory provides an economic perspective on stress that is aligned with social identity (Hobfoll, 2001) and meaning making in the marketplace. This complements rather than contradicts the stress transaction theory and expands the construct of stress with two principles (Hobfoll, 1998).

COR Principle 1: Primacy of Resource Loss. Life is lived in trade; success depends on profitable ventures. Stress occurs when resources are lost, threatened, or diminished in inefficient trade or investment. Thus there is a negativity bias attached to loss. The perception of loss is more powerful than the perception of gain. Gains become more important in the context of previous loss, that is, there is more emotional energy invested in recouping something of value that was lost than the energy invested in its acquisition. Resource loss is more stressful than low resources; that is, there is less perceived stress in dealing with low resources if one has never experienced high resources. Positive life events are not stressful if they are equated with gain. They are only stressful inasmuch as they include loss in subevents. For example, a promotion is not stressful for the gain in prestige or cash, but in the loss of the social network of equals incurred in leaving previous employment.

COR Principle 2: The Necessity of Resource Investment. The community is a dynamic and fluid marketplace of resources, and life in the community requires strategic investment. Resources must be invested to protect against future loss, recoup actual loss, and hopefully to amass resources as a form of well-being. In this psycho-socio-economic model, people who have limited resources consequently have little capacity to increase their "wealth" and suffer proportionally more from loss. Access to resources is positively correlated with capacity to orchestrate resource gain and negatively correlated with vulnerability for loss of resources.

Those who are vulnerable to loss are vulnerable to "loss spirals" as current loss begets future loss (Hobfoll, 1998, 2001). Cascading loss associated with at-risk populations exponentially exacerbates stress as vulnerable persons transact in increasingly frustrating systems with fewer and fewer resources. Families that lack a reservoir of resources tend to take a defensive approach to conservation rather than an investing approach that would have a better probability to ameliorate the loss and create gains. They do not see a way to risk-manage what they have, as they are not in a position to gamble. Consequently, they hang on without leverage and eventually lose again. There is a difference between learned helplessness and a defensive resource conservation strategy. Learned helplessness is succumbing; it is giving up. In a defensive posture, austerity is used as a coping strategy. But they eventually end up in the same place as loss spirals down, and efficacy erodes. This describes the dynamics of Wright's (1983) concept of succumbing. Succumbing is a stress response of last resort, the last choice at the end of the spiral. In this way, poverty creates poverty and stress spreads from the economic to the social and psychological.

Coping, Disability, and Identity

Coping is a normal function of everyday life. Coping with disability does not engender new coping strategies, although it often requires an enhanced portfolio of options. The appraisal of harm, threat, or challenge associated with disability is multifaceted and requires a concerted coping response that varies in its orchestration across individuals, within groups, and over time. The vast potential for variance and its idiosyncratic application makes coping a personal art navigating many possible outcomes (Haslam et al., 2005). Capacity for coping depends on both access to resources and skills to mobilize them.

Social Supports

We start with social support because any internalized skill that might be brought to bear first requires an environment that is conducive to implementation. Social support provides the conduit to resources and the relationships required to solve problems and achieve goals. Social support comes from being embedded in a social network that is responsive to one's needs. This implies a deeper set of relationships and stronger socioemotional bonds than casual or formal professional connections allow (Pearlin et al., 1981, p. 340). Social support comes from one's family and friends because it is based on sustainable interdependence.

Instrumental (Problem Solving)

Problem solving is the most straightforward approach to dealing with stress, wherein one strives to resolve the problem directly. Most strategies are variations on a strategic, highly cognitive approach (Isaksen & Treffinger, 2004) that moves stepwise from problem identification, to solution finding, to plan development, to implementation and evaluation of outcomes. Problem solving is most useful when it cycles through repeatedly as an organizational learning process. Problem solving may not be directly effective when you are not in control of the source of the problem or there is no solution to be found (Newth & DeLongis, 2004).

Problem Solving With Resources

Solving problems defined within a transactional model are aimed at resolving issues surrounding events and thus tend to be reactive. Problems and solutions in the COR theory are defined in terms of resources and more easily take on a proactive approach to problem solving. Strategic planning revolves around efforts to build reservoirs of resources and orchestrate them to best advantage in recouping loss, preemptive action to prevent future loss and loss spirals, and encouraging synergistic gain spirals that fortify a healthy social position. Immediate strategies include (a) resource replacement (get back what you lost), (b) resource substitution (lose peace at home, increase investment in work), (c) optimize what you already have, and (d) compensate for lack of fit with support (e.g., adaptive technology, social support). Emphasis on optimizing environmental resources facilitates the development of underlying personal characteristics such as self-efficacy (Freedy & Hobfoll, 1994), optimism, self-esteem, sense of coherence, learned resourcefulness, social support, and personal hardiness (Hobfoll, 2001).

Affective Coping

Alternatively, emotional response to stress can be changed. Reappraisal initiates all emotional coping. Acceptance of the situation is a positive reframing. Self-blame is a negative reframing (Gross & John, 2003). Emotional distance, avoidance, and suppression attempt to negate appraisal completely. There is a general consensus to view positive framing as superior and the others as potentially dysfunctional coping. In practice, there are times when emotional distance, avoidance, and suppression are the more healthy coping alternatives.

Meaning Making as Coping

Rogers (1951) opined that healthy adjustment comes from being able to incorporate all of one's experiences into a relationship with one's self-concept. Any experience that one does not integrate becomes a threat or stress. As a major theme in this chapter, meaning making has emerged as the loom on which we weave our identities. It follows that stressful challenges to identity send us back to the loom, and there we find a particularly potent exercise in the family processes.

Family Narrative (Stories and Myths). Families create shared meaning in the stories they tell of themselves and of each other. There is the everyday story, like the news, that explains what we did and why. It reifies the routines of our lives, "The children were gathering eggs on Saturday morning . . ." puts the story in a role, at time, in a place, and for a purpose that is known in a special way to the family. The most powerful stories become family mythologies that carry deeper meaning. The communion of storytelling creates a sense of coherence among family members. It normalizes the stress-filled event and reassures the teller's place in the family by the tacit approval of the attentive audience (Pasupathi & Hoyt, 2009). The family participates in the meaning making of the story with its asides and commentary. Shared values are accentuated. Out-group villains are vilified. Reasons for optimism are found and value is mined in lessons learned (Saltzman et al., 2011). The story of the individual becomes the story of the group, thereby reaffirming solidarity in social identity (McClean & Pasupathi, 2012) in times of adversity.

Meaning Making in Action: Routines and Rituals. Meaning making also takes place in cooperative action. Family life gets its sense of stability from the habits of individuals and the routines of the group (Fiese, 2006). These are the basic proximal processes (Bronfenbrenner, 1977) that construct personal and social identity. There is comfort in the pattern of routine, and a sense of competence comes from mastering it (Fiese et al., 2002). Caring for a loved one is a potent path for meaning making. The meaning of a caring act deepens and intensifies with repetition. Loving care captured in routine creates a moment in time when the array of other demands are put into perspective. It becomes an applied and practiced acceptance of the present and a renewal of the value of this particular relationship (Larson, 2010). The act being charged with symbolic meaning becomes more than routine; it becomes a ritual (Fiese et al., 2002).

Rituals exist for daily activities (e.g., pledge of allegiance), scheduled events (e.g., weddings), and in response to the unforeseen, providing structure to life. They are celebrations, traditions, or patterned family interactions (Costa, 2013) that communicate meaning through the generations and most importantly reify membership and create a role for everyone. Rituals around family care routines of loved ones have been shown to improve cohesion and compliance with treatment regimens (Santos, Crespo, Silva, & Canavarro, 2012). Disability is incorporated into family stories and myths, and routines and rituals through traditional family channels (Fiese et al., 2002) and thus becomes an integral feature of evolving family life (Larson, 2010).

Relational Coping. Relational coping arises out of dyads and is used to strengthen the individuals and preserve the relationship (Marin, Holtzman, DeLongis, & Robinson, 2007). Parental dyads often engage in mutual emotional support and collaborative problem solving (Donato, Iafrate, Bradbury, & Scabini, 2012) to deal with larger issues of family stress (DeLongis & Holtzman, 2005) and the logistics of disability/care within the family (Kramer, 1993). The salience of group membership acts as a buffer against stressors that attack the family (Haslam & Reicher, 2006). Relational coping is most obvious in moments of trauma, when families come together to comfort each other and to make meaning out of chaos and tragedy (Marin et al., 2007).

Manifestations of Coping: Family Resilience

Unabated stress and strain have negative biological, psychological (Haslam, 2004), and social consequences (Saltzman et al., 2011). Ineffective coping strategies only slow the rate of decline. The experience of disability often poses such risks to families. Even under the best of circumstances, it is doubtful that family members' first attempts at coping with the complexities of care are particularly efficacious. But they learn. Coping is social learning (Layne, Warren, Watson, & Shalev, 2007) with family at the core in both character and process (Werner & Smith, 2001). Disability is experienced as the history of a shared adaptation to adversity (Luthar, 2006). Experience begets wisdom, a portfolio of coping strategies, and a worldview infused in the social identity that bespeaks emotional lessons learned.

This positive manifestation of stress and coping is called family resilience. Walsh (2006) saw family resilience as the capacity to withstand crises, endure hardships, and grow through adversity as a functional unit. She saw this capacity coming out of family strengths tested against challenge. Family resilience, Walsh states, "involves many interactive processes over time—from a family's approach to a threatening situation, through its ability to manage disruptive transitions, to varied strategies for coping with emerging challenges in the immediate and long-term aftermath" (p. 23). Walsh finds the family's shared beliefs, norms, and rituals at the balanced center of family resilience. Identity is the foundation on which resilience grows.

Meaning Making in Family Resilience

Patterson (1995) observed that the meaning-making processes were the social learning engine that turns coping experience into integrated resilience. Meaning making builds resilience through its capacity to (a) redefine threat and challenge in the appraisal process; (b) reconstitute a coherent family identity capable of developing new coping strategies; and (c) reimagine family relationships with other groups and social systems (Patterson, 2002).

Relational Aspect of Family Resilience

The strength of family resilience is the synergistic effect of individual resilience in the collective. The individual is fortified by the confidence that comes from family membership and is thus motivated to advocate on the family's behalf. Responding to challenge in the collective, no one individual need master all aspects of coping or be particularly resilient 100% of the time (Patterson, 2002). Shared problems and orchestrated response allow that individuals can contribute according to their strengths, and seek support according to their needs.

Social Support of Family Resilience

Resilience is learned, but it is not entirely a personal or group attribute. Just as individual resilience depends on family support, family resilience depends on the social support of the community (Corrigan & Phelan, 2004). The character of the family's social network determines the kind, amount, quality, and timing of informal support and care resources available. The constellation, structures, and processes of community services similarly determine the societal contribution to the raw material of family resilience (Farrell, Bowen, & Swick, 2014). Rehabilitation counseling stands among these formal resource offerings. Its value in building resilience, as with all social support, depends largely on the fit between service and need and the family's ability to turn potential into plan and practice.

Implications for Rehabilitation Counseling

Client-centered rehabilitation counseling maintains the individual with a disability at its core. All counseling activity must be maximally under client control and evaluated on the basis of its contribution to the full community inclusion of the individual. The family is recognized as the first community, a social extension of the client that experiences threats to its collective inclusion in community and thus has a legitimate and direct relationship with rehabilitation counseling. Family is recognized as an essential component of efficient and effective service in the present and sustaining inclusion into the future. It is the prerogative of the client to define what the family is in the collective sense, who its constituents are, and the role family members will play in the development, execution, and evaluation of rehabilitation counseling plans and services. To serve the family and the fundamental mission, rehabilitation counseling is transacted in the community with two instrumental expressions: (a) to facilitate client inclusion within the family; and (b) to facilitate family inclusion in the rehabilitation process.

Working Alliance

Rehabilitation counselors approach the family as an outsider, a stranger, and, worse, a stranger with an agenda. At the door, the family knows nothing of rehabilitation counseling but the stereotype and its previous experience with health care, insurance, and/or governmental systems. Imagine the family connotations of "I'm from the government and I'm here to help," or "I represent your employer and I'm here to get you back to work." The rehabilitation counselor is an outsider at entry and potentially a threat to a family in need. The counselor must often act on whatever motivation and good will accompanies him or her to the initial contact and begin negotiating a better relationship immediately. He or she must form a bond of trust and communication that starts with the client (Strauser, Lustig, & Donnell, 2004) and will grow into a working alliance with the family (Thompson, Bender, Lantry, & Flynn, 2007).

Preconditions for a Working Alliance. A working alliance in a group setting might as well be called community development. The rehabilitation counselor seeks a place in the family's social constellation. The rehabilitation counselor's position should be peripheral and deferent to the family dynamic, close and trusted enough to participate in the family business of caring for the client, and emic enough as scientist-practitioners to accurately and empathetically document the family's lived experience of disability. The counselor strikes this balance: not to join the family, but to become a bona fide part of the family's community.

Finding that balance under current vocational rehabilitation service structures may make this level of family communion problematic, but nevertheless, it is what is likely to be effective when the family's engaged cooperation is desired. A social model worldview is required to make this work, and it begins by embracing more egalitarian relationships and eschewing the power of the expert role. The proper relationship is a partnership of equals, with each partner to be respected and valued in his or her contribution.

The second requirement is to reject pathology. The family in community-based rehabilitation counseling is assumed to be healthy, normal, and performing to the best of its abilities. The problem that precipitated the partnership is defined as a temporary gap between where the family is and where the family wishes to be. The solution is in closing the gap, not fixing the person. The rehabilitation counselor must be slow to label behavior as maladaptive or pathological. When pathology cannot be denied and exists as a threat to self, other, or progress, it is time for a referral. The rehabilitation counselor cannot fill a dual role as family therapist and expect to succeed in either.

The third requirement is to embrace a positive, community-based psychology (see Lopez & Snyder, 2009). Rehabilitation counseling with families focuses on strengths, opportunities, and solutions. It communicates a realistic sense of optimism and models the sense of individual flexibility, group efficacy, and mutual esteem that undergirds effective collaboration. It transpires in the space where the family lives: at the kitchen table, in the workplace, at the community center. It remains consistently focused on client-controlled processes and outcomes, but everyone has a voice to be heard and a role to play.

Strategic Collaboration

Given this proactive and resilient worldview, rehabilitation counseling builds community with the family within a very focused set of shared values, meanings, beliefs, goals, and actions. The medium through which this exchange happens is instrumental problem solving. It is a normal family process and the most productive of coping strategies. The problem-solving process also mirrors brief and solution-focused counseling as well as models of the learning organization and continuous improvement logic models in quality assurance. In the identification of problems and goals, the family shares meaning. In the generation of solutions, the family explores resources. In the development of the plan, the family clarifies roles and relationships. In the implementation of the plan, the family masters the process and itself, growing in resilience through every failure and success. In time, this effort becomes identity and part of the stories it tells about community.

REFERENCES

Aneshensel, C. S., Pearlin, L. I., & Shuler, R. H. (1993). Stress, role captivity, and the cessation of caregiving. *Journal of Health and Social Behavior, 34,* 54–70.

Bandura, A. (1998). Personal and collective efficacy in human adaptation and change. In J. G. Adair, D. Belanger, & K. L. Dion (Eds.), *Advances in psychological science Volume 1: Personal, social and cultural aspects.* Hove, England: Psychology Press.

Bronfenbrenner, U. (1977). Lewinian space and ecological substance. *Journal of Social Issues, 33,* 199–212.

Burnes, B. (2004). Kurt Lewin and the planned approach to change: A re-appraisal. *Journal of Management Studies, 41,* 977–1002.

Camp, D. L., Finlay, W. M. L., & Lyons, E. (2002). Is low self-esteem an inevitable consequence of stigma? An example from women with chronic mental health problems. *Social Science & Medicine, 55*(5), 823–834.

Clare, L., Rowlands, J., & Quin, R. (2008). Collective strength: The impact of developing a shared social identity in early-stage dementia. *Dementia: The International Journal of Social Research and Practice, 7,* 9–30.

Corrigan, P. W., & Phelan, S. M. (2004). Social support and recovery in people with serious mental illnesses. *Community Mental Health Journal, 40*(6), 513–523.

Costa, R. P. (2013). Family rituals: Mapping the postmodern family through time, space and emotion. *Journal of Comparative Family Studies, 44*(3), 269–289.

Cox, L. M., & Lyddon, W. J. (1997). Constructivist conceptions of self: A discussion of emerging identity constructs. *Journal of Constructivist Psychology, 10,* 201–219.

Deaux, K. (2001). Social identity. *Encylopedia of women and gender.* New York, NY: Academic Press.

DeLongis, A., & Holtzman, S. (2005). Coping in context: The role of stress, social support, and personality in coping. *Journal of Personality, 73,* 1–24.

Dewey, J. (1922). *Human nature and conduct: An introduction to social psychology.* New York, NY: Holt, Rinehart and Winston. Retrieved from http://www.archive.org/details/humannaturecondu00deweiala

Deyhle, D. (2009). *Reflections in place.* Tucson: University of Arizona Press.

Donato, S., Iafrate, R., Bradbury, T. N., & Scabini, E. (2012). Acquiring dyadic coping: Parents and partners as models. *Personal Relationships, 19,* 386–400.

Epstein, N. B., Ryan, C. E., Bishop, D. S., Miller, I. W., & Keitner, G. I. (2003). The McMaster model: A view of healthy family functioning. In F. Walsh (Ed.), *Normal family processes* (3rd ed., pp. 581–607). New York, NY: Guilford.

Erikson, E. (1968). *Identity: Youth and crisis.* New York, NY: Norton.

Farrell, A. F., Bowen, G. L., & Swick, D. C. (2014). Network supports and resiliency among U.S. military spouses with children with special health care needs. *Family Relations, 63*(1), 55–70.

Feigin, R. (1994). Spousal adjustment to a postmarital disability in one partner. *Family Systems Medicine, 12*, 235–247.

Fiese, B. H. (2006). *Family routines and rituals.* London, NY: Yale University Press.

Fiese, B. H., Tomcho, T. J., Douglas, M., Josephs, K., Poltrock, S., & Baker, T. (2002). A Review of 50 years of research on naturally occurring family routines and rituals: Cause for celebration? *Journal of Family Psychology, 16*(4), 381–390.

Freedy, J. R., & Hobfoll, S. E. (1994). Stress inoculation for reduction of burnout: A conservation of resources approach. *Anxiety, Stress, and Coping, 6*, 311–325.

Goffman, E. (1963). *Stigma: Notes on the management of spoiled identity.* New York, NY: Simon & Schuster.

Gross, J. J., & John, O. P. (2003). Individual differences in two emotional regulation processes: Implications for affect, relationships, and well-being. *Journal of Personality and Social Psychology, 85*, 348–362.

Haslam, S. A. (2004). *Psychology in organizations: The social identity approach* (2nd ed.). London, England: SAGE.

Haslam, S. A., O'Brien, A., Jetten, J., Vormedal, K., & Penna, S. (2005). Taking the strain: Social identity, social support and the experience of stress. *British Journal of Social Psychology, 44*, 355–370.

Haslam, S. A., & Reicher, S. D. (2006). Stressing the group: Social identity and the unfolding dynamics of stress. *Journal of Applied Psychology, 91*, 1037–1052.

Hobfoll, S. E. (1989). Conservation of resources: A new attempt at conceptualizing stress. *American Psychologist, 44*, 513–524.

Hobfoll, S. E. (1998). *Stress, culture, and community: The psychology and philosophy of stress.* New York, NY: Plenum.

Hobfoll, S. E. (2001). The Influence of culture, community, and the nested-self in the stress process: Advancing conservation of resources theory. *Applied Psychology: An International Review, 50*(3), 337–421.

Hogg, M. A., & Abrams, D. (1988). *Social identifications: A social psychology of intergroup relations and group processes.* London, England: Routledge.

Isaksen, S. J., & Treffinger, D. J. (2004). Celebrating 50 years of reflective practice: Versions of creative problem solving. *Journal of Creative Behavior, 38*(2), 65–92.

Iyer, A., Jetten, J., Tsivrikos, D., Postmes, T., & Haslam, S. A. (2011). The more (and the more compatible) the merrier: Multiple group memberships and identity compatibility as predictors of adjustment after life transitions. *British Journal of Social Psychology, 48*, 707–733.

Kallezi, B., Reicher, S., & Cassidy, C. (2009). Surviving the Kosovo conflict: A study of social identity, appraisal of extreme events, and mental well-being. *Applied Psychology, 58*(1), 59–83.

Kelly, G. J., & Steed, L. G. (2004). Communities coping with change: A conceptual model. *Journal of Community Psychology, 32*(2), 201–216. doi:10.1002/jcop.10090

King, L. A., & Hicks, J. A. (2006). Narrating the self in the past and the future: Implications for maturity. *Research in Human Development, 3*, 121–138.

Klein, D. C. (1991). The humiliation dynamic: An overview. *Journal of Primary Prevention, 12*(2), 93–121.

Kramer, B. J. (1993). Expanding the conceptualization of caregiving coping: The importance of relationship-focused coping strategies. *Family Relations: Interdisciplinary Journal of Applied Family Studies, 42*, 383–391.

Larson, E. (2010). Psychological well-being and meaning-making when caregiving for children with disabilities: Growth through difficult times or sinking inward. *Open Journal of Therapy and Rehabilitation, 30*(2), 78–86.

Latrofa, M., Vaes, J., Cadinu, M., & Carnaghi, A. (2010). The cognitive representation of self-stereotyping. *Personality and Social Psychology Bulletin, 36,* 911–922.

Layne, C. M., Warren, J., Watson, P., & Shalev, A. (2007). Risk, vulnerability, resistance, and resilience: Towards an integrative conceptualization of posttraumatic adaptation. In M. M. Friedman, T. M. Keane, & P. A. Resick (Eds.), *Handbook of PTSD: Science and practice* (pp. 497–520). New York, NY: Guilford.

Lazarus, R. S. (1993). From psychological stress to the emotions: A history of a changing outlook. *Annual Review of Psychology, 44,* 1–21.

Lazarus, R. S., & Folkman, S. (1984). *Stress, appraisal and coping.* New York, NY: Springer.

Lewin, K. (1936). *Principles of topological psychology.* New York, NY: McGraw Hill.

Lopez, S. J., & Snyder, C. R. (Eds.). (2009). *Oxford handbook of positive psychology* (2nd ed.). New York, NY: Oxford University Press.

Luthar, S. S. (2006). Resilience in development: A synthesis of research across five decades. In D. Cicchetti & D. J. Cohen (Eds.), *Developmental psychopathology: Risk, disorder, and adaptation* (pp. 740–795). New York, NY: Wiley.

Marcia, J. E. (1966). Development and validation of ego identity status. *Journal of Personality and Social Psychology, 3,* 551–558.

Marin, T., Holtzman, S., DeLongis, A., & Robinson, L. (2007). Coping and the response of others. *Journal of Social and Personal Relationships, 24,* 951–969.

McAdams, D. P. (2001). The psychology of life stories. *Review of General Psychology, 5,* 100–122. doi:10.1037/1089-2680.5.2100

McGoldrick, M., & Carter, B. (2003). The family life cycle. In F. Walsh (Ed.), *Normal family processes* (3rd ed., pp. 375–398). New York, NY: Guilford.

McKellin, W. H. (1995). Hearing impaired families: The social ecology of hearing loss. *Social Science Medicine, 40,* 1469–1480.

McLean, K. C., & Pasupathi, M. (2012). Processes of identity development: Where I am and how I got there. *Identity: An International Journal of Theory and Research, 12*(1), 8–28.

McMillan, D. W., & Chavis, D. M. (1986). Sense of community: A definition and theory. *Journal of Community Psychology, 14*(1), 6–23.

Nario-Redmond, M. R. (2010). Cultural stereotypes of disabled and non-disabled men and women: Consensus for global category representations and diagnostic domains. *British Journal of Social Psychology, 49,* 471–488.

Newth, S., & DeLongis, A. (2004). Individual differences, mood, and coping with chronic pain in rheumatoid arthritis: A daily process analysis. *Psychology & Health, 19,* 283–305.

Oliveri, M. E., & Reiss, D. (1981). A theory-based empirical classification of family problem-solving behavior. *Family Processes, 20,* 409–418.

Oliveri, M. E., & Reiss, D. (1982). Families' schemata of social relationships. *Family Process, 21,* 295–311.

Pals, J. L. (2006). Narrative identity processing of difficult life experiences: Pathways of personality development and positive self-transformation in adulthood. *Journal of Personality, 74*(4), 1079–1110. doi:10.1111/j.1467-6494.2006.00403.x

Park, C. L., & Folkman, S. (1997). Meaning in the context of stress and coping. *Review of General Psychology, 1,* 115–144.

Pasupathi, M., & Hoyt, T. (2009). The development of narrative identity in late adolescence and emergent adulthood: The continued importance of listeners. *Developmental Psychology, 45*, 558–574.

Patterson, J. M. (1995). The role of family meanings in adaptation to chronic illness and disability. In A. P. Turnbull, J. M. Patterson, S. K. Behr, D. L. Murphy, J. G. Marquis, & M. J. Blue-Banning (Eds.), *Cognitive coping, families, and disabilities* (pp. 221–238). Baltimore, MD: Brookes.

Patterson, J. M. (2002). Integrating family resilience and family stress theory. *Journal of Marriage and Family, 64*(2), 349–360.

Pearlin, L. I. (1983). Role strains and personal stress. In H. B. Kaplan (Ed.), *Psychosocial stress: Trends in theory and research* (pp. 3–32). New York, NY: Academic Press.

Pearlin, L. I. (1991). The study of coping: An overview of problems and directions. In J. Eckenrode (Ed.), *The social context of coping* (pp. 261–276). New York, NY: Plenum.

Pearlin, L. I., Aneshensel, C. S., & LeBlanc, A. J. (1997). The forms and mechanisms of stress proliferation: The case of AIDS caregivers. *Journal of Health and Social Behavior, 38*, 223–236.

Pearlin, L. I., Menaghan, E. G., Lieberman, M. A., & Mullan, J. T. (1981). The stress process. *Journal of Health and Social Behavior, 22*, 337–356.

Perrewé, P. L., & Zellars, K. L. (1999). An examination of attributions and emotions in the transactional approach to the organizational stress process. *Journal of Organizational Behavior, 20*, 739–752.

Putnam, R. D. (2000). *Bowling alone: The collapse and revival of American community*. New York, NY: Simon & Schuster.

Reicher, S. D., Spears, R., & Haslam, S. A. (2010). The social identity approach in social psychology. In M. S. Wetherell & C. T. Mohanty (Eds.), *SAGE identities handbook* (pp. 45–62). London, England: SAGE.

Rogers, C. (1951). *Client-centered therapy: Its current practice, implications and theory*. London, England: Constable.

Rolland, J. S. (2012). Mastering family challenges in serious illness and disability. In F. Walsh (Ed.), *Normal family processes* (4th ed., pp. 452–482). New York, NY: Guilford.

Saltzman, W. R., Lester, P., Beardslee, W. R., Layne, C. M., Woodward, K., & Nash, W. P. (2011). Mechanisms of risk and resilience in military families: Theoretical and empirical basis of a family-focused resilience enhancement program. *Clinical Child and Family Psychology Review, 14*, 213–230. doi:10.1007/s10567-011-0096-1

Santos, S., Crespo, C., Silva, N., & Canavarro, M. C. (2012). Quality of life and adjustment in youths with asthma: The contributions of family rituals and the family environment. *Family Process, 51*(4), 557–569.

Schmitt, M. T., & Branscombe, N. R. (2002). The meaning and consequences of perceived discrimination in disadvantaged and privileged social groups. *European Review of Social Psychology, 12*, 167–199.

Schwartz, S. J. (2001). The evolution of Eriksonian and New-Eriksonian identity theory and research: A review and integration. *Identity, 1*(1), 7–58.

Skaff, M. M., & Pearlin, L. I. (1992). Caregiving: Role engulfment and the loss of self. *The Gerontologist, 32*(5), 656–664. doi:10.1093/geront/32.5.656

Steinglass, P., Bennett, L., Wolin, S., & Reiss, D. (1987). *The alcoholic family*. New York, NY: Basic Books.

Stets, J. E., & Burke, P. J. (2000). Identity theory and social identity theory. *Social Psychology Quarterly, 63*, 224–237.

Strauser, D. R., Lustig, D. C., & Donnell, C. (2004). The relationship between working alliance and therapeutic outcomes for individuals with mild mental retardation. *Rehabilitation Counseling Bulletin, 47*(4), 215–223.

Tajfel, H., & Turner, J. C. (1979). An integrative theory of intergroup conflict. In W. G. Austin & S. Worchel (Eds.), *The social psychology of intergroup relations* (pp. 33–47). Monterey, CA: Brooks/Cole.

Tajfel, H., & Turner, J. C. (1986). The social identity theory of intergroup behaviour. In S. Worchel & W. G. Austin (Eds.), *Psychology of intergroup relations* (2nd ed., pp. 7–24). Chicago, IL: Nelson-Hall.

Thompson, S. J., Bender, K., Lantry, J., & Flynn, P. M. (2007). Treatment engagement: Building therapeutic alliance in home-based treatment with adolescents and their families. *Contemporary Family Therapy, 29*(1–2), 39–55.

Turner, J. C. (1982). Towards a cognitive redefinition of the social group. In H. Tajfel (Ed.), *Social identity and intergroup relations* (pp. 15–40). Cambridge, England: Cambridge University Press.

Turner, J. C. (1991). *Social influence.* Milton Keynes, England: Open University Press.

Turner, J. C. (1999). Some current issues in research on social identity and self categorization theories. In N. Ellemers, R. Spears, & B. Doosje (Eds.), *Social identity: Context, commitment, content* (pp. 6–34). Oxford, England: Blackwell.

Turner, J. C., Hogg, M. A., Oakes, P. J., Reicher, S. D., & Wetherell, M. S. (1987). *Rediscovering the social group: A self-categorization theory.* Oxford, England: Blackwell.

Turner, H. A., & Schieman, S. (Eds.). (2008). *Stress across the life course. Advances in life course research.* New York, NY: Elsevier.

Verkuyten, M., & Reijerse, A. (2008). Intergroup structure and identity management among ethnic minority and majority groups: The interactive effects of perceived stability, legitimacy, and permeability. *European Journal of Social Psychology, 38,* 106–127.

Walsh, F. (2006). *Strengthening family resilience* (2nd ed.). New York, NY: Guilford.

Weeks, T. L., & Pasupathi, M. (2010). Autonomy, identity, and narrative construction with parents and friends. In K. C. McLean & M. Pasupathi (Eds.), *Narrative identity development in adolescence: Creating the storied self* (pp. 65–92). New York, NY: Springer.

Werner, E., & Smith, R. (2001). *Journeys from childhood to midlife: Risk, resilience, and recovery.* Ithaca, NY: Cornell University Press.

World Health Organization. (2013, October). *How to use the ICF: A practical manual for using the International.* Geneva, Switzerland: Author.

Yeates, G., Henwood, K. L., Gracey, F., & Evans, J. (2007). Awareness of disability after acquired brain injury and the family context. *Neuropsychological Rehabilitation, 17*(2), 151–173.

Wright, B. A. (1983). *Physical disability: A psychosocial approach.* New York, NY: Harper & Row.

CHAPTER 3

Counseling in the Context of Family Empowerment

Terri Lewis, Michael J. Millington, and Irmo Marini

What do we direct and what directs us?

Power is ideally expressed in community as "influence" or "trust" (McMillan, 1996; McMillan & Chavis, 1986) depending on whether the emphasis is placed on action or effect, respectively. Community members negotiate power to establish a predictable, stable, and safe environment conducive to trade and transactions in all manner of resources. Roles in community specialize around tasks, authorities, and responsibilities that facilitate complex undertakings, like raising children. Role behavior is sanctioned and orchestrated by tradition, rules, regulations, policy, and law. Everyone in the family gives up a certain level of autonomy to live in its community. For instance, parents may exercise significant control over the child's life, but they are also responsible for the child's well-being. When the child is in need, care takes precedence over self-centered parental pursuits. Compliance with role expectations buys the individual the security of knowing his or her place, knowing what is expected, and knowing the consequences of his or her choices and actions. Compliance rewards the person with access to the power of the collective when the family acts on the behalf of individual members in public matters. Compliance is the part of the dues one pays to earn status within interfamily negotiations.

In a robust family or community, members are engaged in a variety of evolving roles in a fair give-and-take of power. Members participate with a stake in group processes and outcomes. They are fortified and made resilient by fully inhabiting a multifaceted social identity anchored to the other members of the group in a web of influence and obligation. Power, properly balanced and fairly applied, creates healthy individuals and a strong family unit. Social justice, actively pursued, creates an empowered constituency and a strong democracy.

The ideal is useful inasmuch as it points the way to better community function and brings the gap between aspiration and reality into bold relief. However, disability is operationally defined by diminished participation in the contexts of community life and with it diminished access to social justice. The social history of disability since the mid-20th century has been framed by the sociopolitical response of persons with disabilities and their families to the systemic misappropriation of power. In rejecting a medicalized interpretation of their lived experience, people with disabilities claimed the right to define themselves. In constructing a collective identity as a minority group unified in self-advocacy, they became a movement and force in their own right. The ideal as aspiration becomes powerful when it drives people to act with a sense of community.

The disability rights movement is the quintessential case study for empowerment and a window into rehabilitation counseling's challenges in conceptualizing family practice. Although empowerment has been a popular topic in rehabilitation counseling, the profession has never reconciled its power relationship with the client vis-à-vis its quasiclinical stance on counseling expertise. It has been called a paradox (Szymanski, Parker, & Patterson, 2005) and a likely barrier to the development of family service. How does one empower from a position of expert authority? From the perspective of a client-centered counseling dyad, we define empowerment in psychosociological terms, but we stay resolutely within the person of the client. There is no room to empower the family when family is outside of the working alliance. And so the family remains in the waiting room with the rest of the disability community, its movement, and its collective identity.

The presence of a paradox tends to indicate that one is operating on the wrong set of assumptions. The disability rights movement brought about a paradigmatic change that has yet to become rehabilitation counseling's worldview. From the perspective of the profession, the new paradigm is more in line with Lewin's (1948) old conception of social psychology as social justice (Jost & Kay, 2010) rather than group-friendly psychotherapy. From political resistance to the pursuit of the "justice motive" that drives people to act beyond self-interest (Lerner, 2003), social psychology has had a voice in society's search for equity in resource distribution, interpersonal treatment, citizenship (Danermark & Gellerstedt, 2004), and justice in all affairs. Embracing social justice reveals a broader professional obligation to community counseling than traditional rehabilitation counseling models allow (Lewis, Ratts, Paladino, & Toporek, 2011; Sandler, 2007; Todman & Mansager, 2009). To embrace the disability community, we must join it, reinterpret ourselves within it, and find our role as advocates for clients and their families (Ratts, 2009).

Hahn (1991) believed that integrating empowerment into rehabilitation counseling would require a paradigmatic shift in the professional identity. The current effort to integrate family into a rehabilitation counseling model has us confronting

Hahn's existential challenge. Family has been a party to the disability rights movement (Dybwad & Bersani, 1996) as well as an advocating force for an empowering approach to family care support (Singer & Powers, 1993) for decades. It has emerged with a voice in the same sociopolitical context as disability identity (Hahn, 1997), that is, an identity forged in the struggle *against* an internalized oppression and *for* empowerment in the home, community, and society (Fleischer & Zames, 2001). It follows that as we reconcile empowerment with counseling in the community, we will once again find the family standing with the client, and with empowering aspirations of its own.

POWER AND DISABILITY

The opposite of empowerment is not disempowerment, it's oppression.

Empowerment requires an introduction. It implies instrumentality with power, social power specifically, and for our purposes power must be interpreted through the experience of disability. The political discourse between social power and disability exemplified in the disability rights movement is the space within which empowerment resides. Rehabilitation counseling must enter this politicized space to fully understand what empowerment means.

Defining Power

Power is inseparable from the concept of identity. Like identity, it is fundamentally relational (Neal & Neal, 2011). We form the narrative of who we are in our efforts to impress our values and beliefs on other people, and they respond in kind. Identities and power are negotiated in the transaction. Just as we find different facets of identity nested in individual, social, and collective relationships, we also find power redefined across these contexts.

Individual Identity and Relational Power

Relational power arises out of a social transaction between individuals. It is predicated on an asymmetrical distribution of resources and the efforts of both parties to effect change in that status (Serrano-Garcia, 1994). Relational power is about the possession of resources, ability to make decisions about the use and exchange of resources possessed, and agency in the execution of their planned use and exchange (Neal & Neal, 2011). It is the most personal expression of power as it deals with direct acquisition and control. It is often about conflict and always about change.

Social Identity and Social Power

The social aspect of power is the ability to move groups of people (Neal & Neal, 2011). It is exercised through (a) the manipulation of resources to reward or punish, (b) control of the public discourse and agendas, and (c) influence over how people feel and think about the subject of discourse. This is the power of leadership. It acquires adherents and allies. It is the power of the individual to shape the community to one's values and purposes.

Collective Identity and Psychopolitical Power

Individual identity and power are subordinate to the will of the group in psychopolitical power. Power here turns to social transformation and the pursuit of social justice (Speer, 2008) through collective action in the public sphere. The targets of collective action are primarily the processes and artifacts of governance. The change sought is at the policy level and can entail political, economic, and environmental issues; civil rights; and any other causes that respond to community advocacy. There is less focus on people and more focus on movements (Prilleltensky, 2008). The activist individual is not the subject of change; the system is the subject of change. Psychopolitical power is the means by which the individual can impose his or her will on the macrolevel forces that otherwise control him or her.[1]

Approach to Power. There are three approaches to power in these social contexts (Berger, 2005). The power exercised in organizational hierarchies is an example of *power over* others. In the chain of command, authority is invested in the role and delegated top-down. There are many variations on the theme, but the power relationship is always about dominance and submission based on position. *Power over* creates control and accountability within the group. It is also the primary instigator of oppression. *Power to* is the power to resist *power over*. It is generally exercised in the collective. The power relationship is negotiated between power of position and power of the movement. *Power with* is the power to come together where "dialog, inclusion, negotiation, and shared power guide decision making" (Berger, 2005, p. 5). All three forms of power, namely, top-down, bottom-up, and in-community, are potentially at work to balance order against change—or, more darkly, oppression against liberation.

Oppression and Response

Power is neither distributed nor wielded justly in U.S. society. For each nested level of power relationships, there is a corresponding violation of community values and negation of identity. The bully attacks, one on one. The social clique ostracizes and humiliates the outsider. The society formalizes discrimination against a minority group. Oppression is systemic, pervasive, purposeful, and strategic. The perpetrators gain power by wielding power and seek ever more power. The intent of oppression is to isolate, disempower, and exploit those who cannot defend themselves. The concentration of wealth and political power in the hands of the hyperrich, the growth of a permanent underclass of the working poor, the rise of the precariat class (people whose employment and survival is always in question), and the stripping of the social safety net in the name of programmatic austerity are not policy accidents. They are the business and political objectives of an economic ruling class. This is the pervasive downward force of oppression that is aimed at the general populace. The focused forms of oppression have been reserved historically for minority groups (see also Millington, 2012).

The United Nations Human Rights Committee (2014) recently profiled its concerns with U.S. treatment of minorities. Among the abuses noted were (a) racial disparity in criminal prosecution and sentencing, killings by police, and discriminatory application of "stand your ground laws"; (b) exploitation of immigrant workers and their families; (c) violence against women; (d) coercive psychiatric treatment (forced medication, electroconvulsive therapy) for people with mental illness; and (e) criminalization of the homeless. Political oppression is sometimes boldly obvious (e.g., The Defense of Marriage Act [P.L. 104-199]). Sometimes a pretense is offered. The voter-ID legislation in North Carolina was recently passed ostensibly to stop nonexistent voter fraud. The actual purpose was to make voting more difficult for low-income minority households.

Oppression is effected in the sabotage of poorly integrated, underfunded, deficit-model service systems. Under the cover of the neoliberal language of self-sufficiency and self-empowerment (Clark & Krupa, 2002), provider networks have been retracted, caseloads multiplied, and waiting lists extended. The depth and corruptive influence of systematic oppression is often revealed when disaster strikes (e.g., Hurricane Katrina; see Millington, 2005). Oppression can be found within the family itself as enforced expectations lock the person with a disability into a role not of his or her choosing.

Oppression is insinuated most personally in the microaggressions of day-to-day life that constantly remind people with disabilities and their families of their inferior status (Sue, 2010). Often the microaggressive oppressors are unaware of the deleterious impact of their actions as they reflexively express the prejudices of their culture, often with the best intentions. The inaccessible toilet stall, the condescending pat on the head, and any number of insulting assumptions made on the person's behalf in social negotiations are a dispiriting daily trial. Sue said that microinvalidation is perhaps the most insidious of the microaggressions. This refers to the dominant voice that opines, "I do not see you as a person with a disability," and thus communicates a denial of an empowering identity and discounts the experience of being disabled by societal attitudes, while simultaneously assuaging the oppressor's discomfort with the obvious difference.

Oppression is expressed in every social sphere, at every level. The artifacts of oppression remain quasipermanent, if covert, fixtures in the social and physical landscape (Prilleltensky, 2008). Oppression functions in a blind spot in the medical model because it is a political phenomenon, not a psychological one. It requires a different type of response.

Resistance as Response

Resistance is the empowered response to oppression. It is the application of the *power to* (Berger, 2005). Through resistance, people with disabilities are activists "operating in all directions of the social sphere and across paradigmatic boundaries" (Gabel & Peters, 2004, p. 594). Resistance takes place at the individual level as a response to relational power, that is, the ability to personally reject unequal treatment in specific situations. However, the emphasis of resistance is on its expression at social and collective levels. Resistance is about identity politics and the building of a disability community.

Resistance theory trades at the nexus of social control: Disability activists seek power, not integration or parity (Armstrong & Thompson, 2009). Activists reject the dominant narrative of disability and define themselves (Campbell & Oliver, 1996; Peters, Gabel, & Symeoniduo, 2009) by a collective identity that demands to be recognized and engaged in all public forums. Education is the primary tool used to emancipate the public from its unenlightened views on disability (*conscientization*; Peters et al., 2009). Proselytizing his or her point of view and appropriating the language of disability in the ensuing discourse make the movement and the person. Individuals with disabilities seek and find the balance between difference and solidarity in community membership (Charlton, 1998) as they engage their own psychological and political emancipation.

EMPOWERMENT

> *Empowerment is the ability to resist oppression and offer an inclusive alternative.*

Empowerment's definition varies, depending on its intended purpose (Neal & Neal, 2011). Kosciulek (1999, 2004, 2005) has sought to establish a working definition for rehabilitation counseling in his consumer-directed theory of empowerment (CDTE). In the CDTE, empowerment is an outcome (Kosciulek, 2001) of (a) applied consumer direction of rehabilitation efforts through control, direction, and choice of service options, access to information and support, and participation in policy development; and (b) active community integration. Empowerment is characterized therein by psychological, that is, "sense of control, competence, responsibility, participation, and future orientation" (p. 211), and psychosocial aspects, that is, "control over resources; interpersonal, work, and organizational skills; and 'savvy', or the ability to 'get around' in society" (p. 211). Kosciulek (2004) cites the oppressive repercussions of castification (Szymanski & Trueba, 1994) as an exacerbating factor in the client's presenting issues surrounding disability and a potential corrupting influence on the rehabilitation counseling process itself. The CDTE has been an important bridge between the social justice issues of oppression and the advancement of rehabilitation counseling practice. It provides an essential point of departure for clarifying empowerment in the context of families and community-based rehabilitation counseling.

For our community-based purposes, we will begin by defining empowerment as "a group-based, participatory, developmental process through which marginalized or oppressed individuals and groups gain greater control over their lives and environment, acquire valued resources and basic rights, and achieve important life goals and reduced societal marginalization" (Maton, 2008, p. 5). Here, empowerment is a sociopolitical term, not a psychological one. It is a process tool that belongs to minority groups, among them people(s) with disabilities. As the identity politics of the disability rights movement asserts, castification is not a danger to rehabilitation systems; it is a feature. Oppression is found in all spheres of power—relational, social, and psychopolitical (Clark & Krupa, 2002; Labonte, 1990). Empowerment is the means by which oppression is resisted *by the oppressed* wherever it is found. People with disabilities do not need to wait for rehabilitation counselors, or anyone else, to empower them. It is a disability community struggle, a collective will-to-meaning (Frankl, 1988) that creates identity and in identity finds the power to respond to oppression. Empowerment for people with disabilities began with the movement and is sustained by the community that formed in its wake. Rehabilitation counseling's role in empowerment will be found there, in the community that owns the rights.

The aspect of empowerment that surfaces within the rehabilitation counseling purview has an important relationship with identity and resilience. Empowerment is an expression of identity. In *power over*, one gives voice to "I am." In *power to*, one gives voice to "We are." Even in the most extreme of circumstances, people can choose not to relinquish the meaning they attach to life and are empowered even in that most desperate moment (see Frankl, 1988). Empowerment's relationship with resilience is symbiotic. Resilience supports efforts to exert and acquire power. Empowering experiences, successful or not, are life lessons that inform identity and shape resilience. But empowerment is not a psychological characteristic of the person. It sits squarely on the "×" in the person × environment equation. As resilient as one may be, one can only be as empowered as the environment will allow.

The ecological approach to empowerment theory is in the very early stages of development (Peterson, 2014) and open to philosophical interpretation. To reinterpret Kosciulek's (1999) clinically oriented approach to empowerment into a community-based model, we turn to and interpret this basic structure in accordance with our social justice values. Thus our discussion of empowerment will reflect the psychosocial origins and resolve in a sociopolitical end.

Psychological Aspects of Empowerment

Psychological empowerment is a developmental product of social transactions (Maton, 2008). It takes different forms with different people across different contexts (Wilk & Speer, 2011) and its composition changes over time (Zimmerman, 1995). Psychological empowerment has affective, cognitive, behavioral, and relational dimensions (A, C, B, and R in Figure 3.1, respectively) that constitute our sense of empowerment.

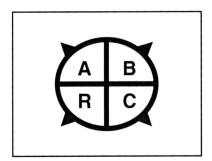

FIGURE 3.1 Psychological empowerment.

Affective: Motivation and Meaning

The interpersonal aspect of empowerment captures the affective component and entails the psychological preconditions of motivation. To act, the person must identify a desired goal. The person must feel that the goal is obtainable and that he or she has the skills and resources to achieve the goal, and have an optimistic view of the plan and the chances for success. Confidence, self-efficacy, self-worth, hope, and optimism are the emotional watchwords for empowerment. How empowered one feels is situationally dependent. It is based on an ongoing appraisal of one's personal capacity to affect the desired outcome in a given situation. Together, as a generalized and healthy self-concept, these psychological characteristics raise the level of motivation to engage across challenging situations, increase persistence in effort, positively skew interpretation of outcomes, and increase the chances for success.

Cognitive: Capacity and Intention

The interactional aspect of empowerment captures the cognitive component and entails the ability to conceptualize and plan for action. The person confronts a challenge with an explicit intention to enact change toward a desired goal. Efficacy is enhanced by access to pertinent information and a set of generalizable, strategic, problem-solving skills. The ability to conceptualize the gap between need and goal requires critical thinking about the cause and effect of power transactions. Planning includes complex considerations of contingencies, evaluative comparisons of alternate paths to solutions, choosing among options with incomplete information, and the ability to integrate tactics into an orchestrated strategy. Implementing the plan requires attention to detail, monitoring progress, and the cognitive flexibility to adjust to changes on the fly.

Behavior: Response and Participation

The behavioral aspect of empowerment is the physical translation of plan into action. It entails what one actually does to achieve desired ends. It is expressed through community participation (Christens, Peterson, & Speer, 2011). Behaviors are the external manifestations of affective and cognitive processes in the social environment. They are facilitated by physical function or the accommodation thereof and engage the array of coping behaviors used to influence others and sustain oneself in the struggle for influence.

Relational: Social Connection and Process

Given that social power is relational in all instances, Christens (2012) thought it illustrative to add a relational component to the traditional model of psychological empowerment. Relational empowerment entails collaborative competence. The relational component appears to suggest an additional set of community-oriented affective qualities and cognitive skills that facilitate social and collective empowerment. Collaborative behaviors include ability to work in groups, create group identity, and strong group cohesion; bridging differences in the group; celebrating and finding the value in diversity; resolving conflicts with respect; facilitating the empowerment of others; mobilizing people in the network to act; passing on knowledge and supporting the next generation; sharing power and information; and integrating social learning.

Christens's psychosocial integration provides an individual foundation for the social and collective empowerment models to come. Psychological empowerment at the individual level integrates perceptions of self-efficacy, proactive and directed action in life, a critical appraisal of the sociopolitical environment, and facility in defining one's role and options across social situations (Dempsey & Foreman, 1997; Zimmerman, 1995). At the root of empowerment, there is the individual, his or her experience, and his or her psychological state. It behooves us to remember this, as the strength of all empowerment efforts is dependent upon the physical and psychological well-being of this essential personage in any social movement.

Social Empowerment

As central as psychological empowerment is, it is extremely limited in its potential for response to systemic oppression. It is the individual against the world. The relational tools of psychological empowerment lead the individual to the essential well of resources beyond his or her person. True empowerment begins as *power with* (Berger, 2005), where inclusion begets sharing and psychological, physical, social, logistic, economic, spiritual, and other forms of support are offered (Parsons, 1991). Personal empowerment can only grow through the exercise of strengths on loan from the family (Dunst, Trivett, & LaPointe, 1992) and other social groups.

The psychologically empowered individual is free to negotiate membership into communities. In doing so, he or she freely chooses to subordinate selfish desires to group (family[2]) goals, and in doing so embraces a shared identity. An important distinction is raised here. Compliance to family norms does not equate to oppression, nor

FIGURE 3.2 Social empowerment.

does it necessarily impinge upon empowerment. We choose to belong. By belonging, we inherit roles that give us authority within the group as well as obligations. Through membership we are empowered. We have role-based influence over others. We have access to family resources. In return, we have an obligation to work within our role to empower the family (Dempsey & Dunst, 2004; Zimmerman, 1995).

Social empowerment is insinuated in the balanced relationship between role-empowered individuals within the family and in the family's ability to advocate for its members in the larger community (Nachshen & Minnes, 2005). The empowered family consists of empowered individuals (see Figure 3.2) and exhibits the same characteristics at an organizational level. Social empowerment requires the acquisition of shared knowledge, skill, and resources (see Farber & Maharaj, 2005). Empowered groups embrace belief systems that inspire confidence, promote group efficacy, value members and see their potential as resources, and offer a clear unifying vision beyond personal agendas. Members are engaged in strategic planning and implementing group tasks that they find meaningful. Support systems are responsive to the changing needs of its membership. Leadership acts decisively, yet collaboratively, on behalf and in behest of the family. Family focuses on continuous social learning so as to be responsive and adaptive to circumstance. Members are capable of bridging internal differences for the common good, celebrating diversity, and resolving conflict. Acting outside of the family, members actively build relationships with helpful others and access external resources (see Dempsey & Dunst, 2004) for communal use.

Collective Empowerment

Because a society that is not universally inclusive is predisposed to disempowering individuals with disabilities, empowerment interventions must at some point be operationalized as a form of community development (Maton, 2008). Empowerment in community development ranges from issues of self-advocacy and civic engagement in the most proximal of environments (family, school, work) to mobilizing citizenry in community change at municipal, state, and global levels. Community empowerment is effected through building social networks across organizations,

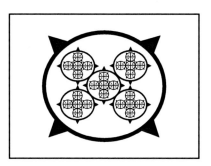

FIGURE 3.3 Collective empowerment.

that is, coalitions of communities (Figure 3.3; Zimmerman, 1995). The defining characteristic of collective advocacy is its focus on policy rather than people. Collective
advocacy changes law and builds accessible parks. It celebrates disability in civic arts
projects, raises awareness through mass media events, and establishes advocacy and
support groups. It builds alliances between disability groups and disability-neutral
groups. Collective empowerment transforms the system in the development of a
more accessible world and, through social learning, a more resilient and empowered
person and family (Maton, 2008). Although individuals within the collective are not
the subject of change, they evolve with the collaborative effort to resist injustice and
work toward positive social change (Prilleltensky, 2012).

Empowerment and the Family in Rehabilitation Counseling

Having defined empowerment as a psychosociopolitical response to systemic
oppression, what remains is to clarify the rehabilitation counseling role in facilitating empowerment in the context of the family. Without a history of practice in a
community-based model to consult, we can only present the broadest of extrapola-
tions from existing frameworks (Kosciulek, 2001) and look to community rehabilitation models outside of traditional counseling frameworks for inspiration.

Working Alliance and Empowerment

All counseling ventures are predicated on the working alliance. The working alliance
is the work of client and counselor over a set of shared goals and coordinated tasks
that generates a socioemotional bond between them. It is on the strength of this bond
that counseling stakes its relevance to practice (Lustig, Strauser, Rice, & Rucker, 2002).
Properly executed, the working alliance is generically conducive to empowerment
(Kosciulek, 2004). Affectively, empowerment in the working alliance is enhanced
by the counselor's unconditional positive regard for the client, the well-honed
microskills of counseling that communicate full engagement, an air of confident optimism, and a focus on strengths and possibilities. Cognitively, empowerment in the

working alliance is enhanced by strengths-based, solution-focused, and problem-solving strategies that can be taught and generalized to other life situations. Behaviorally, empowerment is enhanced by a fully collaborative partnership that is built on an assumption of growth, stepwise progress, mobilizing resources, continuous learning, and client autonomy in managing his or her life (Emener, 1991).

In traditional models of rehabilitation counseling, the working alliance tends to be viewed as a rather exclusive dyad. Counselor and client collaborate in assessing the client's current situation, desired ends, and the plans to achieve them with little direct recognition of the import of the client's family and extended support network. It is an approach that psychologically empowers, but ignores the potential for social empowerment. An alternative approach to the working alliance would be to expand into a team effort with the family. The core values and microskills remain constant, but counseling professionals can enhance social empowerment by (a) involving family in the development, implementation, and evaluation of interventions; (b) becoming a member of the community and part of the family social network; (c) working as equal partners toward shared goals; and (d) creating opportunities for the development of skills among family members that enhance independent function separate from professional support (Zimmerman, 1995).

Client/Family-Directed Service

The empowered client remains at the center of all service and maximally in control of planning, implementation, coordination, and evaluation (Kosciulek, 2001). Family systems theory affirms the client-centric approach, but recognizes that the family must also be considered as a locus of choice and control in the rehabilitation issues that matter to it (Knox, Parmenter, Atkinson, & Yazbeck, 2000). This is a tacit recognition of the social nature of decision making and authority across family roles. The person with a disability remains the center of rehabilitation counseling service, but that does not mean he or she makes unilateral decisions about family affairs. Family decision-making processes are idiosyncratic. Influence shifts between stakeholders as the family matures. The autonomy of children changes with maturity. The autonomy of adults can change with events (Kirkendall, Waldrop, & Moone, 2012) or the exacerbation of symptoms (McDaid & Delaney, 2011). The empowered family shares in the control and direction of client service in a reflection of the client's desires.

Person-centered planning integrated with a family-focused approach takes place in the client's world, in the client's language, and under the client's control, with family and advocates in attendance as active collaborators in the decision-making process. As with all roles, authority is paired with responsibility. Inasmuch as family is included in goal setting, planning, and monitoring services, it is obliged to take on tasks itself. These are processes that must be learned, and so there is training. Choices must be informed, and so there is research. Family engagement in choice and control is facilitated by knowledgeable case workers, who know the system and can provide actionable information (Knox et al., 2000). The family comes to the table as a resource to be mobilized, and so the family evaluates its own potential to support the plan. To be treated as equals is to contribute as equals.

Capacity and Support

By actively entering into the rehabilitation process, family becomes a resource to be nurtured and thereby a legitimate recipient of direct service. Support that facilitates family stability, better coping, or the acquisition of skills can be a strategic benefit for the client. Wraparound services that reduce the burden of care for family members (Kilmer, Cook, & Munsell, 2010) increase the potential for successful client outcomes.

Among the most potent of family support resources is the disability community itself. Peer support groups coalesce around disability experiences and can be as formal and organized as the National Alliance on Mental Illness (https://www.nami .org) or as informal as an ad hoc group of parents meeting at the community center. Peer-support groups are communities of practice expressly designed to include people with disabilities and their families. They are experts in the direct experience of disability and recognize the expertise of those who share their experience. They often provide social support through education and peer counseling, but most importantly they represent one instance of complete community inclusion.

The self-advocacy movement represents a more politically oriented community of practice. Self-advocacy has been an outgrowth of the disability rights movement that actively attacks the dominant and oppressive worldview of disability (Goodley, 1997). Self-advocacy is an individual act of resistance, sponsored by the group, working in collaboration with others for the cause of justice. Group work in self-advocacy is a social learning experience (see Smith, 2013). Groups organize around advocacy training and sponsor advocacy projects to educate, raise awareness, and ultimately create positive systems change (Goodley, Armstrong, Sutherland, & Laurie, 2003; Smith, Reynolds, & Rovnak, 2009). For rehabilitation counselors, a referral to an established community of people who share their client's experience and have a collected reservoir of resources and an agenda for forward movement is the definitive expression of the professional's capacity to empower.

Professional Advocacy

Counselors are citizens as well as members of the profession. Their potential roles in advocacy are as liaisons and allies for their clients and client families and more directly as activists in community development representing themselves and their profession in crafting a more accommodating and fair world. The American Counseling Association (ACA) provides a profile of the community-based counselor in its recitation of competencies in social justice advocacy (Lopez-Baez & Paylo, 2009). The ACA profile suggests strategies for action as much as qualities of the change-agent role.

Counseling Through Community Collaboration. In this strategy, the focus is on community development. During the course of service, the counselor identifies barriers to client development or barriers to desired environmental adaptations. All stakeholder groups are alerted and informed of the need for action. The counselor seeks out and develops alliances with advocacy groups in the course of resolving the community-based barrier, inasmuch as an environmental barrier for one is likely an environmental barrier for others. The counselor is actively engaged in social networking and the development of partnerships. He or she engages the advocacy group in collaborative work or dialog, seeks to understand the advocating group's point of view, evaluates group strengths and available resources germane to systems change, and communicates his or her recognition and respect of the group for these strengths and resources. In return, the counselor offers valued trade in the emerging community of practice. He or she identifies and offers counseling skills that potentially add value to the group's collaborative efforts. As collaborative work is engaged, on behalf of the client or for the group, the counselor monitors all: his or her contribution, the group, and the impact of counselor collaboration in the community for present and future use.

Counseling Through Systems Advocacy. Starting from the same perspective of identified environmental barriers, the second strategy focuses on a self-advocacy approach to systems change. The emphasis here is on resistance, raising awareness of and resolving injustice. In this strategy, the counselor researches social justice issues and presents a needs assessment to the group (be it advocacy group, job club, or family) and demonstrates the urgent need for advocacy. Working with concerned stakeholders, the counselor collaborates in the development of a shared vision of aspirational change, collaborative evaluation of the situation, consensual development of an intervention plan, and cooperative advocacy efforts in implementation. Given that this is a more actively advocacy-oriented approach to empowerment, contingency plans are made for conflict resolution and other issues surrounding social response to acts of resistance. As before, the counselor monitors the impact of systems advocacy in its effect on both the system and the advocates.

Rehabilitation counseling is perfectly situated to give counseling support to activists and activist groups. Rehabilitation counselors can play an important role as a consultant (Cone, 1999) or advisor to advocacy groups, if invited. As with any organizational consultants, advisors are a potential resource for forming groups, helping to establish processes, facilitating group growth, and the development of sustainability . . . and enriching both.

Infusing Empowerment in the Rehabilitation Counseling Identity

Empowerment does suggest some very directed counselor action, but it is more an attitude of practice than a type of intervention. The community-based rehabilitation (CBR) model (World Health Organization [WHO], 2010) that has admittedly been the core inspiration for the approach we have taken in conceptualizing family service has a particularly informative perspective in this matter. The CBR matrix identifies four contexts in which full community inclusion is pursued: health, education, livelihood, and social contexts (see Table 4.1). Family, community volunteers, para-professionals, professionals, and most importantly the person with a disability shape service within events and experiences that fill these spaces. The fifth component of the matrix is not a context at all; it is empowerment, and it cuts across the action and space of the other four with identifiable tasks of its own. It is the antidote for medical model rehabilitation that creates dependencies and cannot be sustained further than the expert will allow. From the preamble of the empowerment section of the CBR Guidelines (WHO, 2010), empowerment "begins to happen when individuals or groups of people recognize that they can change their situation, and begin to do so. It is a process that involves things like awareness and capacity-building leading to greater participation, to greater decision-making power and control, and to action for change" (p. 1). Empowerment is operationalized in the CBR through advocacy and communication, so people with disabilities can speak for themselves; through community mobilization, so the community can be empowered to remove barriers and actively include people with disabilities and their families; through political participation, so people with disabilities can stand up and be counted in political and public life; through self-help groups, so people with disabilities and their families can participate freely and fully in the resolution of common problems, build their own strength, and improve their own quality of life without external meddling; and, finally, through disabled people's organizations, so they can be a collective force in the advancement of the Convention on the Rights of Persons With Disabilities and a collective author of inclusive community development at all levels of society. As the CBR is a matrix mapping potential services, each of these empowerment goals qualifies how services are to be expressed in each of the community contexts. And so it is, or should be, for rehabilitation counseling. Although the CBR matrix is not well known in the United States, it suggests a broad field of potential rehabilitation counseling roles in community inclusion beyond the expert role that presently contains it. Empowerment is the key to the profession finding itself and the family in a shared community space.

NOTES

1. This capstone of power reflects the bridge between Dewey and Lewin that was discussed in Chapter 1.
2. Social empowerment applies to any group of people who unite in a community of practice. We will refer to the family throughout this exposition instead of the generic "group" while acknowledging that the construct is broader than our present interests.

REFERENCES

Armstrong, C., & Thompson, S. (2009). Parity of participation and the politics of status. *European Journal of Political Theory, 8,* 109–122.

Berger, B. K. (2005). Power over, power with, and power to relations: Critical reflections on public relations, the dominant coalition, and activism. *Journal of Public Relations Research, 17*(1), 5–28.

Campbell, J., & Oliver, M. (1996). *Disability politics: Understanding our past, changing our future.* London, UK: Routledge.

Charlton, J. I. (1998). *Nothing about us without us: Disability oppression and empowerment.* Berkeley, CA: University of California Press.

Christens, B. D. (2012). Toward relational empowerment. *American Journal of Community Psychology, 50,* 114–128.

Christens, B. D., Peterson, N. A., & Speer, P. W. (2011). Community participation and psychological empowerment: Testing reciprocal causality using a cross-lagged panel design and latent constructs. *Health, Education & Behavior, 39,* 229–238.

Clark C. C., & Krupa, T. (2002). Reflections on empowerment in community mental health: Giving shape to an elusive idea. *Psychiatric Rehabilitation Journal, 25*(4), 341–349.

Cone, A. A. (1999). Profile of advisors to self-advocacy groups for people with mental retardation. *Mental Retardation, 37*(4), 308–318.

Danermark, B., & Gellerstedt, L. C. (2004). Social justice: Redistribution and recognition—A non-reductionist perspective on disability. *Disability & Society, 19*(4), 339–353.

Dempsey, I., & Dunst, C. J. (2004). Helpgiving styles and parent empowerment in families with a young child with a disability. *Journal of Intellectual & Developmental Disability, 29*(1), 40–51.

Dempsey, I., & Foreman, P. (1997). Toward a clarification of empowerment as an outcome of disability service provision. *International Journal of Disability, Development and Education, 44,* 287–303.

Dunst, C. J., Trivette, C. M., & LaPointe, N. (1992). Toward clarification of the meaning and key elements of empowerment. *Family Science Review, 5,* 111–130.

Dybwad, G., & Bersani, H. (Eds.). (1996). *New voices: Self-advocacy by people with disabilities.* Cambridge, MA: Brookline.

Emener, W. G. (1991). An empowerment philosophy for rehabilitation in the 20th century. *Journal of Rehabilitation, 57*(4), 7–16.

Farber, M. L., & Maharaj, R. (2005). Empowering high-risk families of children with disabilities. *Research on Social Practice, 15,* 501–515.

Fleischer, D., & Zames, F. (2001). *The disability rights movement: From charity to confrontation.* Philadelphia, PA: Temple University Press.

Frankl, V. (1988). *The will to meaning: Foundations and applications of logotherapy.* New York, NY: Meridian.

Gabel, S., & Peters, S. (2004). Presage of a paradigm shift? Beyond the social model of disability toward resistance theories of disability. *Disability & Society, 19*(6), 585–600.

Goodley, D. (1997). Locating self-advocacy in models of disability: Understanding disability in the support of self-advocates with learning difficulties. *Disability & Society, 12*(3), 367–379. doi:10.1080/09687599727227

Goodley, D., Armstrong, D., Sutherland, K., & Laurie, L. (2003). Self-advocacy, "learning difficulties," and the social model of disability. *Mental Retardation, 41*(3), 149–160.

Hahn, H. (1991). Alternate views of empowerment: Social services and civil rights. *Journal of Rehabilitation, 57*(4), 17–19.

Hahn, H. (1997). An agenda for citizens with disabilities: Pursuing identity and empowerment. *Journal of Vocational Rehabilitation, 9,* 31–37.

Jost, J. T., & Kay, A. C. (2010). Social justice: History, theory, and research. In S. T. Fiske, D. T. Gilbert, & G. Lindzey (Eds.), *Handbook of social psychology* (Vol. 2, 5th ed., pp. 1122–1165). Hoboken, NJ: John Wiley.

Kilmer, R. P., Cook, J. R., & Munsell, E. P. (2010). Moving from principles to practice: Recommended policy changes to promote family-centered care. *American Journal of Community Psychology, 46,* 332–341.

Kirkendall, A. M., Waldrop, D., & Moone, R. (2012). Caring for people with intellectual disabilities and life-limiting illness: Merging person-centered planning and patient centered, family focused care. *Journal of Social Work in End-of-Life & Palliative Care, 8,* 135–150.

Knox, M., Parmenter, T. R., Atkinson, N., & Yazbeck, M. (2000). Family control: The views of families who have a child with an intellectual disability. *Journal of Applied Research in Intellectual Disability, 13,* 17–28.

Kosciulek, J. F. (1999). The consumer-directed theory of empowerment. *Rehabilitation Counseling Bulletin, 42,* 196–213.

Kosciulek, J. F. (2001). Structural analysis of the consumer-directed theory of empowerment. *Rehabilitation Counseling Bulletin, 44*(4), 209–216.

Kosciulek, J. F. (2004). Empowering people with disabilities through vocational rehabilitation. *American Rehabilitation, 28*(1), 40–47.

Labonte, R. (1990). Empowerment: Notes on community and professional dimensions. *Canadian Research on Social Policy, 26,* 64–75.

Lerner, M. J. (2003). The justice motive: Where social psychologists found it, how they lost it, and why they may not find it again. *Personality and Social Psychology, 7,* 388–399.

Lewin, K. (1948). *Resolving social conflicts.* New York, NY: Harper.

Lewis, J. A., Ratts, M. J., Paladino, D. A., & Toporek, R. L. (2011). Social justice counseling and advocacy: Developing new leadership roles and competencies. *Journal for Social Action in Counseling and Psychology, 3*(1), 5–16.

Lopez-Baez, S. I., & Paylo, M. J. (2009). Social justice advocacy: Community collaboration and systems advocacy. *Journal of Counseling & Development, 87,* 276–283.

Lustig, D. C., Strauser, D. R., Rice, N. D., & Rucker, T. F. (2002). The relationship between working alliance and rehabilitation outcomes. *Rehabilitation Counseling Bulletin, 46,* 25–33.

Maton, K. I. (2008). Empowering community setting: Agents of individual development, community betterment, and positive social change. *American Journal of Community Psychology, 41,* 4–21.

McDaid, S., & Delaney, S. (2011). A social approach to decision-making capacity: Exploratory research with people with experience of mental health treatment. *Disability & Society, 26*(6), 729–742.

McMillan, D. W. (1996). Sense of community. *Journal of Community Psychology, 24*(4), 315–325.

McMillan, D. W., & Chavis, D. M. (1986). Sense of community: A definition and theory. *Journal of Community Psychology, 14,* 6–23.

Millington, M. J. (2005). Disability, poverty, and Hurricane Katrina. *Journal of Rehabilitation, 71*(4), 3.

Millington, M. J. (2012). Culturally different issues and attitudes towards disability. In I. Marini, N. M. Glover-Graf, & M. J. Millington (Eds.), *Psychosocial aspects of disability: Insider perspectives and counseling strategies* (pp. 61–95). New York, NY: Springer.

Nachshen, J. S., & Minnes, P. (2005). Empowerment in parents of school-aged children with and without developmental disabilities. *Journal of Intellectual Disability Research, 49*(12), 889–904.

Neal, J. W., & Neal, Z. P. (2011). Power as a structural phenomenon. *American Journal of Community Psychology, 48*, 157–167.

Parsons, R. J. (1991). Empowerment: Purpose and practice principle in social work. *Social Work with Groups, 14*(2), 7–21.

Peters, S., Gabel, S., & Symeonidou, S. (2009). Resistance, transformation and the politics of hope: Imagining a way forward for the disabled people's movement. *Disability & Society, 24*(5), 543–556.

Peterson, N. A. (2014). Empowerment theory: Clarifying the nature of higher-order multidimensional constructs. *American Journal of Community Psychology, 53*, 96–108.

Prilleltensky, I. (2008). The role of power in wellness, oppression, and liberation: The promise of psychopolitical validity. *Journal of Community Psychology, 36*, 116–136.

Prilleltensky, I. (2012). Wellness as fairness. *American Journal of Community Psychology, 49*, 1–21.

Ratts, M. J. (2009). Social justice counseling: Toward the development of a "fifth force" among counseling paradigms. *Journal of Humanistic Counseling, Education, and Development, 48*, 160–172.

Sandler, J. (2007). Community-based practices: Integrating dissemination theory with critical theories of power and justice. *American Journal of Community Psychology, 40*, 272–289.

Serrano-Garcia, I. (1994). The ethics of the powerful and the power of ethics. *American Journal of Community Psychology, 22*, 1–10.

Singer, G. H., & Powers, L. E. (1993). Contributing to resilience in families: An overview. In G. H. Singer & L. E., Powers (Eds.), *Families, disability, and empowerment: Active coping skills and strategies for family interventions* (pp. 1–25). Baltimore, MD: Paul H. Brookes.

Smith, D. H. (2013). Deaf adults: Retrospective narratives of school experiences and teacher expectations. *Disability & Society, 28*(5), 674–686.

Smith, S. D., Reynolds, C. A., & Rovnak, A. (2009). A critical analysis of the social advocacy movement in counseling. *Journal of Counseling & Development, 87*, 483–491.

Speer, P. W. (2008). Social Power and forms of change: Implications for psychopolitical validity. *Journal of Community Psychology, 36*(2), 199–213.

Sue, D. W. (2010). Microaggressions, marginality, and oppression: An introduction. In D. W. Sue (Ed.), *Microaggressions and marginality: Manifestation, dynamics, and impact* (pp. 3–22). Hoboken, NJ: John Wiley.

Szymanski, E. M., Parker, R. M., & Patterson, J. B. (2005). Beyond the basics: Sociopolitical context of rehabilitation counseling practice. In R. M. Parker, E. M. Szymanski, & J. B. Patterson (Eds.), *Rehabilitation counseling: Basics and beyond* (4th ed., pp. 395–412). Austin, TX: PRO-ED.

Szymanski, E. M., & Trueba, H. T. (1994). Castification of people with disabilities: Potential disempowering aspects of classification in disability services. *Journal of Rehabilitation, 60*, 12–20.

Todman, L. C., & Mansager, E. (2009). Social justice: Addressing social exclusion by means of social interest and social responsibility. *Journal of Individual Psychology, 65*(4), 311–318.

United Nations Human Rights Committee. (2014, March). *Concluding observations on the fourth report of the United States of America: Advanced unedited version.* Retrieved from http://tbinternet.ohchr.org/Treaties/CCPR/Shared%20Documents/USA/INT_CCPR_COC_USA_16838_E.doc

Wilk, L. A., & Speer, P. W. (2011). The mediating influence of organizational characteristics in the relationship between organizational type and relational power: An extension of psychological empowerment research. *Journal of Community Psychology, 39*(8), 972–986.

World Health Organization. (2010). *Community-based rehabilitation: CBR guidelines.* Geneva, Switzerland: Author.

Zimmerman, M. A. (1995). Psychological empowerment: Issues and illustrations. American *Journal of Community Psychology, 23,* 581–600.

CHAPTER 4

Rehabilitation Counseling in the Context of Family Capital

Sue Lukersmith, Charlotte Scarf, and Michael J. Millington

The term *capital* is used here with a caveat. Modified with the family adjective, we seek to highlight the dynamic aspect of the term while minimizing the economic connotations. A family's capital is its reservoir of resources (Hobfoll, 1989, 2001) put into social circulation for the family good. The term capital implies an intent to invest and trade between parties. The resource can be any asset: for example, goods, services, structures, systems, formal and informal care, paid and volunteer work, knowledge, experience, skills, policies, relationships, trust, resilience, opportunities, personal attributes, values and beliefs, time, and space. The investment is in the physical, psychological, or social advancement of the family or its members. Trade or exchange in family life is much more than economic. It is the commerce of social wellness.

Trade in family capital builds on the family identity. The interdependence of family members is defined in their transactions. Family trade is negotiated through family roles. The individual gives to family according to his or her roles and resources. He or she takes from the family according to his or her roles and needs. The cost of membership is family participation, and participation is its own reward. For example, the morning routine is an exchange of role-defined contributions to family life (making beds, cooking breakfast, washing dishes, etc.) that resolves in outcomes that serve the individual and the collective (a meal, an ordered house, coordinated schedules, and a comforting sense of familiarity). Routine upon routine, the trade between roles articulates the individual and sustains the social-emotional bonds that bind him or her.

Family invests in its members as they trade in the public marketplace through roles outside the family. Students trade attention for knowledge. Workers trade labor for cash. Shoppers trade cash for merchandise. Volunteers trade time for a better community. The family benefits in its support of the student, worker, shopper, and volunteer through the acquisition of new resources that fortify its position in society. The family also engages trade at the organizational level. Neighborhoods negotiate ordinances with local government, and families are represented. Families organize in advocacy for inclusive causes and create communities of mutual support around issues of recovery. Trade in its most basic sense of exchange drives the action of community and society at every level. Every member of a community participates in this trade. Participation, as the defining characteristic of community inclusion, requires it.

Disability changes the dynamics of trade, and thus the nature of the relationships within the family and between the family and other groups. Trade in the context of disability as conceived in the International Classification of Functioning (ICF; World Health Organization [WHO], 2001) tends to be characterized by diminished access to capital under conditions of heightened need. What starts as compromised biological structure and function within the individual does not become a disability until it results in diminished community participation for the individual and the family. Diminished participation in community trade takes many forms and consequences including social isolation, poverty, unemployment, exacerbated health problems, and oppression (Marmont & Wilkinson, 2007; WHO & International Spinal Cord Society, 2013; WHO & World Bank, 2011).

A person who does not participate and cannot engage in trade may be physically present in the marketplace, but he or she is not part of the community in any meaningful sense. Conversely, a society that alienates its members from trade may be thought of as diminished by its collusion in exclusion. The health of the individual and the collective revolve around a free exchange of capital in all its forms. This is the purpose of the social safety net. Society provides for citizens who are politically, economically, socially, or otherwise at risk so they may ideally trade as equals in community. What society spends on the social contract is an investment in the public as well as individual well-being.

Although an agent of the client, the rehabilitation counselor is also working on behalf of the funding source in compliance with policy and law and in cooperation with a constellation of stakeholders (i.e., service and advocacy groups) with potentially competing interests. Best practice lies in the balance between maximizing the client's control over process and outcomes while making the most efficacious use of limited resources. The profession advocates for the client through the context of trade and does so in two approaches to family capital:

- *Community development (CD)* that builds environmental capacity for family trade in valued resources and
- *Case management*, orchestrating the family trade that occurs.

Moving effectively in these systems roles is predicated on (a) mastery of and influence on formal care and support systems; (b) building capacity within formal care and support systems to better serve clients and families; (c) understanding of and acceptance in the informal care and support systems of the individual, family, and their extended social care network; (d) building family capacity to identify, acquire, orchestrate, and direct capital to best effect; and (e) networking all systems in collaborative and strategic implementation of client-centered rehabilitation plans and CD.

COMMUNITY DEVELOPMENT

CD has its roots in the social justice movement as it applies to the economic struggles of low-income communities and countries around the world. A network of nongovernmental organizations (NGOs), trade unions, faith-based organizations, women's associations, human rights organizations, activists, and concerned citizens and families arose in opposition to the failed market-based development strategies they saw as an oppressive tool of economic globalization. A progressive policy alternative to neoliberal strategies was sought in the populist discourse. They conceived a wealth redistribution scheme that championed a more human-centered and sustainable approach to development that was locally planned and controlled by the intended beneficiaries. While it was impossible to reduce the multitude of voices into a coherent policy platform, together they embraced and advanced community-friendly alternatives to resolving local issues in a process that became known as CD.

The CD/Rehabilitation Counseling Connection

CD is an outgrowth of the same social movement that spawned the rehabilitation counseling profession and gave voice to the family within it. There is a synomorphic[1] resonance between the two, united as they are in social justice values. CD's focus on distributive social justice at the collective level is a counterpoint to rehabilitation counseling's focus on the interactional social justice of Lewin's social psychology (Jost & Kay, 2010). The service models meet in the larger mission of full community inclusion. As rehabilitation counseling increasingly recognizes the community aspect of that mission, the resonance between CD and rehabilitation counseling practice becomes clearer.

Contemporary CD translates democratic values to action through empowerment strategies in local decision making and collective problem solving that addresses power inequity in relations and structures that are the root causes of poverty and injustice. CD is based on the belief that there is a wealth of social capital within every community that can be creatively channeled into collective action for the common good. Social capital within the community is cultivated and traded through the social networks that make it a cohesive entity and connect it to society. The value of social capital is negotiated through cooperative relationships toward shared goals (Putnam, 1995, 2001).

Rehabilitation counseling is part of the networked social capital that serves the family. Its value to the family depends on its instrumental impact on family goals. The family goals that rehabilitation counseling can best serve are pragmatic ones, such as helping a member of the family become gainfully employed or facilitating family transitions in care situations. Families turn to rehabilitation counseling for resources, not direct care. These resources are the stuff of rehabilitation counselor's trade and trade requires reciprocation from the family. The rehabilitation counselor wants access to the family social capital as well. They share a goal, the family and counselor, but for different outcomes. The family seeks improvement in its standing in the community and more resilient well-being. The counselor seeks the most efficient and effective path to successful case closure.

Achieving these ends requires that family resources be put to optimal use (thereby increasing realized social capital) toward the shared goal. For example, job placement efforts could be greatly enhanced if the task became part of family practice. By engaging otherwise-fallow resources, like the family's social connections, less overall capital need can be invested to achieve better employment outcomes faster (see Gorman & Marsden, 2001; Granovetter, 1974). For the counselor's part, collaborating in the development of a job club through the local community center becomes an investment paying dividends when future families connect and share their social networks, thus further expanding opportunities for the job seeker and support for the family. This example illustrates the profession's connection to CD at the client/family level, that is, trading in social capital for mutual strategic gain.

Shared Values and Principles of CD

The values of CD are the values of rehabilitation counseling in an aggressively empowered setting. *Participation* is not simply the goal in CD; it is an emancipatory learning process for the family (Freire, 1970). The lived experience of disability, including the social response of rehabilitation, leads the family to a critical analysis of the world it attempts to change. CD supports participation as the means to action-based learning and an understanding of the steps toward achieving social justice (Chambers, 1997). The rehabilitation counselor in this setting is a citizen professional (see Doherty, Mendenhall, & Berge, 2010) and fellow learner who offers tools and resources, not answers or direction. *Inclusion* of diversity is essential in CD to ensure that marginalized groups are not excluded from the benefits flowing to individuals and the wider community. This value accords with the global disability advocacy movement's meme of "nothing about us without us," which emphasizes applied social justice from the client-centered perspective. *Sustainability* is an approach to planning that resolves system issues rather than surface symptoms. It is a critical approach to ensuring long-term contributions to quality of life and well-being in the communities CD is meant to serve. Sustainability in rehabilitation counseling involves orchestrating and investing in "caravans" of resources as Hobfoll (2001) puts it; that is, manifold streams of accumulating resources that attract other resources, building capital upon capital. Sustainability applies as well to family learning and skill development that can be retained and practiced into the future. It is a service contribution to family resilience (Walsh, 2006).

Toolbox: Basic Themes

CD intervention strategies evolve independently as unique, value-driven responses to local realities. They are not applied as discrete programs but approaches that are adapted and blended to suit the situation. The following themes provide a profile of CD tools in common practice. Rehabilitation counseling in the United States, being new to the community base, has yet to interpret CD tools into its core roles and functions (see Leahy & Phillips, 2010), and so they stand here as undeveloped professional capital.

Economic Development. Microfinance provides financial services, including credit, loans, savings, insurance, and payment services to low-income households through creative and nontraditional structures. CD projects have established microfinancing through NGOs, credit unions, cooperative banks, building societies, and smaller commercial banks (Prahalad, 2004). Financial services are delivered via individual and group-based models to support microentrepreneurs and small business (Yunus, 2003). Of course, microfinance provides a platform for small-scale commercial ventures, but in keeping with CD principles, social entrepreneurship is also encouraged. These are small-scale businesses designed to support social causes. They implement cooperative and innovative business practices that fill community need through community mobilization. People with disabilities often find integrative training and employment opportunities as service providers in such settings (Yunus, 2010) as well as accessing resources as consumers.

Community Education and Networking. Community education activities are organized by local people in response to community needs. Community education is informal adult education, open to all interested parties, and does not usually lead to formal qualifications. It does act as a bridge to more formal training, thereby reducing the barriers faced by some in gaining work-related skills and credentials. For others, community education is a means to achieve personal goals such as learning a language or playing a musical instrument; or fulfilling social goals such as building a community garden or volunteering in respite care. These activities allow participants to cultivate personal strengths and attributes like self-esteem, while building positive relationships with others.

Community networking provides opportunities for social interaction among local people for the expressed purpose of building the simple social capital of friends and acquaintances. This differs from CD activities where social capital is a desired by-product, not the primary goal. In communities with dense social networks, people participate in CD because their friends or neighbors are involved, or they want to meet new people. In communities with low social capital, it can be difficult to organize and mobilize people to participate in community-building activities. Community networking is useful in dealing with these more fundamental issues as a precursor to bigger CD plans. It is accomplished simply by creating spaces, virtual or real, for people to come together on any topic of mutual interest. Internet technologies and social media play an important and pervasive role in social net-working, but physical face-to-face interaction is more potent for developing strong and enduring social bonds.

Cultural Development. Community-controlled media provide a space for local peo-ple to share their stories, discuss local issues, promote local businesses, and advertise local events, using local languages. Community media projects strive to provide an alternative to homogeneous commercial media offerings. Programming is driven by, and features the voices of, culturally and linguistically diverse groups that are in the community but not widely heard. All media including community radio, public-access television, print publications, virtual communities, and even local kiosks pro-vide an opportunity to amplify minority points of view and build them into informed and engaged communities (Rennie, 2006).

Community arts projects take communication into the sphere of cultural celebra-tion that strengthens social identity and cohesion within minority groups while build-ing bridges to the larger community. Events encourage local participation in arts-based creative processes, provide resources and venues to local artists while creating a safe public space to explore, challenge, and celebrate our shared humanity. Projects sup-port the participation of disadvantaged and minority groups in the arts, and use the arts as a vehicle to open up new ways of looking at the life of the community, its his-tory, and its future. Techniques can be diverse and include visual and performing arts, crafts, literature, and design. Community arts projects promote community building and neighborhood renewal by drawing on and enriching local culture, and strengthen-ing creative community capacity and resilience (Goldbard, 2006).

Political Development. CD plays an important advocacy role in working with people denied justice because of their common identity or the nature of their issues in the legal system. Activities focus on individuals seeking their legal rights and entitle-ments or groups advocating for legislative reform to eliminate unfair discrimination. The approach is of increasing importance in CD as a precondition for human rights-based programming, as well as being an important means to strengthen disadvan-taged people's choices to seek and obtain a remedy for grievances.

Citizen engagement links local interest groups with public policy processes with a view to improving recognition of community needs and aspirations by state institu-tions. In many established democracies, reforms in governance have generated a pro-fusion of new spaces for citizen engagement, from participation in resource allocation to citizen's juries. These fora provide an entirely different kind of interface with policy processes than other avenues through which citizens can articulate their demands, such as protest and lobbying. They are participatory and deliberative spaces for knowledge exchange and negotiation by citizens and the state. CD activities in this area aim to build the capacity of disadvantaged groups and their representatives to access and make their voices heard in these spaces (Cornwell & Coelho, 2007).

Toolbox Specific: Community-Based Rehabilitation. One particular CD tool should be singled out as the most promising CD investment for the global growth of rehabilitation counseling. Community-based rehabilitation (CBR) is a CD strategy designed specifically to facilitate community participation of people with disabilities and their families (WHO, 2004). CBR evolved over decades (WHO, UNESCO, International Labour Organisation, & International Disability Development Consortium, 2010) as a response to the absence of human resources in rehabilitation, failures of mainstream services, and the impracticality of the center-based Western medical model applied in low-resource settings. CBR applied CD principles to the provision of rehabilitation services and has become recognized as an important strategy for advancing human rights of persons with disabilities (United Nations, 2006; World Health Organization, 2014) and an effective ecological approach to community inclusion and participation. Now with decades of implementation and development in its past, an emerging movement toward evidence-based research in its present (Lukersmith et al., 2013), and a standardized approach to development and dissemination planned in its future, CBR is the greatest untapped conceptual resource available to rehabilitation counseling to date.

This integrated service model conceptualizes community directed CD in health, education, livelihood, social, and empowerment domains (Table 4.1; WHO et al., 2010).

The first four domains have been articulated in the CBR matrix to describe the primary foci of CD projects across life spaces. The fifth domain cuts across all others as a principled approach to service development and a set of integrated services based on empowerment. This domain advances inclusion and participation of persons with disabilities and their family members in all aspects of CBR development and delivery. Community projects are grassroots in development, locally resourced and managed, and unique in content and style. CBR programs are unified by their adherence to process management strategies as evidenced in the four-stage management cycle promulgated in the guidelines (i.e., situation analysis, planning and design, implementation and monitoring, and evaluation). CBR is relevant for any

TABLE 4.1 CBR Matrix

HEALTH	EDUCATION	LIVELIHOOD	SOCIAL	EMPOWERMENT
Promotion	Early childhood	Skills development	Personal assistance	Advocacy and communication
Prevention	Primary	Self-employment	Relationships, marriage, and family	Community mobilization
Medical care	Secondary and higher	Wage employment	Culture and arts	Political participation
Rehabilitation	Nonformal	Financial services	Recreation, leisure, sports	Self-help groups
Assistive devices	Lifelong learning	Social protection	Justice	Disabled people's organizations

community where structural or environmental barriers, economic restrictions, and resource limitations restrict opportunities for participation (WHO, 2004; WHO & World Bank, 2011). Accordingly, a growing number of rural and remote communities in high-resourced countries have adopted CBR, although it often goes by other names. In the future, the fact that CBR stands as a community-based model alternative to medical model hegemony will likely find expressions at all strata of society where social justice remains elusive for people with disabilities.

CBR CASE STUDY

In the context of counseling in capital, the following exemplifies how a CD strategy of microfinance benefited the individual with a disability, the family, and the village community in a low-resource setting. The CBR community worker linked a family with a microfinance program sponsored by the CBR program. The family configuration was a mother (Komal) and her son (Sanjiv), who lived in a small village. Her husband had died a year ago. Her oldest son was overwhelmed by the responsibilities of supporting his mother and younger brother that had passed onto him since his father had died. He left the village to seek a life elsewhere and no longer had contact with his mother or brother.

Komal and Sanjiv did not have their own place to live and lived in a cramped two-room house with her sister, brother-in-law, and their three children. They were isolated in the village, and did not interact with many in the village. She was a widow and he had a disability. Sanjiv had spent much of his first 15 years of life restricted to home and grounds due to the mobility impairments associated with cerebral palsy. He could not walk but could stand to move from one seat to another. He did not have a wheelchair and could not afford to buy one. Over the years, he had developed hip contractures because of the spasticity in his muscles. Sanjiv was a slow learner, but interacted with others and was independent in his self-care.

The CBR worker supported Komal to apply for a small loan through a microfinance program, a housing subsidy, and organized for a hand-crank tri-wheelchair with a small trolley to carry goods hitched to the back. This wheelchair was supplied through and subsidized by the CBR program (funded by an NGO). Within 1 month of the housing subsidy, Komal and Sanjiv moved to their own small house, which had a small yard. Komal had grown up on a farm and knew about caring for dairy cattle. She bought a milking cow with the loan. She fed the cow and milked her every day. Sanjiv's job was to carry the milk pails each day, 7 days per week in his trolley at the back of his wheelchair, to sell to a shop owner in the village. Delivery of produce was a man's job, and Sanjiv grew more confident with his new role. Fresh milk was needed in the village. Most people in the village were crop farmers and did not have the knowledge or time to care for and milk a cow each day.

Over the next 2 years, Komal had paid back most of the loan, had bought two more cows and the family had savings. Sanjiv had become well known in the village with people saying hello and talking to him as he made his way each day to the shop. He would often linger in the shop and talk with local people. Over time, he had developed a strong network of friends and acquaintances. Komal was now respected in the community, as many people had been impressed at her small business enterprise. Their profile and value to the community had changed.

CASE MANAGEMENT

The evolutionary history of case management mirrors the social movement's rights-based struggle of people with disabilities to be served as equals in society. Case management began as a social justice response to the deinstitutionalization of persons with psychiatric disabilities (Dieterich, Irving, Park, & Marshall, 2010; Mas-Exposito, Amador-Campos, Gomez-Benitor, & Lalucat-Jo, 2014). Institutional care did not prepare the newly discharged to survive in such an unstructured and demanding environment. The consequences of state-sponsored abandonment were overwhelmingly catastrophic. The original case management model that sought to remedy the resultant personal and family crises was called the broker model. It focused on clinical assessment, planning, and referral processes that emphasized service coordination and the input of experts. This systems-focused approach to case management framed the client as the dependent and passive recipient of care. Success was measured in client and family compliance.

The broker model expanded across in-patient and out-patient settings (Kerbergen, 1996). The decentralization of health care services led to improved models that gave case managers enhanced levels of clinical input and judgment (medical/clinical case management). Increasing health care costs led to cost containment models that redefined the case manager as gatekeeper (discharge planner; see Fox et al., 2013) to service and a proxy for management interests in the client's rehabilitation plan.

These models focused on *medical/health* systems response to illness and the coordination of services rather than the client's goals and aspirations. The approach is rational and the decision making is algorithmic; to wit, if the client has been referred, the need has been met. Client feedback is not necessary and typically does not occur in these models. Client capacity building, self-management, and determination are not features. Referral does not enhance one's relationship within the health care system, as one passes from service to service as a vessel that is acted on but not often consulted.

A hybrid model (assertive case management [ACM]) addressed the social deficits of early case management. Personalizing activities were added to the traditional system throughput. Rehabilitation case managers, trained in mental health counseling, provided both clinical supports and brokerage. Monitoring functions addressed progress toward client goals and purposeful community engagement. Outcome evaluations began to consider quality-of-life indices that proper care should affect, such as recidivism and repeat hospitalizations. The ACM social capital focus on client, family, and community strengths expanded across rehabilitation settings and populations in the manner of the brokerage model before it.

The UN Convention on the Rights of Persons with Disabilities (United Nations, 2006) and the ICF (WHO, 2001) provide the community values and ecological framework that shape the evolution of case management models into the future. Emerging CM models recognize "the valued existing and potential contributions made by persons with disabilities to the overall well-being and diversity of their communities" (UNCRPD, 2013, p. 2) and structure service accordingly. Valuing community participation as the central, instrumental goal leads to *social* systems interventions as a new core skill set for case managers that includes (a) an emphasis on clear and effective communication at all levels, (b) social networking, (c) knowledge dissemination and utilization, (d) individual and group advocacy, (e) plan and program monitoring, (f) consensus building, and (g) optimizing resource utilization to the benefit of all parties involved. The systems-oriented approach to case management has been adapted to a variety of settings (e.g., clinical, rehabilitation, nursing, medical, legal, and advocacy) with a variety of emphases (e.g., intensive case management, care coordination, strengths based, networking, generalist, peer assisted, managerial), providing a diverse array of possibilities (Bedell, Cohen, & Sullivan, 2000; Chamberlain & Rapp, 1991; Fraser & Strang, 2004; MacNeil Vroomen et al., 2012; Petersen, 2004; Rosen & Teesson, 2001; van Houdt, Heyrman, Vanhaecht, Serveus, & De Lepeleire, 2013).

Case Management and Rehabilitation Counseling Connection

The expression of case management service in rehabilitation counseling varies by context. The fundamental mission does not change, for that is the essence of the profession, but policies, politics, and economics create a service environment to which value-driven models must adapt. The history of case management is a case in point. Case management development is revolutionary in its sea change of fundamental values (from medical to social worldview), and evolutionary in its adaptation across settings. Rehabilitation counseling is practiced in three sectors (a) public, which is eclipsed in the United States by the state/federal Vocational Rehabilitation (VR) program; (b) private nonprofit, which may serve people with disabilities in a variety of settings with financial support of VR or other public and private entities, and (c) private for-profit, where rehabilitation counselors primarily populate worker compensation systems and specialize in return to work, disability management, and forensic work. Each system has its own drivers, resources, and barriers that must be negotiated by the case manager who serves, in a sense, as the agent for the greater professional identity of rehabilitation counseling. Case management will naturally look different in each sector. Within sectors, case management is an imperfect approximation of ideal service, a work in progress as it were. At the local point of delivery, case management becomes whatever the agency decides it to be. It is not surprising that rehabilitation counselors in the field report feeling underprepared as case managers (Roessler & Rubin, 2006). Implementation is free to vary throughout the rehabilitation counseling system with extant empirical support for case management as best practice in general (Leahy, Muenzen, Saunders, & Strauser, 2009), but little support for specific models in any sector (see Selander & Marnetoft, 2005; Upton & Beck, 2002).

Shared Values and Principles

We do have our democratic values and the guiding principles that come from them to unite all models. Client-centered practice is, at this point, a given universal principle. Case management in rehabilitation counseling is resolutely client centered in all professional trade. Except where a significant other has legal claim to guardianship or proxy, the client is empowered to define his or her family, for case management purposes, in his or her supporting roles in the rehabilitation process. Family members are free to choose whether or not to accept these terms, as is their right, but the rehabilitation counseling case manager is there to ensure that the client maintains maximal control.

Social Justice and Human Rights

Participating family members have a fiduciary relationship with service that requires a guarantee of their rights. Fundamentally, families are ensured (a) access to an equitable portion of all resources due to them as players in the process and people in need; (b) ethical treatment on par with the client in terms of informed consent, confidentiality, respect and preservation of dignity, safety, and access to redress of grievances; and (c) active participation in decision-making processes that impact their lives, so they may be heard and have fair influence; and (d) to be treated with dignity as a full partners and persons of worth. The rehabilitation counselor is obligated to see these rights met, doubly so, as instrumental players to the welfare of the client, and as persons in their own right.

Strengths-Based Practice and Resilience

The case management model that best reflects the sensibilities of CBR counseling is a strengths-based approach. People become resilient by navigating their own way through adversity, using their own resources, and developing their own potential. They tend to choose this more autonomous path if they perceive that they have access to sufficient internal and external resources to succeed (Rapp & Goscha, 2006). The assumption of strengths-based case management is normalcy, optimism, and confidence in the family. The family members come as experts to the process, capable and deserving of self-determination, and in possession of a potentially large and untapped reservoir of potential capital. The community beyond the family is not a barrier, but a wealth of resources to be appropriated for the client's plan. As the client transcends the pathology of the medical model, the counselor descends from the favored status of expert, and the twain meet as citizens in the community. Case management is practiced in the family's world, not in the counselor's office (Selander & Marnetoft, 2005). Client-centered, strengths-based case management still looks at the family as instrumental to the client's needs. It recognizes that this is best served when the family knows its own strengths as well as the strengths of the client; protects its rights and advocates effectively; is skilled in self and group development, learning, and care; is embedded in a functional support system; and is proficient and proactive in accessing all available community resources (Bailey et al., 2006).

Toolbox of Approaches

The tools of case management work in any model and all models will employ these tools within a predictable process common to any strategic management situation (see Tague, 2005): (a) evaluate the client's current situation in light of identified goals and the gap between current and desired states; (b) take stock of all available resources that can be used to reach identified goals and make a plan replete with intermediate steps—objectives; (c) implement the plan; (d) monitor progress toward goals and objectives and repeat the process and adapt the plan until success is reached. This borrowing of continuous improvement framework is fitting when case management becomes a group effort with the family, rather than an extension of individual counseling (Kierpiec, Phillips, & Kosciulek, 2010).

Working Alliance. The working alliance is still the first and most fundamental tool of case management. The working alliance is earned through a collaborative social process entered into by equals and gained through successful implementation of a consensual plan. It comes from an overtly and aggressively positive psychology. The needs analysis does not begin with "What is the problem and why is it a problem?" The family relationship with the rehabilitation counselor does not revolve around identifying and resolving its physical, emotional, or social/economic shortcomings. Because the profession is client centered and community based, the family × counselor nexus revolves around the question: How can family capital be orchestrated, enhanced, and implemented to best strategic effect in achieving and sustaining client goals? It is in answer to this question that the tools of case management are employed.

Counseling Within Case Management. There are two primary reasons why families would receive counseling support within the case management context: (a) help the family cope with the stress of change and (b) facilitate well-informed decisions in the change process. Counseling accompanies the cycle like a form of brief, solution-focused therapy. Where are you now? Where do you want to be? What's in your way? What have you tried? How did it work? And most importantly, what do you do next? Beyond this, the choice of approach depends on counselor expertise, and the context. Acceptance and commitment therapy, for instance, seems particularly well suited to some applications in case management. The emphasis is on supporting the family as it faces hard choices, helping it to move through a process of accepting (rather than avoiding) that which is outside of its control, create new meanings for adversity, and define itself as validated in its ownership of decisions and commitment to life as it is (Hayes, Luoma, Bond, Masuda, & Lillis, 2006).

Positive Risk Taking. Taking acceptable risks is something all humans do in all aspects of our lives, in order that we may develop, experience, and so change our life. Risks can be calculated and managed, or impulsive or emotionally driven. For individuals with an acquired disability through trauma, risk aversion is a natural response from the individual and family, particularly where the injury arose from engaging in risk-taking behavior. However, risk is an everyday experience and the person with a disability should be provided with the opportunity to have the responsibility and choice to take acceptable risks. Positive risk taking recognizes the positive benefits of risk, weighs potential for harm (risk assessment), exercises informed choice, and studiously plans to maximize the potential for success.

Supported Decision Making. Supported decision making involves conscious planning for supports to enable a person to make key decisions affecting his or her life, across the arc of life. Supports might be as simple as facilitated communication of information (in a medium suited to the person), or as involved as a structured stepwise approach where the potential options, outcomes, and responsibilities are presented in a fashion customized to the client, situation, and presenting issue. The process works within the family to facilitate client inclusion in all aspects of plan design. Understanding the person's capacity is an important first step, and the process is adjusted according to individual and family needs.

Knowledge and Skill Acquisition. Neither the content nor processes of the rehabilitation plan is likely to be well integrated into the family's functions without training. Families need a great deal of information, some of it quickly, to be informed partners to the process. Initially the learning focus is on orientation to systems, and service. Moving forward, the family needs increasing individualized knowledge and understanding of the disability and its implications, guidance on how to negotiate within the formal care system, and useful information about the efficacy and availability of services and strategies provided by the rehabilitation counselor. As the plan progresses, need for knowledge focuses more pragmatically on advancing the plan. Needs change, but the demand for learning is ever present. Putting the right knowledge in the hands of the right people, at the right time, in the right space, and in a format they can use becomes a critical empowerment tool in community-based case management. Knowledge dissemination and utilization at the consumer level is an exercise of capital that has been overlooked in rehabilitation counseling to date. The default is informal training and brochures without regard to potential for informed choices and strategic delivery (Kingston, 2012).

Fortified with content, family members can develop thinking skills with specific applications. Families alternately have need for critical reasoning skills to distill complex issues into salient decision points, creative strategies for generating divergent options, and problem-solving models that combine the two (Parnes, 1992). Problem-solving strategies and critical thinking in case management move the family from uncertainty to positive outcomes (Kelley, 2003). They are skills that can be learned, practiced, and generalized in application.

Goal Setting and Planning. Goals belong to the person with a disability, not the case manager or the family. Goals that are meaningful to the client can increase motivation, the task performance, and the level of engagement participation (Locke, 1996). Goals need to be specific, measurable, achievable, realistic, and time targeted (S.M.A.R.T. goals).

Planning is more than a conversation; it allows the person with a disability and his or her family to think ahead. Planning involves the person with a disability identifying what steps are needed to assist him or her to achieve his or her goal. Active involvement of the person with a disability in planning means thinking about his or her goals, contributing to planning tasks, ideas for supports (e.g., knowledge of the local community), having choices, making decisions, and having control and responsibilities.

Referral and Networking. At the center of every plan is a concrete outcome for the client with a disability, be it a home, a job, or an education. Building the bridge from current need to resolved outcome often requires the coordination of services across disparate and disjointed service agencies. Family access to service within the plan facilitates the family's ability to support the individual in achieving the goal, including respite care, training to provide specialized care (monitoring medical regimes in the home), assistants for home care, assistive devices they may use in the process of care (e.g., transfer hoist), and ancillary welfare or other economic support to which they may otherwise be entitled. If family dysfunction is indeed present and disrupting the plan, referrals could be made for family counseling as well.

Advocacy. Advocacy refers to completing tasks; speaking or writing on behalf of another to promote, protect, or defend his or her needs or circumstances; and arguing in that person's favor. Individual advocacy comes primarily through the work done in the person's environment, and typically aims to mediate the environment barriers that are negatively influencing the participation of the client. In some models of CM, advocacy is integral to the service goal, others less so. As a case manager, advocacy can be at the micro level (attitudes of family) or at the meso level (influential policy at the workplace).

Building Purposeful Networks. In CM, particular strategies can be used to purposefully build or extend the networks of the person with a disability and his or her family. Networks potentially strengthen the connection to the community and lead to better or broader exchange of resources. "Circles of support" refer to the identification and sometimes the formalization of a circle of people that provide a network of social support to the person with a disability. The people may be friends, key workers, service organization, or volunteers. Other purposeful networks may be relevant community groups such as special interest groups (e.g., organic gardening), social and sports clubs, peer-support group or more formalized peer-support programs, and advocacy groups.

CASE STUDY

George was referred to the rehabilitation counselor for assistance to return to work. George had been diagnosed several years ago with multiple sclerosis and had recently changed from using a walking aid to a manual wheelchair. George was of Maltese origin. As the sole income earner in his family, he had worked for 10 years as an employed manager of a retail store that sold vacuum cleaners. He had been made redundant 4 years ago. Now, his wife worked part time and he had two primary school–aged children.

The rehabilitation counselor had completed vocational assessment and identified book-keeping and accounts as an appropriate retraining option given that George had been exposed to small business and had had some financial responsibilities as manager of the store, although not accounting. He was attending a technical college three times per week and doing well with his studies. He needed some work experience to be able to compete for paid employment on the open job market as a bookkeeper, assistant to an accountant.

At a community program network meeting, the rehabilitation counselor met a CD colleague who was looking toward developing a program to support children with severe disabilities in long-day child care centers for children below 5 years. Many of the parents had come to the organization (which certified these child care centers) seeking a placement for their children but were not accepted due to a higher staff–child ratio of care needed subsequent to disability (roughly two children to one staff member whereas usually it is five or eight children to one staff member depending on the child's age). The parents of these children were not able to work because of a lack of options with child care. Furthermore, their children were not able to access mainstream child care services, a human rights issue. Child care centers struggle to mainstream children with severe disabilities because of the staff–child ratios and lack of funding.

The CD colleague got together a steering committee to form a community group, the birth of Adina Children's Program. The management was 12 people—parent representative, specialist child care worker, director of child care center staff, health professional, and George (as the finance expert). The group submitted for government funding, which targeted community groups to stimulate employment for unemployed people with mild to moderate disabilities. Submission was successful (and subsequent renewals for a further 5 years). The local baby health center provided office accommodation for the Adina program coordinator and a space for the management committee to meet. The local unemployment office referred people who were interested in a position. Interviews were held and six adults with mild to moderate disabilities were employed as child care support workers by the community group (insurances taken out). The support workers worked alongside the child care center staff, with primary responsibility for the child with a disability that was then placed in the center. A maximum of four children were placed at each center (so each child attended 1–4 days each depending on the circumstances). George managed the salaries, financial bookkeeping, banking, and so forth. George continued in a voluntary capacity for 2 years while he finished his studies (2 financial years, so he had relevant experience). Identified outcomes included the following:

- *George gained recent industry experience in accounting and bookkeeping. His role within his family had improved and self-confidence increased.*
- *Children with disability attending the center (having exposure to each other) learned from experiences.*
- *Parents were able to return to work part time and their well-being improved.*
- *Rights of children with disabilities and their families were advanced through mainstream recognition and participation.*
- *Adults with disability were employed and gained industry experience. Three of the employees in the first year were employed by the child care centers where they worked.*
- *Child care center staff learned skills and increased confidence in caring for children with disabilities.*

INTEGRATING COMMUNITY REHABILITATION COUNSELING IN THE CONTEXT OF FAMILY CAPITAL

Case management effectiveness depends on the strength, depth, and span of the case managers' knowledge of how to strengthen and build formal and informal support networks. The basic case management model is not alien to rehabilitation counseling. We have understood that case management and counseling are inseparable. Here they are the same thing. And, in a sense, this last discourse starts to unify the others as we see families not as clients, but as partners in growth and consultants to the family business of caring for their member with a disability. VR is one application (Selander & Marnetoft, 2005) that stands to benefit from this paradigm shift. In vocational case management, there is often a disconnect between the capacity of the person with a disability, as measured and assessed in a uniform or standard environment such as a clinic or work-assessment facility, and his or her performance in actual life situations. Retooled with a systems understanding of CD and strengths-based case management, VR has the potential to conceive tools and strategies that harness resources to best effect in employment and careers. Indeed, rehabilitation counseling interpreted into the community paradigm has the potential to expand on its present identity in new and innovative family practice.

NOTES

1. Synomorphy was introduced in Chapter 1 as a systems argument for finding parallel structures serving the same thematic values at different levels and in different situations. Here, CD and rehabilitation counseling are shown to be different expressions of social justice and thus likely to share synomorphic structures and processes.

REFERENCES

Bailey, D. B., Bruder, J. M. B., Hebbeler, K., Carta, J., Defosset, M., Greenwood, C., . . . Barton, L. (2006). Recommended outcomes for families of young children with disabilities. *Journal of Early Intervention, 28*, 227–251. doi:10:1177/105381510602800401

Bedell, J. R., Cohen, N. L., & Sullivan, A. (2000). Case management:The current best practices and the next generation of innovation. *Community Mental Health Journal, 36*(2), 179–194.

Chambers, R. (1997). *Whose reality counts? Putting the last first.* London, England: ITDG Press.

Chamberlain, R., & Rapp, C. A. (1991). A decade of case management: A methodological review of outcome research. *Community Mental Health Journal, 27*(3), 171–188.

Cornwell, A., & Coelho, V. S. (Eds.). (2007). *Spaces for change? The politics of citizen participation in new democratic arenas* (Vol. 4). London, England: Zed Books.

Dieterich, M., Irving, C. B., Park, B., & Marshall, M. (2010). Intensive case management for severe mental illness. *Cochrane Database of Systematic Reviews*, 10, Art No: CD007906. doi:10.1002/14651858.CD007906.pub2

Doherty, W. J., Mendenhall, T., & Berge, J. M. (2010). The families and democracy and citizen health care project. *Journal of Marital and Family Therapy, 36*, 389–402.

Fraser, K. D., & Strang, V. (2004). Decision-making and nurse case management: A philosophical perspective. *Advances in Nursing Science, 27*(1), 32–43.

Freire, P. (1970). *Pedagogy of the oppressed.* New York, NY: Continuum.

Fox, M. T., Persaud, M., Maimets, I., Brooks, D., O'Brien, K., & Tregunno, D. (2013). Effectiveness of early discharge planning in acutely ill or injured hospitalized older adults: A systematic review and meta-analysis. *BMC Geriatrics, 13*, 70. doi:10.1186/1471-2318-13-70

Goldbard, A. (2006). *New creative community: The art of cultural development.* Oakland, CA: New Village Press.

Gorman, E. H., & Marsden, P. V. (2001). Social networks, job changes, and recruitment. In I. Berg & A. L. Kalleberg (Eds.), *Sourcebook on labor markets: Evolving structures and processes* (pp. 467–502). New York, NY: Kluwer Academic/Plenum.

Granovetter, M. S. (1974). *Getting a job: A study of contacts and careers.* Cambridge, MA: Harvard University Press.

Hayes, S. C., Luoma, J. B., Bond, F. W., Masuda, A., & Lillis, J. (2006). Acceptance and commitment therapy: Model, processes and outcomes. *Behaviour Research and Therapy, 44*(1), 1–25. doi:10.1016/j.brat.2005.06.006

Hobfoll, S. E. (1989). Conservation of resources: A new attempt at conceptualizing stress. *American Psychologist, 44*, 513–524.

Hobfoll, S. E. (2001). The Influence of culture, community, and the nested-self in the stress process: Advancing conservation of resources theory. *Applied Psychology: An International Review, 50*(3), 337–421.

Jost, J. T., & Kay, A. C. (2010). Social justice: History, theory, and research. In S. T. Fiske, D. T. Gilbert, & G. Lindzey (Eds.), *Handbook of social psychology* (Vol. 1, 5th ed., pp. 1122–1165). New York, NY: John Wiley.

Kelley, T. A. (2003). Critical thinking and case management. *Case Manager, 14*(3), 70–72.

Kerbergen, A. (1996). Case Management: A rich hisotry of corodinating care to control costs. *Nursing Outlook, 44*(4), 169–172.

Kierpiec, K. M., Phillips, B. N., & Kosciulek, J. F. (2010). Vocational rehabilitation caseload size and the working alliance: Implications for rehabilitation administrators. *Journal of Rehabilitation Administration, 34*(1), 5–14.

Kingston, J. (2012). Choosing a knowledge dissemination approach. *Knowledge and Process Management, 19*(3), 160–170.

Leahy, M. J., Muenzen, P., Saunders, J. L., & Strauser, D. (2009). Essential knowledge domains underlying effective rehabilitation counseling practice. *Rehabilitation Counseling Bulletin, 52,* 95–106. doi:10.1177/0034355208323646

Leahy, M. J., & Phillips, B. (2010). Certification: Practitioner certification in the delivery of vocational rehabilitation services to individuals with disabilities in the United States. In J. H. Stone & M. Blouin (Eds.), *International encyclopedia of rehabilitation.* Retrieved from http://cirrie.buffalo.edu/encyclopedia/en/article/42/

Locke, E. A. (1996). Motivation through conscious goal setting. *Applied and Preventive Psychology, 5,* 117–124.

Lukersmith, S., Hartley, S., Kuipers, P., Madden, R., Llewellyn, G., & Dune, T. (2013). Community-based rehabilitation (CBR) monitoring and evaluation methods and tools: A literature review. *Disability and Rehabilitation, 35*(23), 1941–1953.

MacNeil Vroomen, J., Van Mierlo, L. D., van de Ven, P. M., Bosmans, J. E., van den Dungen, P., . . . van Hout, H. P. (2012). Comparing Dutch case management care models for people with dementia and their caregivers: The design of the COMPAS study. *BMC Health Service Research, 12,* 132. doi:10.1186/1472-6963-12-132

Marmont, M., & Wilkinson, R. G. (Eds.). (2007). *Social determinants of health* (2nd ed.). New York, NY: Oxford University Press.

Mas-Exposito, L., Amador-Campos, J. A., Gomez-Benitor, J., & Lalucat-Jo, L. (2014). Depicting current case management models. *Journal of Social Work, 14,* 133–146. doi:10.1177/1468017313477296

Parnes, S. J. (Ed.). (1992). *Source book for creative problem solving: A fifty year digest of proven innovation processes.* Buffalo, NY: Creative Education Foundation Press. ISBN: 0-930222-922

Petersen, V. M. (2004, March/April). When quality management meets case management. *Lippincott's Case Management, 9*(2), 108–109.

Prahalad, C. K. (2004). *The fortune at the bottom of the pyramid.* Upper Saddle River, NJ: Wharton School Publishing.

Putnam, R. D. (1995). Bowling alone: America's declining social capital. *Journal of Democracy, 6*(1), 65–78.

Putnam, R. D. (2001). *Bowling alone: The collapse and revival of American community.* New York, NY: Simon and Schuster.

Rapp, C. A., & Goscha, R. J. (2006). *The strengths model: Case management with people with psychiatric disabilities* (2nd ed.). New York, NY: Oxford University Press.

Rennie, E. (2006). *Community media: A global introduction*. Lanham, MD: Rowman and Littlefield.

Roessler, R. T., & Rubin, S. E. (2006). Mission, role, and competencies of the rehabilitation counselor. In R. T. Roessler & S. E. Rubin (Eds.), *Case management and rehabilitation counseling* (4th ed., pp. 1–27). Austin, TX: PRO-ED.

Rosen, A., & Teesson, M. (2001). Does case management work. *Australian and New Zealand Journal of Psychiatry, 35*, 731–746.

Selander, J., & Marnetoft, S. (2005). Case management in vocational rehabilitation: A case study with promising results. *Work, 24*, 297–304.

Tague, N. R. (2005). *Quality toolbox* (2nd ed.). Milwaukee, WI: ASQ Quality Press.

Upton, T. D., & Beck, R. (2002). Case management: Rehabilitation applications and administrative implications. *Journal of Rehabilitation Administration, 26*(1), 39–46.

United Nations. (2006). *Convention on the rights of persons with disabilities*. Retrieved from http://www.un.org/disabilities/default.asp?navid=12&pid=150

van Houdt, S., Heyrman, J., Vanhaecht, K., Serveus, W., & De Lepeleire, J. (2013). An in-depth analysis of theoretical frameworks for the study of care coordination. *International Journal of Integrated Care, 13*, 27.

Walsh, F. (2006). *Strengthening family resilience* (2nd ed.). New York, NY: Guilford.

World Health Organization. (2001). *International classification of functioning, disability and health*. Geneva, Switzerland: Author.

World Health Organization. (2004). *CBR: A strategy for rehabilitation, equalization of opportunities, poverty reduction and social inclusion of people with disabilities* (Joint position paper of the International Labour Organization, United Nations Educational, Scientific and Cultural Organization, and the World Health Organization). Geneva, Switzerland: Author.

World Health Organization. (2014, April). *Disability. Draft WHO global disability action plan 2014-2021: Better health for all people with disability*. Retrieved from http://apps.who.int/gb/ebwha/pdf_files/WHA67/A67_16-en.pdf

World Health Organization, UNESCO, International Labour Organisation, & International Disability Development Consortium. (2010). *Community-based rehabilitation (CBR) guidelines*. Geneva, Switzerland: World Health Organization.

World Health Organization & International Spinal Cord Society. (2013). *International perspectives of spinal cord injury*. Geneva, Switzerland: World Health Organization.

World Health Organization & World Bank. (2011). *World report on disability*. Geneva, Switzerland: World Health Organization.

Yunus, M. (2003). *Banker to the poor: Micro-lending and the battle against world poverty*. New York, NY: Public Affairs.

Yunus, M. (2010). *Building social business: The new kind of capitalism that serves humanity's most pressing needs*. New York, NY: Public Affairs.

CHAPTER 5

Family Care and Support

Michael J. Millington and Irmo Marini

As a term of art, care has suffered from misappropriation in the medical model. Formal care marginalized (Jones, 2006) "informal" family contributions and connotatively reduced care recipients to a passive drain on family resources (Hughes, McKie, Hopkins, & Watson, 2005). Family care research in this vein is framed by the expert outsider and his or her stigmatized constructions of disability (Olkin, 1999). It is not surprising that researchers in the medical model found the family experience of care overwhelmingly negative, as Yuker (1994) complained. Medical model thinking defines disability as deficit and assumes tragedy in its experience. Family care is mischaracterized as unrequited charity to the recipient and a burden to be endured by the carer. Thus the medical model lacks a worldview that can interpret the positive aspects of care as anything more than an anomaly.

Family care is more powerful, more life- and community-affirming, than the constraints of this common conceptualization. We have made the case that family is the touchstone of client identity, a source of client power, and the core of the client's social support network. In this chapter, we advance the concept of care as the medium through which all community grows. We repurpose care as a term of art for community use and describe the relationship between family and rehabilitation counseling within the context of care. We define care in terms of the family ethos and a preliminary model emerges. By building from the values that link care to community, we redefine and start to operationalize a new understanding of how rehabilitation counseling enters into the caring relationship—how we are, as a value-driven profession, obligated to provide support for the caring family.

DEFINING CARE

The word *care* has etymological roots in lamentation, which means to call out in pain or sorrow. It also has more familiar roots in the Latin, *caritas*, which refers to the applied practice of agape, that is, unconditional love for humanity and its expression in acts of kindness. The word kindness itself reflects the idea of kinship. To say that one has received a kindness is to infer that one has been treated like family. The kindness that is the family ethos is the ethos of care. It is a feminist voice for a moral philosophy of relationships and interdependence (Gilligan, 1982) that emerged as a counterpoint and balance to the rugged individualism of the liberal justice perspective on moral development (Kohlberg & Hersh, 1977). The ethics of care is local, intrinsic to proximal process, embedded in the family (Gilligan & Wiggins, 1987), and epitomized in motherhood. Criticized early on for its inability to speak to power at a global scale (Friedman, 2006), the ethics of care has since found its own path to justice and advocacy through community activism (Noddings, 1984) and earned its forum in the disability community. As with Dewey, the caring response to social justice begins in the home (Noddings, 2002) and is expressed through local action.

Psychosocial Character of Care

Care is both the call to, and response of, community. It is a pervasive occupation for individuals within groups. The tales of community history that reflect our better nature tell the story of people rallying around the beleaguered town or strife-torn neighborhood. Individual lives are replete with small, transient acts of caring, as we hold the door, give up our seat, or return a lost dog. These selfless acts of caring, however heroic or common, are the transactional manifestations of community. Care is motivated through the spirit of *gemeinschaft*, that is, community built on social identity rather than individual profit. It is through the act of caring that we share in something larger than ourselves because caring makes that larger thing real.

Care Is a Reciprocal Relationship

Care is first a value, then a social exchange, then a relationship. The care recipient benefits from a kindness, as previously described. The caregiver benefits by being afforded the opportunity to live his or her values (Jones, 2006). Roles emerge and social–emotional bonds form (Dembo, Leviton, & Wright, 1975) in the proximal process of caring practiced over time. We give and receive care throughout our lives in predictable and unpredictable circumstances, and in needs great and small. The reciprocal nature of care creates interdependence (Condelucci, 1995) and builds social obligations between the person and the group. Care is a currency of community inclusion. The carer, even if unpaid and lacking any other form of external reward, still obtains a sense of purpose and meaning and is intrinsically rewarded for his or her acts of kindness.

Family Is the Proximal Source of Care

Family care is characterized by deep emotions, shared history, shared intimacy, and reciprocity. It is qualitatively different from the formal care of professionals, even where the service is the same. Caring is networked in the family system and orchestrated in its delivery through every family role. Spouses care for their partners, parents care for their children, and siblings care for each other in a complex web of prescribed relationships (Bauman, Foster, Silver, Berman, Gamble, & Muchaneta, 2006). These caring roles adjust to changes and challenges and evolve over time. Caregivers negotiate multiple roles within the family (Bainbridge, Cregan, & Kulik, 2006) and take their identity from the synthesis of these practiced roles. Objectively, there may be no difference between the outputs of family care and professional care as both deliver a nutritious meal, a hot bath, or scheduled medication. Subjectively, family care communicates genuine unconditional love as a subtext of the act. Family care is intimate and familiar. Family care is family ritual. Family care is more than a meal.

Formal Care Is Distal Care

Where the needs of a family member exceed the local community's ability to provide care and support, care is sought through formal expert networks. Professional care is characterized by reserved emotions, limited history, lack of intimacy, and constrained reciprocity in the application of advanced technical knowledge and skill. Formal care is defined by its interventions rather than its relationships, and that is the crucial difference. Formal care is subordinate to the proximal care of family as a means to full community inclusion. Indeed, distal (formal) care alone is isolating—an institutional substitute for community. Formal care must ultimately serve the system of informal care where inclusion resides.

THE EXPERIENCE OF FAMILY CARE AND DISABILITY

Disability is expressed through impairments in body structures and functions, limitations in activities, and restrictions in participation (World Health Organization [WHO], 2013). The family response to disability is to provide care that satisfies the complex of needs across these domains. The caring response is complex and systemic. At the most elementary level, care is expressed in dyads through the roles of the family (see Figure 5.1). Each role represented in Figure 5.1 is relational. The parent role implies care for a child with a disability, the sibling role implies care for a brother or sister, and so on. Each family member potentially has role-defined care duties built into his or her relationships.

   Care can be direct in the client dyad or indirect in support of caring others. Family roles are subject to change and shift in their interrelationships as the group adapts to the reality of care and support for the person with a disability. Care is embedded in this network of support, extending outward from the client to whomsoever the person embraces as family or friend. In this way, the task load is shared and all needs are potentially met in a balanced and sustainable way.

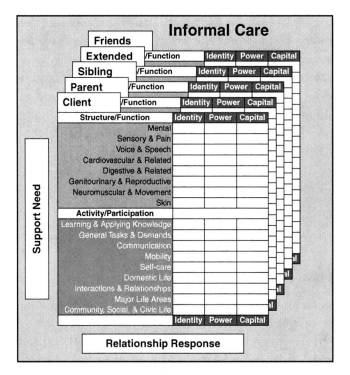

FIGURE 5.1 Care and support for disability in the family.

Instrumental Family Support in Body Structures and Functions

Disability issues of body structure and function are the primary concern of health care professionals. The diagnosis and treatment of medical conditions require the direction and supervision of formal care expertise, but families have an instrumental and growing role in its administration. The consumer movement, evidence-based practice, and the economics of health care have moved medical monitoring and management tasks into the home (Lakin, Prouty, & Coucouvanis, 2007). Formal care is time limited. Health care professionals intervene in emergencies and episodic interventions. In the rehabilitation model, they staunch the bleeding, fix what is broken, and cure what is ailing. As structural and functional needs become chronic and care becomes maintenance, their roles necessarily recede into the background tasks of supervision and consultation.

The family provides ongoing support to the medical professional by (a) implementing medical regimens; (b) monitoring health status; (c) identifying emerging health issues and medical complications; and (d) tracking progress in the care plan (Von Korff, Gruman, Schaefer, Curry, & Wagner, 1997). Families monitor and manage medical treatment for a variety of chronic illnesses (e.g., Falloon et al., 1982; Fiese & Wamboldt, 2003). Family partnership in supporting long-term medical care is established practice that continues to expand with innovations in treatment, technology, and home-based strategies (Heaton, Noyes, Sloper, & Shah, 2005).

Instrumental Family Support in Activities and Participation

Activities and participation are complementary aspects of independent and collaborative social behavior, respectively. There is no clear boundary between the two. They represent the behavioral continuum of community inclusion (WHO, 2013). Activities and participation, particularly those more closely associated with activities of daily living, consume the majority of family care resources (National Alliance for Care Giving & AARP, 2009). Family members are commonly engaged in care and support across the International Classification of Functioning (ICF) categories that describe social inclusion (see Figure 5.1). Family care and support advances independence in activities and inclusion in participation via three strategies.

- *Remediation* develops performance through training, practice, and exercise.
- *Adaptation* improves independence and inclusion by modifying the environment to better match the functional performance of the person.
- *Compensation* utilizes assistive devices to increase, maintain, or improve functional capacity (Henderson, Skelton, & Rosenbaum, 2008).

The ultimate success of family care is how well it addresses community inclusion across the range of categories, over the course of a lifetime. Unlike formal care, family is forever.

Applied Community Values in Family Care

The ICF categories that populate the vertical axis in Figure 5.1 represent a taxonomy of client need. The figure itself is a model of the caring response. On the face of the figure, we can project the unique pattern of needs for any client across the ICF categories. In the immediate frames behind the client, we can arrange the supporting family by social distance and appreciate the unique constellation of individual contributions. Further back and at a formal distance, health care agents take their place in a complementary constellation of distal care. Peering through the frames, we can superimpose all care activities provided by all stakeholders, individual and in collaboration, and map the state of care against the client's need profile. In this way, care can be succinctly quantified in all of the instrumental configurations of care: coverage and redundancy, balance and load (across stakeholders), and the gaps between need and response.

The model's third dimension introduces the essential characteristics of care as they were appropriated from sense of community theory (McMillan & Chavis, 1986) in Chapter 1 and given full exposition in Chapters 2 through 4. Identity, power, and capital represent the dimensions that describe how, and how well, care is expressed as a relationship between people in the context of community. The response to need, when community inclusion is the goal, is not arbitrary. A private bath at home with the assistance of a loving and attentive spouse serves the same physical self-care need as a group shower in an institution attended by an orderly. Bereft of identity, stripped of power, and removed from the marketplace, what becomes of the person, however clean he or she may be? What becomes of the custodial orderly who only interacts with people as objects to be cleaned? What becomes of the family that no longer participates in the rituals of care?

If the meaning of care is not anchored in community values, it is vulnerable to corruption and a potential cover for bad behavior. "Caring" relationships range from supportive, to dependent, to contentious and abusive (Nosek, Foley, Hughes, & Howland, 2001). Family beliefs, attitudes, and expectations regarding disability set the stage for self-fulfilling prophesies and the tone for individual and collective self-efficacy in dealing with the challenges of care (Minnes, Woodford, & Passey, 2007). Where expectations emphasize self-direction, care is expressed as partnership. Where expectations emphasize diminished capacity, care is expressed as custodianship. In the absence of caring values, the relationship becomes toxic and care may eventually erode to abuse (Washington, 2009). If care does not set a standard, it cannot be effectively improved.

Thus we argue that care portrayed as a burden to the family is a misappropriation of the term. Care, properly understood, is a hygienic social process that nurtures the individual (both parties to the care dyad), builds cohesion in the group (Jones, 2006), and provides a learning context for the pursuit of resilience (Smyth, Cass, & Hill, 2011). Care in practice is the imperfect expression of a democratic ideal. Burden is not a party to care; it is a consequence of insufficient, deficient, and corrupt systems that attempt to provide care. "Burden of care," defined elsewise, is a covert indictment of the person with a disability and makes victims of those who embrace the caring role.

Benefits and Burdens

Care creates opportunities for reciprocal social exchange (Call, Finch, Huck, & Kane, 1999) of love, warmth, and companionship. This is the exercise of the affective bond that unites and defines family. Its expression has a synergistic quality to it; shared positive emotions enhance the care experience and increase carer motivation (Reid, Moss, & Hyman, 2005). Studies have consistently found that caring for a loved one with a disability is perceived as a normal part of family life. Even as the demands of care tax family resources, care remains something family members often want, and are proud, to do (Buchanan, Radin, Chakravorty, & Tyry, 2009). A qualitative study of parents in Sweden (Lindblad, Holritz-Rasmussen, & Sandman, 2007) observed that among the healthy, caring families observed, the child with a disability was fully included within the family identity and duly valued without conditions. Furthermore, the experience of disability was authentically integrated into family processes. Space had been created to openly discuss and express the sadness and worries that attend parenthood from time to time, and conversely to celebrate the joys and successes.

They found that the experience of caring had changed family structure and processes in positive ways. Parents became less demanding of life in general, more spontaneous, and tolerant of difference. The necessity of recruiting support from their social network reinforced this community-oriented attitude. Engaging with the support network in this sense of community created closer bonds with extended family and friends. The practice of interdependency was seen as life enriching for its promotion of personal growth and empathy (Wang & Barnard, 2008).

Negative Effects of Burden. Flaws in a system of care are the burdens that beget stress. Stress in the moment becomes strain over time (see Brannan, Heflinger, & Bickman, 1997). The chronic strain of care exhausts the caregiver (Heaton et al., 2005). The retraction of the family around the issue of care reduces sibling engagement in physical activity (Bauman et al., 2006) outside of the home. Long-term physical effects are numerous, including exacerbation of chronic health conditions and psychosomatic complaints (Vitaliano, Schulz, Kiecolt-Glaser, & Grant, 1997) and generally poorer physical health (Byrne, Hurley, Daly, & Cunningham, 2010).

Where physical health is compromised, psychological health is at risk (Lounds & Seltzer, 2007). Depression and anxiety are the most commonly identified problems (Roth et al., 2009). Depression can become a secondary disability in the family system, further threatening relationships. Depression can affect siblings at home, not only in their childhood but also into their adulthood. Depression increases in prevalence with the age of the carer (Minnes et al., 2007). Concerns regarding the future, fear of being isolated and alone, and worries over one's diminishing capacity to satisfy increasing care demands take a chronic and mounting toll on carer's emotional and physical health.

Social burden revolves around isolation. Increasing care demands can monopolize the carer's time and energy. The carer role within the family can displace other important family roles. High demand for care of one child can diminish time spent with other children and one's spouse and time spent alone with one's personal pursuits. Lack of time to participate in personal interests shrinks social environments beyond the carer role (Quittner, Gluekauf, & Jackson, 1990). Social networks providing support can erode as the situation becomes chronic (Quittner et al., 1990). Even the spiritual network is at risk when leaders and lay members do not recognize the spiritual life of the person with a disability and, worse, validate some form of social shaming. Rejection by religious community can create a crisis of faith and alienation in the family (Speraw, 2006).

The first consequences of isolation are emotional and economic impoverishment. The family's diminished participation in the workforce (Scott, 2010) results in loss of identity (Shearn & Todd, 2000), reduction in earning capacity, and increased risk of financial collapse brought on by the exorbitant cost of treatment (Birdsong & Parish, 2008). Mothers of children with disabilities are doubly impacted. As traditional carers, they are often expected to take on disability without much in the way of role negotiation. The result is significantly less full-time work, less tenure, more intermittent and permanent exits from the labor market (Scott, 2010), problems with reentry into the labor market (Heller, Caldwell, & Factor, 2007), and significant long-term economic consequences (Parish, Seltzer, Greenberg, & Floyd, 2004). Interestingly, single mothers are often forced to remain in the workforce in low-wage and precarious employment in an effort to avoid abject poverty. Lone carers in an Irish study tended to be older, in poorer health, less engaged in employment, overwhelmingly dependent on social security, and dealing with greater stress than those in more networked support systems (McConkey, 2005).

Burdensome Issues. The burden of care is real. Only now do we start to understand that it is largely caused by a society that takes the carer for granted (Hancock, Jarvis, & L'Veena, 2007). Burden is the consequence of bad fit between care strategies and the needs of all system stakeholders. It stands in the logic model of care as an output that reflexively becomes an input and cycles through the system in increasing toxicity. It is a burden to work at full capacity without relief, day after day. It is more of a burden to rise in the morning depressed, exhausted, sick, and alone and be expected to fill that role again. When the burdened carer finally succumbs, the need for care remains, and the system shifts the burden to others. The dissolution of care continues anew. Alternately, the stakeholders in the system may take it upon themselves to negotiate a sustainable approach to care that sees burden as a diagnostic symptom of a dysfunctional system rather than a feature of the caring process. By looking at the demand placed on the care system across client needs, and the nature of the systemic response, perceived burden can be articulated in a profile of potential counseling and care planning issues.

Severity of Disability. In general, the more severe the impact of disability on biological structures/functions and activities/participation, the greater the demand on the care system. Providing medical care in the home is complicated and difficult to integrate into the parenting role (Wang & Barnard, 2008). It requires training and monitoring, adds a layer of complexity and stress to daily life, and monopolizes family resources. Increasing severity and frequency of behavioral disruptions require greater effort, time, and skill in management, under conditions conducive to increased stress. At-risk populations (suicide, relapse, self-injurious behaviors, fragile health) require heightened levels of supervision, intermittent crises response, and intensive interface between family and trained staff on-call and scheduled (Luiselli & Hurley, 2008). Complex demands across biopsychosocial contexts result in family burden without adequate training, coping, external support, and respite (MacDonald & Callery, 2007).

Role Issues. Caring responsibilities are built into existing family roles. However, disability requires a strategic renegotiation of caring roles to be effective. When it is not well considered, disability-related care tends to be disproportionately ascribed along gendered lines. Mothers are traditionally ensconced in nurturing, familial roles. The traditional role may require mother's selfless dedication to child care. Mothers are made implicitly responsible for all facets of child development in health, education, and moral upbringing regardless of the demands on them, adequacy of resources, or their power to implement (Malacrida, 2009). The pursuit of the impossible demands of the role comes increasingly at the expense of self-care and personal well-being.

Mothers with disabilities find additional struggles defending themselves in a formal care system that is predisposed to see them as unfit for parenting (Prilleltensky, 2004). Help for mothers with developmental disabilities often comes with state supervision, an assumption of incompetence, and service that usurps rather than supports the mothering role (McKeever, Angus, Lee Miller, & Reid, 2003). Fear of the state's judgment and sanctions, including the very real threat of enforced foster care (McConnell & Llewellyn, 2002), coerces mothers into diminished and dependent roles.

Children are often active participants in care capable of contributing to family well-being. The type and amount of care provided by children appears linked to family income (Becker, 2007), in that more is required in homes with fewer economic resources. To a point, the child's helping role can be an extension of accepted and traditional duties. As care demands increase, childhood roles undergo actual structural changes (Warren, 2007). In the extreme, the "parentification" (Stein, Reidel, & Rotheram-Borus, 1999) of the child role, especially where children are caring for parents with disabilities, can disrupt the development of traditional identities (O'Dell, Crafter, de Abreu, & Cline, 2010). A childhood spent providing personal care, performing household tasks and child care, and supplemental family income with paid work can disrupt the customary developmental path of childhood (Earley, Cushway, & Cassidy, 2007) and challenge the development of coping skills (Pakenham, Bursnall, Chiu, Cannon, & Okochi, 2006).

Siblings find their relationships with a brother or sister with a disability redefined in childhood (Rawson, 2009). Maintaining and expanding care responsibilities throughout the life span are common (Heller & Kramer, 2009) and can compete with personal development. Sibling care is often a social negotiation. In general, siblings rise to the occasion and benefit from the relationship (Heller & Arnold, 2010). When care transitions from parent to siblings, one sibling is usually designated for the primary carer role whereas other siblings will provide indirect support, such as financial and other planning consultations (Heller & Arnold, 2010). Lone siblings are often dually encumbered as they inherit responsibilities for sibling care and simultaneously entertain approaching care issues for aging parents (Burke, Taylor, Urbano, & Hodapp, 2012). Additional burden can arise from formal care systems that were not designed for use by siblings, whose lives are physically and temporally removed from the parents (Levine et al., 2005).

Aging and Evolution. Transitions create challenges anew. Parental care for an adult child with a disability changes as the family moves from home care to independent living (Lindsay, 2008). In later life, the aging of the parental carer becomes an issue as mother and father face diminishing physical capacity to perform caring roles. Care becomes an issue of continuity into adulthood as parents look beyond their tenure as aging carers for a family member with developmental disabilities (Minnes et al., 2007).

Sometimes grandparents reassume parental roles in child care (Pit-ten Cate, Hastings, Johnson, & Titus, 2007). This can be a beneficial role support within a network of care, but a concern when aging grandparents replace rather than support the parent in the long term. Many of the challenges facing spousal caregivers arise out of the growing psychological conflict between the desire to sustain deeply engrained roles and the reality of a relationship increasingly dominated by one-sided care, loss of function, and diminished social activity (Ducharme, Levesque, Ethier, & Lachance, 2007).

Stigma. Stigma does not reside so much in the attitudes of loved ones or the act of care as it does in societal attitudes (Ray, 2003), expectations, and value judgments imposed on the family. The burden of care worldview acts to stigmatize young carers. Their lives are cast as a "lost childhood" as their parents with disabilities are simultaneously cast as passive or dysfunctional (Newman, 2002). Mothers once again figure prominently in this prejudice. Stigma, not the severity of disability, tends to reduce the quality of family life (Ones, Yilmaz, Cetinkaya, & Caglar, 2005) and the perceived value of motherhood (Green, 2007). Cultural attitudes toward people with disabilities are engrained in the family worldview and can represent a formidable barrier to autonomy for the family member with a disability. Fear of stigma and the influence cultural taboos result in disabled family roles fraught with low expectations, denial, forced dependency, and shame-based isolation (Millington, 2012).

Capacity and Access. Barriers to access confound care efforts. Specialized services, such as day care for children with disabilities, can be difficult to secure and sustain when they are both dependent on and in conflict with family employment (Ceglowski, Logue, Ullrich, & Gilbert, 2009). Access can be denied by waiting lists (Minnes et al., 2007) and orders of selection. Physical distance is a barrier (McConkey, 2005) to those without transportation. Sometimes service is its own barrier. Inflexible content, delivery, and hours; underresourced or overly bureaucratic structures; and nonsupportive agents exact a high psychological, social, and economic cost from carers (Power, 2009).

SUPPORT FOR THE CARERS

The rehabilitation counselor is a care consultant to the family caregiving process who facilitates efficient, effective, and sustainable care strategies and does so for the expressed purpose of maximizing the client's inclusion in community. The counselor has a concrete service objective coming in, such as competitive employment for the client. Facilitating family care is justified by the assumed connection between family participation in rehabilitation efforts and optimal client outcomes (Resch, Benz, & Elliott, 2012). The case for the connection has been made in the preceding chapters, culminating here in a synthesis of three contexts for counseling that make up a community-based approach for engaging families in rehabilitation counseling.

Supporting Family in a System of Care

The recovery movement that gave voice to the family in rehabilitation counseling extends its influence into practice through the Systems of Care philosophy (SOC; Cook & Kilmer, 2012). SOC was a response to family mistreatment in the fragmented panoply of services systems required in the care of children with mental health issues. Initially, SOC sought to insert community psychology practice and thereby create "change in the community systems that provide support for families" (p. 393). The practices that developed within the SOC were shaped by community principles that also guide rehabilitation counseling and emerging family practice that is (a) client centered; (b) family driven; (c) community based; and (d) culturally competent. Community-based rehabilitation counseling is expressed in a strengths-based case management model that focuses on the acquisition and strategic utilization of resources in accomplishing vocational and related goals (Selander & Marnetoft, 2005). Family care is the point of entry into this system for the rehabilitation counselor. Facilitating successful long-term client goals depends on a synergistic relationship with family care.

Counseling

Framed in case management, rehabilitation counseling is any service that directly or indirectly facilitates client outcomes. The family goal is to facilitate family resilience. At the client's behest, family features in two intertwined service concerns: (a) the primary participation goal of rehabilitation counseling service (e.g., supported employment) and (b) the family care system that will support the person before, during, and after the primary goal is achieved. In both service concerns, the family is engaged as a full and valued partner.

Communication and Partnership. Establishing a working alliance with the family requires clear and open communication; a safe space for self-expression; and a shared belief that everyone will be heard, understood, valued, and influential. Sharing personal experiences about disability reveals care issues (Fisher, 2006), provides an opportunity to deepen trust through disclosure (Goldsmith, 2009), and creates a space for each person to find a voice. By encouraging family members to share their thoughts, emotions, and caring activities, the rehabilitation counselor develops a more holistic family profile that facilitates counselor empathy and understanding. Whether and how the family talks about its disability experience provides insight into the values and beliefs of the group and the specific perspectives of each member (Checton, Greene, Magsamen-Conrad, & Venetis, 2012).

Focus on Strengths. Motivation to act turns on the potential that exists within each person, the power of the collective, and the great untapped resources that are available in the larger community. Problems have solutions. Positive change is possible.

Counseling nurtures self-efficacy and confidence through positive reframing of experience, a climate of optimism, and an accumulating history of planful successes. Helping family members reframe their stories becomes especially important in resisting disempowering social attitudes and stigma. Family members are encouraged to identify and discuss individual and collective strengths that they have otherwise taken for granted in caring for their loved one. Counselors emphasize concepts such as resilience, perseverance, altruism, meaningfulness, and faith/spirituality when appropriate.

Coping. The family's repertoire of problem solving (Nezu, Palmatier, & Nezu, 2004) and other coping skills is its bulwark against distress (Elliott, Shewchuck, & Richards, 2001). Both care and employment outcomes are pursued via a continuous process of strategic evaluation, planning, implementing, monitoring, and adapting group effort in care. Social problem solving is the preferred cognitive–behavioral coping strategy. Where plans do not come to fruition or crisis derails progress, other coping strategies are practiced to ameliorate stress and make new and constructive meaning out of otherwise untenable circumstances (Kenny & McGilloway, 2007). Failure is reframed as a learning opportunity and a step toward eventual success.

Rehabilitation counselors should engage family in contingency planning for high-probability complications to the core plan. Contingency planning coordinates roles and processes in the event of a crisis, thus inoculating the family against the chaos and uncertainty. Plans may include having the emergency phone lists and trees posted, alternate "Plan Bs" for predictable disruptions to daily life, and a support network of extended family and friends at the ready. As much as possible, the family strives to maintain its natural routine and rhythm with community support.

Empowerment. The fair distribution of social power is central to any social justice endeavor. Carers and care recipients alike should be intimately aware of the obligations, expectations, and authorities of their role. Their respective roles should reflect a fair distribution of obligation and authority across family members. The person should be capable of enforcing his or her authority and fulfilling his or her obligations and be reasonably satisfied with the arrangement. Within the family, empowerment comes from inclusive discussion and consensus on task delegation.

Care often takes place in a vulnerable space for the recipient. The carer has a stake in the caring task and must move with some level of autonomy. The proper balance of power is constantly being negotiated between "caring for" and "caring about." Maximizing care recipient control over the caring process is important. Where choice and self-direction are possible, they should be supported. Minimizing time spent in the care recipient role is desirable to a point. Diversifying roles for the family member with a disability to include his or her fair share of care-giving obligations helps to balance the care load and reaffirm the interdependent nature of family life. Rehabilitation counselors encourage client independence as a family value. Learning to master one's environment is critical to one's self-esteem and prospects beyond the home.

Power is also negotiated in the family's transactions in formal care systems (Swain & Walker, 2003). Families confront byzantine health care systems as advocates for their loved ones. System empowerment can take place at a personal level in negotiations with the service providers in strategic planning, accessing service, monitoring and evaluation, or in family input into networking other forms of care across care systems (e.g., education, residential, employment, transportation). Where choices in care providers and models (Deegan, 1988) are possible, they should be entertained. The principled push in a strengths-based model is to have families lead and control the care that enters their lives, standing as equals in the dialog with formal care professionals (Caldwell & Heller, 2007; Dempsey & Dunst, 2004).

The perceived and actual amount of power families can reasonably assert with health care and related community providers are dependent on several factors—some controllable, some not. Family members become more empowered when they are educationally prepared and can articulate (assertively when necessary) their loved one's needs. Rehabilitation counselors can assist family members in developing appropriate medical and related service inquiries, thereby establishing a partnership of equals that affords the family the time and respect necessary to become fully informed (Yuker, 1988). Families that are more directly engaged in formal care decisions are less likely to passively defer to authority. Families may struggle with professionals who exert an authoritative medical model approach to care (whether it is appropriate or not). In such instances, rehabilitation counselors may choose to advocate on behalf of the family/client, equip the family with strategies to self-advocate for its rights, refer clients to client assistance programs (CAPs), or seek out alternative providers if necessary.

Peer Support and Advocacy

Peer support is a resource based on the resilient properties of social identity that initially emerged from the mental health recovery movement (Nelson et al., 2007). It is an empowerment model designed by people with disabilities who live engaged and inclusive lives in the presence of symptoms. They seek support and strength from each other (rather than experts) and express their well-being in coping, planning, and advancing in employment, advocacy, education, community life, and health care alternatives. Care among peers is mutual. It runs the gamut from need to empowerment, but one in which the "taking responsibility for. . ." is excised. In this model, responsibility is retained in the individual, and thus he or she must work for him- or herself and define his or her own goals. Even choosing to be cared for must be an informed decision. This emphasis on *choosing* operationalizes empowerment and focuses peer work in a peer community. Peers find it easier to create a safe place where people can be challenged and in which self-sufficiency and the underlying values can be taught.

Referral to a Center for Independent Living or other peer-support groups who have persevered with similar disabilities are not empowering and supportive for a newly adapting family who may otherwise feel isolated by its circumstances. The universality of experience assures family members that their experience is normative and their response is common. Strength in numbers that peers represent opens the doors to untapped resources and possibilities for new solutions. Self-advocacy has a readymade booster group that knows ways around system barriers, strategies for applying collective pressure on unresponsive services, and a louder voice for social justice change. Although the rehabilitation counseling literature rarely addresses the importance of peer-support referrals, their significance cannot be overstated in assisting individuals and families to adapt in many areas of their lives (Marini, Bhakta, & Graf, 2009).

Knowledge and Skill Acquisition

Care is learned behavior. Family capacity for care can be expanded through training that typically focuses on disability information, coping skills, and accessing available resources (Von Korff et al., 1997). Formal and informal training may be facilitated by professionals, peer groups, or informed stakeholders, depending on the nature of the objective. Medical care training and monitoring for secondary complications is a formal and requisite component of the parent–medical care partnership when monitoring, maintenance, and even therapeutic duties are expected in the home care. Social problem-solving training enhances carer resilience (Nezu et al., 2004) and well-being (Elliott & Berry, 2009) by replacing counterproductive strategies and attitudes with functional ones (Elliott et al., 2001). It is generally provided by counselors and is integrated into the plan. Parental and disability-specific support groups can provide a valuable range of skills training from the consumer perspective (Minnes et al., 2007).

Supporting the Social Network

Perhaps one of the most consistent findings in the literature regarding caregiving is that solitary caregivers responsible for almost around-the-clock care without respite are more prone to mental and physical health problems such as depression, anxiety, isolation, back pain, and fatigue (Byrne et al., 2010; McDonald & Callery, 2007). Where multiple family caregivers can orchestrate a balance of care and respite days, the amount of direct care and potential stress placed on any one individual can be dramatically reduced (see Bainbridge et al., 2006). When the informal resources are not sufficient to support a sustainable balance of care, the family must look to paid home care providers for respite. Paid support often takes the form of direct care provided to the family member with a disability. In these instances, establishing trust in the continuity of care for a loved one becomes paramount (Soodeen, Gregory, & Bond, 2007). Primary caregivers are often reluctant to leave their loved one without full assurance in the training and temperament of the home care provider. Respite can also take the form of domestic support in which home care assumes housekeeping duties. Respite is the consistently most requested and psychologically most beneficial family service request (Hanks, Rapport, & Vangel, 2007), and demand just as consistently exceeds supply (see Ryan, Nolan, Reid, & Enderby, 2008).

Besides respite, families often have the option to partake in leisure activities with their disabled loved one. Peer-support role models can be effective in demonstrating to families that there are a number of experiences (e.g., camping, swimming) they can engage in, and rehabilitation counselors can provide information regarding adaptive equipment for camping, sports, and related activities. These normalizing and otherwise pleasurable events are beneficial for all family members and more importantly helps those who become stuck in the medical-model-hospital atmosphere of the home (Downs, 2008).

Family Participating in Employment. Employment for children with emotional and behavioral disabilities depends on integrated formal and informal community supports (job coach, sheltered employment), where participation is not simply thought of as the worker, but of the community and of reciprocity among worker, family, community, and employment (Kagan, Lewis, & Brennan, 2008). For parents, a working child can have many positive effects on the family. Child self-esteem may be improved, family members receive respite for leisure or to engage in employment themselves, and an overall sense of normalcy envelops the family.

Parental employment has also been shown to be a buffer from caregiver stress. Provencher, Perreault, St. Onge, and Rousseau (2003) found that those caregivers who were employed full-time outside the home reported lower levels of stress in caring for a loved one with a severe psychiatric illness. Among the recommendations, Provencher et al. noted the need for respite and leisure time for caregivers as well as establishing a support network. Depending on the loved one's age, there are a number of community supports available for caregivers to be employed if desired. Early childhood education, after school programs, day care centers, and adult day care programs are available to care for a loved one. Overall, respite for caregivers in some form has consistently shown to reduce mental and physical health problems for caregivers.

CONCLUSION: THE FOURTH SENSE OF COMMUNITY

This chapter provided a synthesis of the three fundamental aspects of community-based counseling that we derived from McMillan and Chavis's (1986) sense of community theory. There is a fourth sense of community. It was alternately called Art/Shared Emotional Connection in Time and Space, depending on the emphasis placed on the products of community or its relationships. The fourth sense is the culmination of the other three senses played out over time. It is expressed in the artifacts of community that arise out of membership, trust, and trade. It is found in the history, the culture and its rituals, and the physical environments that we have shaped according to our values.

In our emerging model, care is the fourth sense of community in community-based rehabilitation. In the abridged accounting of possible rehabilitation counseling supports for care in the family, we see the imperfect integration of counseling, case management, and advocacy. In the case studies of the middle chapters that follow, people with disabilities and their families tell their stories of care, given and received, over time. In these stories, we see families reaching into the community, and at times we see rehabilitation counseling responding in kind. We see transactions in identity, power, and capital. In an imperfect system, we can see efforts at a dialog between counselor and client and a search for this shared community of care. It is this idea of community that finally links family to care, and care to practice. In building healthy, inclusive communities through care, rehabilitation counselors fully serve their clients and fundamental mission.

REFERENCES

Bainbridge, H. T., Cregan, C., & Kulik, C. T. (2006). The effect of multiple roles on caregiver stress outcomes. *Journal of Applied Psychology, 91*(2), 490–497.

Bauman, L. J., Foster, G., Silver, E. J., Berman, R., Gamble, I., & Muchaneta, L. (2006). Children caring for their ill parents with HIV/AIDS. *Vulnerable Children and Youth Studies, 1*, 56–70. doi: http://dx.doi.org/10.1080/17450120600659077

Becker, S. (2007). Global perspectives on children's unpaid caregiving in the family: Research and policy on "young carers" in the UK, Australia, the USA and Sub-Saharan Africa. *Global Social Policy, 7*(1), 23–50.

Birdsong, S., & Parish, S. L. (2008). The Healthy Families Act: Vital support for families of people with developmental disabilities. *Intellectual and Developmental Disabilities, 46*(4), 319–321.

Brannan, A. M., Heflinger, C. A., & Bickman, L. (1997). The caregiver strain questionnaire: Measuring the impact of the family of living with a child with serious emotional disorders. *Journal of Emotional and Behavioral Disorders, 5*, 212–222.

Buchanan, R. J., Radin, D., Chakravorty, B. J., & Tyry, T. (2009). Informal care-giving to more disabled people with multiple sclerosis. *Disability and Rehabilitation, 31*(15), 1244–1256.

Burke, M. M., Taylor, J. L., Urbano, R., & Hodapp, R. (2012). Predictors of future caregiving by adult siblings of individuals with intellectual and developmental disabilities. *American Journal of Intellectual and Developmental Disabilities, 117*, 33–47.

Byrne, M. B., Hurley, D. A., Daly, L., & Cunningham, C. G. (2010). Health status of care-givers of children with cerebral palsy. *Child: Care, Health & Development, 36*(5), 696–702.

Caldwell, J., & Heller, T. (2007). Longitudinal outcomes of a consumer-directed program supporting adults with developmental disabilities and their families. *Intellectual and Developmental Disabilities, 45*(3), 161–173.

Call, K. T., Finch, M. D., Huck, M. A., & Kane, S. M. (1999). Caregiver burden from a social exchange perspective: Caring for older people following hospital discharge. *Journal of Marriage and the Family, 61*, 688–699

Ceglowski, D. A., Logue, M. E., Ullrich, A., & Gilbert, J. (2009). Parents' perceptions of child care for children with disabilities. *Early Childhood Education Journal, 36*(6), 497–504.

Checton, M. G., Greene, K., Magsamen-Conrad, K., & Venetis, M. K. (2012). Patients' and partners' perspectives of chronic illness and its management. *Families, Systems, & Health, 30*, 114–129.

Condelucci, A. (1995). *Interdependence: The route to community.* Youngsville, NC: Lash & Associates.

Cook, J. R., & Kilmer, R. P. (2012). Systems of care new partnerships for community psychology. *American Journal of Community Psychology, 49*, 393–403.

Deegan, P. E. (1988). Recovery: The lived experience of rehabilitation. *Psychosocial Rehabilitation Journal, 11*, 11–19.

Dembo, T., Leviton, G., & Wright, B. A. (1975). Adjustment to misfortune: A problem of social-psychological rehabilitation. *Artificial Limbs, 3*, 4–62.

Dempsey, I., & Dunst, C. J. (2004). Helpgiving styles and parent empowerment in families with a young child with a disability. *Journal of Intellectual & Developmental Disability, 29*(1), 40–51. doi:10.1080/13668250410001662874

Downs, M. L. (2008). Leisure routines: Parents and children with disability sharing occupation. *Journal of Occupational Science, 15*(2), 105–110.

Ducharme, F., Levesque, L., Ethier, S., & Lachance, L. (2007). "Masculine" care: Caregiver experiences and perceptions of services helping elderly couples. *Canadian Journal of Community Mental Health, 26*(1), 143–159.

Earley, L., Cushway, D., & Cassidy, T. (2007). Children's perceptions and experiences of care giving: A focus group study. *Counselling Psychology Quarterly, 20*, 69–80.

Elliot, T. R., & Berry, J. W. (2009). Brief problem-solving training for family caregivers of persons with recent-onset spinal cord injuries: A randomized controlled trial. *Journal of Clinical Psychology, 65*, 406–422. doi: 10.1002/jclp.20527.

Elliott, T. R., Shewchuk, R. M., & Richards, J. S. (2001). Family caregiver social problem-solving abilities and adjustment during the initial year of the caregiving role. *Journal of Counseling Psychology, 48*(2), 223–232.

Falloon, I. R., Boyd, J. L., McGill, C. W., Ranzani, J., Moss, H. B., & Gilderman, A. M. (1982). Family management in the prevention of exacerbation of schizophrenia: A controlled study. *New England Journal of Medicine, 306*, 1437–1440.

Fiese, B. H., & Wamboldt, F. S. (2003). Tales of pediatric asthma management: Family based strategies related to medical adherence and health care utilization. *Journal of Pediatrics, 143*, 457–462.

Fisher, L. (2006). Research on the family and chronic disease among adults: Major trends and directions. *Families, Systems, & Health, 24*, 373–380.

Friedman, M. (2006). Beyond caring: The de-moralization of gender. In V. Held (Ed.), *Justice and care: Essential readings in feminist ethics* (pp. 61–77). Boulder, CO: Westview.

Gilligan, C. (1982). *In a different voice.* Cambridge, MA: Harvard University Press.

Gilligan, C., & Wiggins, G. (1987). The origins of morality in early childhood relationships. In J. Kagan & S. Lamb (Eds.), *The emergence of morality in young children* (pp. 277–305). Chicago, IL: University of Chicago Press.

Goldsmith, D. J. (2009). Uncertainty and communication in couples coping with serious illness. In T. D. Afifi & W. A. Afifi (Eds.), *Uncertainty and information regulation in interpersonal contexts: Theories and applications* (pp. 204–225). New York, NY: Routledge.

Green, S. E. (2007). "We're tired, not sad": Benefits and burdens of mothering a child with a disability. *Social Science & Medicine, 64*(1), 150–163.

Hancock, P. J., Jarvis, J. A., & L'Veena, T. (2007). Older carers in ageing societies: An evaluation of a respite care program for older carers in Western Australia. *Home Health Care Services Quarterly: The Journal of Community Care, 26*(2), 59–84.

Hanks, R. A., Rapport, L. J., & Vangel, S. (2007). Care-giving appraisal after traumatic brain injury: The effects of functional status, coping style, social support and family functioning. *Neuro Rehabilitation, 22,* 43–52.

Heaton, J., Noyes, J., Sloper, P., & Shah, R. (2005). Families' experiences of caring for technology-dependent children: A temporal perspective. *Health and Social Care in the Community, 13,* 441–450.

Heller, T., & Arnold, C. K. (2010). Siblings of adults with developmental disabilities: Psychosocial outcomes, relationships, and future planning. *Journal of Policy and Practice in Intellectual Disabilities, 7,* 16–25.

Heller, T., & Kramer, J. (2009). Involvement of adult siblings of persons with developmental disabilities in future planning. *Intellectual and Developmental Disabilities, 47*(3), 208–219.

Heller, T., Caldwell, J., & Factor, A. (2007). Aging family caregivers: Policies and practices. *Mental Retardation and Developmental Disabilities Research Reviews, 13*(2), 136–142.

Henderson, S., Skelton, H., & Rosenbaum, P. (2008). Assistive devices for children with functional impairments: Impact on child and caregiver function. *Developmental Medicine & Child Neurology, 50*(2), 89–98.

Hughes, B., McKie, L., Hopkins, D., & Watson, N. (2005). Love's labours lost? Feminism, the disabled people's movement and an ethic of care. *Sociology, 39,* 259–275.

Jones, K. (2006). Informal care as relationship: The case of the magnificent seven. *Journal of Psychiatric and Mental Health Nursing, 13*(2), 214–220.

Kagan, C., Lewis, S., & Brennan, E. M. (2008). Building community supports for work–life integration. In J. M. Rosenzweig & E. M. Brennan (Eds.), *Work, life, and the mental health system of care: A guide for professionals supporting families of children with emotional or behavioral disorders* (pp. 325–349). Baltimore, MD: Paul H. Brookes.

Kenny, K., & McGilloway, S. (2007). Caring for children with learning disabilities: An exploratory study of parental strain and coping. *British Journal of Learning Disabilities, 35*(4), 221–228.

Kohlberg, L., & Hersh, R. H. (1977). Moral development: A review of the theory. *Theory into Practice, 16*(2), 53–59.

Lakin, K., Prouty, R., & Coucouvanis, K. (2007). HCBS recipients are increasingly likely to live with parents or other relatives. *Intellectual and Developmental Disabilities, 45,* 359–361.

Levine, C., Hunt, G. G., Halper, D., Hart, A. Y., Lautz, J., & Gould, D. A. (2005). Young adult caregivers: A first look at an unstudied population. *American Journal of Public Health, 95*(11), 2071–2075. doi:http://dx.doi.org/10.2105/AJPH.2005.067702

Lindblad, B., Holritz-Rasmussen, B., & Sandman, P. (2007). A life enriching togetherness-meanings of informal support when being a parent of a child with disability. *Scandinavian Journal of Caring Sciences, 21,* 238–246.

Lindsay, P. (2008). "Sunrise, sunset"—The transitions faced by the parents of adults with learning disabilities. *Advances in Mental Health and Intellectual Disabilities, 2*(3), 13–17.

Lounds, J. J., & Seltzer, M. M. (2007). Family impact in adulthood. In S. L. Odom, R. H. Horner, M. E. Snell, & B. Jan (Eds.), *Handbook of developmental disabilities* (pp. 552–569). New York, NY: Guilford.

Luiselli, J. K., & Hurley, A. D. (2008). Systems supports for individuals with intellectual disability and suicidality. *Mental Health Aspects of Developmental Disabilities, 11*(1), 31–32.

MacDonald, H., & Callery, P. (2007). Parenting children requiring complex care: A journey through time. *Child: Care, Health and Development, 34*(2), 207–213.

Malacrida, C. (2009). Performing motherhood in a disablist world: Dilemmas of motherhood, femininity and disability. *International Journal of Qualitative Studies in Education, 22*(1), 99–117. doi:http://dx.doi.org/10.1080/09518390802581927

Marini, I., Bhakta, M. V., & Graf, N. (2009). A content analysis of common concerns of persons with physical disabilities. *Journal of Applied Rehabilitation Counseling, 40*(1), 44–49.

McConkey, R. (2005). Fair shares? Supporting families caring for adult persons with intellectual disabilities. *Journal of Intellectual Disability Research, 49*(8), 600–612.

McConnell, D., & Llewellyn, G. (2002). Stereotypes, parents with intellectual disability and child protection. *Journal of Social Welfare and Family Law, 24*(3), 297–317.

McKeever, P., Angus, J., Lee Miller, K., & Reid, D. (2003). It's more of a production: Accomplishing mothering using a mobility device. *Disability & Society, 18*, 179–197.

McMillan, D. W., & Chavis, D. M. (1986). Sense of community: A definition and theory. *Journal of Community Psychology, 14*(1), 6–23.

Millington, M. J. (2012). Culturally different issues and attitudes toward disability. In I. Marini, N. M. Glover-Graf, & M. J. Millington (Eds.), *Psychosocial aspects of disability: Insider perspectives and counseling strategies* (pp. 61–95). New York, NY: Springer.

Minnes, P., Woodford, L., & Passey, J. (2007). Mediators of well-being in ageing family carers of adults with intellectual disabilities. *Journal of Applied Research in Intellectual Disabilities, 20*(6), 539–552.

National Alliance for Caregiving & AARP (2009). *Caregiving in the U.S.* [White paper]. Retrieved from http://www.caregiving.org/data/Caregiving_in_the_US_2009_full_report.pdf

Nelson, G., Ochocka, J., Janzen, R., Trainor, J., Goering, P., & Lomorey, J. (2007). A longitudinal study of mental health consumer/survivor initiatives: Part V—Outcomes at 3 year follow-up. *Journal of Community Psychology, 35*, 655–665.

Newman, T. (2002). Young carers and disabled parents: Time for a change of direction. *Disability & Society, 17*, 613–625.

Nezu, C. M., Palmatier, A., & Nezu, A. M. (2004). Social problem-solving training for caregivers. In E. C. Chang, T. J. D'Zurilla, & L. J. Sanna (Eds.), *Social problem solving: Theory research, and training* (pp. 223–238). Washington, DC: American Psychological Association.

Noddings, N. (1984). *Caring: A feminine approach to ethics and moral education.* Berkeley: University of California Press.

Noddings, N. (2002). *Starting at home: Caring and social policy.* Berkeley: University of California Press.

Nosek, M. A., Foley, C. C., Hughes, R. B., & Howland, C. A. (2001). Vulnerabilities for abuse among women with disabilities. *Sexuality and Disability, 19*, 177–189.

O'Dell, L., Crafter, S., de Abreu, G., & Cline, T. (2010). Constructing "normal childhoods": Young people talk about young carers. *Disability & Society, 25*(6), 643–655.

Olkin, R. (1999). *What psychotherapists should know about disability.* New York, NY: Guilford.

Ones, K., Yilmaz, E., Cetinkaya, B., & Caglar, N. (2005). Assessment of the quality of life of mothers of children with cerebral palsy (primary caregivers). *Neurorehabilitation and Neural Repair, 19*(3), 232–237.

Pakenham, K. I., Bursnall, S., Chiu, J., Cannon, T., & Okochi, M. (2006). The psychosocial impact of caregiving on young people who have a parent with an illness or disability: Comparisons between young caregivers and noncaregivers. *Rehabilitation Psychology, 51*(2), 113–126. doi:http://dx.doi.org/10.1037/0090-5550.51.2.113

Parish, S. L., Seltzer, M. M., Greenberg, J. S., & Floyd, F. (2004). Economic implications of caregiving at midlife: Comparing parents with and without children who have developmental disabilities. *Mental Retardation, 42*(6), 413–426.

Pit-ten Cate, I. M., Hastings, R. P., Johnson, H., & Titus, S. (2007). Grandparent support for mothers of children with and without physical disabilities. *Families in Society, 88*(1), 141–146.

Power, A. (2009). "It's the system working for the system": Carers' experiences of learning disability services in Ireland. *Health & Social Care in the Community, 17*(1), 92–98.

Prilleltensky, O. (2004). My child is not my carer: Mothers with physical disabilities and the wellbeing of children. *Disability & Society, 19,* 209–223.

Provencher, H. L., Perreault, M., St. Onge, M., & Rousseau, M. (2003). Predictors of psychological distress in family care-givers of persons with psychiatric disabilities. *Journal of Psychiatric and Mental Nursing, 10,* 592–607.

Quittner, A. L., Glueckauf, R., & Jackson, D. (1990). Chronic parenting stress: Moderating versus mediating effects of social support. *Journal of Personality and Social Psychology, 59,* 1266–1278.

Rawson, H. (2009). "I'm going to be here long after you've gone"—Sibling perspectives of the future. *British Journal of Learning Disabilities, 38,* 225–231.

Ray, L. D. (2003). The social and political conditions that shape special-needs parenting. *Journal of Family Nursing, 9*(3), 281–304.

Reid, C. E., Moss, S., & Hyman, G. (2005). Care-givers reciprocity: The effect of reciprocity, carer self-esteem and motivation on the experience of care-giver burden. *Australian Journal of Psychology, 57*(3), 186–196.

Resch, J., Benz, M. R., & Elliott, T. R. (2012). Evaluating a dynamic process model of well-being for parents of children with disabilities: A multi-method analysis. *Rehabilitation Psychology, 57*(1), 61–72. doi:http://dx.doi.org/10.1037/a0027155

Roth, D. L., Perkins, M., Wadley, V. G., Temple, E. M., & Hatey, W. E. (2009). Family caregiving and emotional strain: Associations with quality of life in a large national sample of middle-aged and older adults. *Quality of Life Research, 18,* 679–688.

Ryan, T., Nolan, M., Reid, D., & Enderby, P. (2008). Using the senses framework to achieve relationship-centred dementia care services: A case example. *Dementia, 7,* 71–93.

Scott, E. K. (2010). "I feel as if I am the one who is disabled": The emotional impact of changed employment trajectories of mothers caring for children with disabilities. *Gender & Society, 24*(5), 672–696.

Selander, J., & Marnetoft, S. (2005). Case management in vocational rehabilitation: A case study with promising results. *Work, 24,* 297–304.

Shearn, J., & Todd, S. (2000). Maternal employment and family responsibilities: The perspectives of mothers of children with intellectual disabilities. *Journal of Applied Research in Intellectual Disabilities, 13,* 109–131.

Smyth, C., Cass, B., & Hill, T. (2011). Children and young people as active agents in care-giving: Agency and constraint. *Children and Youth Services Review, 33,* 509–514.

Soodeen, R.-A., Gregory, D., & Bond, J. B., Jr. (2007). Home care for older couples: "It feels like a security blanket..." *Qualitative Health Research, 17*(9), 1245–1255.

Speraw, S. (2006). Spiritual experiences of parents and caregivers who have children with disabilities or special needs. *Issues in Mental Health Nursing, 27*(2), 213–230.

Stein, J., Reidel, M., & Rotheram-Borus, M. (1999). Parentification and its impact on adolescent children of parents with AIDS. *Family Process, 38,* 193–208.

Swain, J., & Walker, C. (2003). Parent–professional power relations: Parent and professional perspectives. *Disability & Society, 18*(5), 547–560.

Vitaliano, P. P., Schulz, R., Kiecolt-Glaser, J., & Grant, I. (1997). Research on physiological and physical concomitants of caregiving: Where do we go from here? *Annals of Behavioral Medicine, 19*(2), 117–123.

Von Korff, M., Gruman, J., Schaefer, J., Curry, S. J., & Wagner, E. H. (1997). Collaborative management of chronic illness. *Annals of Internal Medicine, 127*, 1097–1102.

Wang, K., & Barnard, A. G. (2008) Caregivers' experiences at home with a ventilator-dependent child. *Qualitative Health Research, 18*, 501–508.

Warren, J. (2007). Young carers: Conventional or exaggerated levels of involvement in domestic and caring tasks. *Children & Society, 21*, 136–146.

Washington, L. (2009). A contextual analysis of caregivers of children with disabilities. *Journal of Human Behavior in the Social Environment, 19*(5), 554–571.

World Health Organization. (2013, October). *How to use the ICF: A practical manual for using the International Classification of Functioning, Disability, and Health (ICF) Exposure draft for comment.* Geneva, Switzerland: Author.

Yuker, H. E. (1994). Variables that influence attitudes toward persons with disabilities: Conclusion from that data. *Journal of Social Behavior and Personality, 9*, 3–22.

Yuker, H. E. (Ed.). (1988). *Attitudes towards persons with disabilities.* New York, NY: Springer.

CHAPTER 6

Intellectual and Developmental Disabilities

CHERYL HANLEY-MAXWELL, NANCY MOLFENTER,
AND KRISTIN MAXWELL

Support for persons with intellectual and developmental disabilities (I/DD) is a lifelong proposition for families (Seltzer, Floyd, Song, Greenberg, & Hong, 2011). The activities of support are integral to their lives and part of their identities. Their relationships with formal support providers is part of that experience. As a community, we aspire to a network of formal support providers working in concert and collaboration to provide for the health, education, employment, and general well-being of the person with I/DD. Unfortunately, the families' experience with service providers rarely reflects that ideal and is more honestly portrayed along a continuum anchored by disrespect and marginalization (Bianco, Garrison-Wade, Tobin, & Lehmann, 2009) in an unresponsive, fragmented, and dehumanizing system (McCallion & Toseland, 1993). The relationship between families and formal support providers can be similarly characterized along a continuum of estrangement (Blacher, Neece, & Paczkowski, 2005), starting with the family's entry into a disability service industry they do not understand and are not prepared to negotiate or fight. They learn quickly not to trust (Rueda, Monzo, Shapiro, Gomez, & Blacher, 2005; Valentine, McDermott, & Anderson, 1998) and through experience their role is framed by resistance in lieu of cooperation, as desired by the families.

Families establish beliefs, attitudes, and expectations about these systems well before the rehabilitation counselor arrives. Rehabilitation counseling in the United States currently has no role in the life of the child with I/DD or a stake in the family relationship with early care. It is introduced when the young adult with I/DD seeks to transition from home and school to work and a more independent adult life. Rehabilitation counselors enter as the next expert and offer to facilitate this important family change at the point where the young adult's desire to have less parental involvement (Blacher et al., 2005) meets, and potentially conflicts with (Hatton & Emerson, 2003), the parents' drive to increase their advocacy role in securing services for their adult children (Bianco et al., 2009). Rehabilitation counselors ostensibly represent the family's interests as they facilitate family planning, until the family's objectives begin to conflict with service protocol, the limits of policy, and the intent of legislation (Rueda et al., 2005).

This is the challenge for rehabilitation counseling: to enter the process already defined, to develop a working alliance with potentially wary family members, and to convince them of the rehabilitation counselor's value through facilitating meaningful outcomes (Blacher, Neece, & Paczkowski, 2005). This chapter addresses the strengths, needs, and lives of families of persons with I/DD and considers how these variables affect client/family relationship and partnership with rehabilitation counselors. From the counseling perspective, a working alliance always begins with an appreciation of the person, and family, in his or her environment. For families of a person with I/DD, this will require a thorough understanding of (a) developmental disabilities, (b) issues affecting family participation, (c) environment resources, and (d) considerations for RCs. The chapter begins with two case studies that will illustrate the discussion.

CASE STUDIES

Anna's Family

Anna is a 25-year-old woman with Down syndrome and moderate intellectual disability who lives with her parents. Anna's parents, Martha and Bob, are very involved in her life. Martha helps Anna make many life decisions. Although eligible for retirement, Bob continues to work to build their savings. He worries about Anna's future, but they have made no financial or residential plans. They assume that Anna will eventually live with her younger sister, Becky. Despite health issues of her own, Martha is very active in helping Anna develop home-living skills to prepare her for that future. Martha hopes to have publically funded in-home services to assist Anna in learning additional ADLs (e.g., cooking, cleaning) and engage in community activities (e.g., shopping, movies). Unfortunately, an extensive waiting list prevents Anna from receiving weekly support services for the foreseeable future.

Becky is leaving for college and has mixed feelings about being so far away from home. She has been very close to her sister and worries how Anna will respond to her absence. She is nervous about living in the dorm and adjusting to college life. On the other hand, she is eager to get started and to have some distance from her parents. Becky feels that her parents, especially her mother, still treat her like a child. They don't include her in any decision-making conversations, especially when it comes to Anna. This is frustrating because Becky has been reading books on other family experiences with I/DD and she has ideas she'd like to share.

Martha believes Anna requires supports/supervision to participate safely in leisure and recreation activities and will not let Anna take the bus at night. Unless a family member is willing to travel with her, Anna has limited opportunities to socialize with friends from work. Most evenings, she watches TV with her parents, looks at her magazines, or draws or paints. On weekends, she helps her mother with housework and takes a Saturday painting class sponsored by the local park district, organized by her mother and based on Anna's love to paint and draw. She and her sister also attend exercise classes at the YMCA three times a week. Sometimes, she and her sister go shopping and then out to eat, having a "girls' day out."

Anna works at the sheltered workshop. Although she is satisfied, she'd prefer the part-time housekeeping job she held at the hotel when she was in high school. When she left high school, she had to add another job so that more of her daytime hours were covered by work. This was necessary so that Martha could remain employed in her part-time job. The vocational rehabilitation (VR) counselor recommended that Anna quit her job and attend the sheltered workshop where she would get full-time work and supervision. Anna's teacher and mother argued for a second placement in competitive employment instead. The VR counselor objected to the added expense surrounding transportation and the development of another supported employment site. As a compromise, they agreed on a referral for vocational evaluation at the sheltered workshop to identify community employment options. This is not what happened. Anna simultaneously completed a work trial at a job she said she did not want and a piece-work trial at the workshop. At the completion of the evaluations, Anna was told that her schedule, support constraints, and attitude limited the jobs she could access. As a result, it was "recommended" that she work full-time at the sheltered workshop, making more money and working more hours there than she could in her part-time job at the hotel. In the end, Anna agreed with her parents that the sheltered workshop appeared to be the best option. She has been at the workshop for 3 years.

Bill's Family

Bill is a 35-year-old man who has autism and an uncertain diagnosis of moderate intellectual disability. His severe speech and language and social impairments prevent accurate assessment of his intellectual skills. Bill's mother left when he was 3 years old. His father, Jim, raised Bill alone for 7 years before remarrying. Bill's home life became untenable. He was belligerent and refused to shower, eat meals, or leave his room. As a result, Bill entered supported living and a more structured school setting. He became an emancipated minor to access public financial supports and release his father from financial responsibility for his care.

Bill has made progress in his behavior and independent living. He works on his severe communication and language challenges in therapy. He is practicing behavioral techniques to help with his issues with change and participates in many domestic and community tasks with support. Bill prefers to engage in solitary activities, although he appears to enjoy the proximity of his roommates, and will nominally respond to their presence. He is quite accomplished at using public transport and navigating any environment on foot. After leaving home, tensions between Bill, Jim, and Ann, his stepmother, eased into a new relationship. Jim visits twice per month for an outing to Bill's favorite theater and then his favorite restaurant. Jim is loath to suggest any variation, however. Bill slowly improved in his supported living setting. He now eats regularly, has become less aggressive, is more cooperative, and willingly goes to work.

He has a new job disassembling computers. He was fired from his previous employment when he responded poorly to an abrupt change in routine. Bill's new job seems to be matched perfectly to Bill's interests and skills. VR services were instrumental in creating this match, but accessing services was difficult. Initially, the VR counselor believed that Bill was not capable of independent work and not appropriate for services. Jim was persistent in his demand for services on behalf of his son . . . at considerable expense to his own work schedule. Eventually VR relented and funds and services were procured. Jim hopes this trend will last. He and his wife want to retire early and plan to spend the winter months in a warmer climate.

Anna and Bill have I/DD (American Association on Intellectual and Developmental Disabilities [AAIDD], 2011). I/DD refers to several syndromes; sensory, physical, and health disabilities (Centers for Disease Control and Prevention [CDC], 2013); autism spectrum disorders (ASD); and learning and intellectual disabilities (The Arc, 2013b). I/DD is present at birth or begins in the developmental years (AAIDD) and results in substantial limitations to (a) learning and applying knowledge; (b) social skills required for interpersonal interactions and relationships, as well as communication; and (c) practical skills that are part of mobility, self-care, domestic life, education, work, recreation and leisure, community participation, and civic life (see International Classification of Functioning [ICF]; World Health Organization [WHO], 2001).

FAMILY PARTICIPATION

I/DD changes the constellation and course of family caring roles starting at birth. Even if the I/DD is not apparent at first, families will begin to adjust care reflexively to meet the needs of the newborn (Boyle et al., 2011). As the child grows and developmental issues become more pronounced, traditional activities such as feeding and toileting may be delayed, extended beyond their usual timeframe (Berry & Hardman, 1998) and require more attention and support. At diagnosis, the family interface with formal care begins. Parents can find themselves in a number of novel, quasiprofessional roles (assessor, planner, advocate, case manager, interventionist, trainer, and program evaluator; Bianco et al., 2009) that are quite foreign to customary child care. Grandparents often step into parental care and guardianship roles (Hegar & Scannapieco, 2000). Siblings take on ancillary support roles. Older children may take on supervisory roles with younger siblings to free parents up to focus on the needs of the child with I/DD (Seltzer, Greenburg, Floyd, Pettee, & Hong, 2001). Siblings may stand in for parents (Anderson, Larson, & Wuorio, 2011; Seltzer & Krauss, 2001) and become guardians of their adult sibling with I/DD. The permutations of caring roles within the family are endless and continually evolving as needs and circumstances change. They are socially constructed from the experience of disability (Blacher et al., 2005; Tichá et al., 2012) interpreted through the family's cultural background (Rueda et al., 2005; Valentine et al., 1988; Widmer, Kempf, Sapin, & Galli-Carminate, 2013), their unique family expectations and preferences (Doren, Gau, & Lindstrom, 2012), and the characteristics of the environments in which they move.

There is a tension in caring relationships (Birditt, Miller, Fingerman, & Lefkowitz, 2009) that arises out of shifting assumptions of authority and responsibility for the well-being of the care recipient. Through the family life cycle, each individual negotiates and renegotiates the relationship among family support (Baumrind, 1991), independence, and interdependence (Bianco et al., 2009; Collins & Russell, 1991; Ryan & Lynch, 1989) in his or her evolving role from infant to adult and into old age. By changing the nature and constellation of caring roles, the presence of an individual with I/DD in the family affects this developmental path (Berry & Hardman, 1998; Hanley-Maxwell, Whitney-Thomas, & Pogoloff, 1995). Challenges to people with mild limitations (Van Naarden Braun, Yeargin-Allsopp, & Lollar, 2009) are often straightforward, but any sustained dependency can represent a barrier to growth into autonomy (Fujiura, 2010; Yamaki & Fujiura, 2002).

As needs become more numerous and intense, the path may be dramatically altered for everyone (Seltzer & Krauss, 2001). The person with more severe limitations is increasingly reliant on the support of others to facilitate independence. Sometimes the act of caring itself can get in the way of growth and access to resources (Hegar & Scannapieco, 2000). What constitutes the optimal balance between support giving and independence for a person with I/DD is never certain. In the pursuit of this balance, each member of the family must find his or her own way to support, on his or her own path. There are two fundamental roles around which the forward path is negotiated: the parental role of family authority and responsibility and the sibling role that shares rank in the hierarchy.

Parents' Perspective

The parental role can be filled by anyone taking on the responsibility of keeping the family intact while nurturing the child into adulthood. In general, whether this role is filled by biological parents, grandparents, extended family, or even siblings, what parents want for their loved one with I/DD is to be happy and safe while ensuring that basic needs are being met. Parents see happiness and need fulfillment coming from community inclusion; participation in educational (Anderson et al., 2011), vocational, and avocational pursuits; social relationships (Blacher et al., 2005); community employment; and postsecondary education.

Domestic

Most parents seek to coreside with their adult children with I/DD for the entirety of their lives (Anderson et al., 2011). Success in this commitment to family (Griffiths & Unger, 1994) over residential support programs (Heller & Schindler, 2009), in later years especially, is highly dependent on the demand placed on the parents. Younger persons with mild to moderate I/DD who can communicate verbally (Stancliffe et al., 2012) require less mobility, sensory, or behavior support; have fewer mental health issues (Tichá et al., 2012); and challenge parental resources less. Indeed, the coresiding person with mild to moderate I/DD can provide enriching and reciprocal support to aging parents by contributing to household chores (Pruchno, 2003; Seltzer & Krauss, 2001; Yoong & Koritsas, 2012), providing social connection and emotional support (Seltzer & Krauss, 2001), encouraging increased engagement in community leisure activities, and even generating financial support.

The balance of support shifts as a function of demand and resources. Physical, emotional, and financial demands persist indefinitely (Hodapp, Urbano, & Burke, 2010), while parental strength and stamina diminish with age (Anderson et al., 2011). Intermittent behavioral crises, as those common to persons with ASD, intensify the demand on all resources and threaten family stability (White, McMorris, Weiss, & Lunsky, 2012). For adults with ASD, in particular, change of any kind can precipitate these crises, and in the case of the later transitions, may even precipitate psychiatric symptoms (White et al., 2012). Parents need orchestrated formal support to support diminishing contributions in general, and timely access to crisis support in particular, to sustain the coresiding home life.

This articulated level of service is not often forthcoming. What parents cannot provide, they must acquire. What does not fit for their loved one must be adapted. Thus parents are tasked with quasiprofessional case-management duties (Anderson et al., 2011; McCallion & Toseland, 1993) as well as direct support (Blacher et al., 2005; Seltzer et al., 2011). They persist until lack of agency support (Bianco et al., 2009; Blacher et al., 2005; Valentine et al., 1998) forces them to consider other, less desirable residential options (Hatton & Emerson, 2003).

Family Employment

Full, competitive employment is the optimal goal for person with I/DD and parents, but can be problematic for both. Integrated employment for workers with I/DD are often limited in hours and complicated by transportation needs, making it difficult to coordinate schedules with working parents (Anderson et al., 2011). Sheltered workshops offer predictability, central access to supporting services (Seltzer & Krauss, 2001), and as in the case of Anna, a form of day services that can be more easily matched to parents' vocational needs. Career decisions can come down to a tradeoff between full inclusion in employment for the person with I/DD or the parent. Similarly, career decisions for the parent are also linked to decisions to coreside. It is difficult for both parents to maintain active participation in the workforce and attend to the care needs of the child with I/DD; this demand increases once the young adult leaves school (Anderson et al., 2011). One parent, typically the mother, is tasked with the responsibility, resulting in a career in part-time or episodic employment in lower status employment (Stewart, 2013) and lower earning capacity for mother and household overall.

Family Economic Resources

Diminished earning capacity exacerbates the already taxing cost associated with support. Living alone, the emancipated person with I/DD is typically subsisting at, near, or under the poverty line. Coresiding with parents, the average out-of-pocket cost to parents is $6,000/year (Fujiura, 2010) with very limited access to government-provided financial supports (Seltzer & Krause, 2001). At midlife, parents have saved less than other families (Parish, Seltzer, Greenberg, & Floyd, 2004) and worry more about retirement (Anderson et al., 2011) and their own increasing health-related expenses (Seltzer et al., 2011).

There is economic relief for parents, but it takes effort to secure and comes at a cost. Individuals with I/DD may be able to receive Supplemental Security Income (SSI) and/or Social Security Disability Insurance (SSDI), income supports, and Medicaid or Medicare. Families of adults with I/DD may also be eligible for financial supports through the Medicaid Home and Community-Based Services (HCBS) waiver and other local or state financial/resource supports (Arnold, Heller, & Kramer, 2012; Heller, Miller, & Hsieh, 1999; Rizzolo, Hemp, Braddock, & Schindler, 2009). However, some support is dependent on unemployment of the person, limitations in income, and stipulations in living arrangements and guardianship. Attempts to improve one's position can have unintended repercussions on the financial health of the family as a whole, where most or all sources of income are factored into budgeting.

Family Social Life and Wellness

The social impact of parenting children/adults with I/DD is complex. Divorce rates appear slightly elevated, more so for parents who do not coreside with an adult child with ASD (Hartley et al., 2010). It has little effect on participation in social groups or social networks compared with other parents at midlife (Seltzer et al., 2001). However, parents coresiding with adults with I/DD at midlife and beyond report fewer relationships outside the family and engage in fewer leisure activities (Yoong & Koritsas, 2012). Interestingly, aging parents who do not coreside with their adult children with I/DD report less social–emotional support than those who do (Seltzer et al., 2011). Parents' physical and mental health may also affect their social lives. At midlife, parenting an adult with I/DD is associated with increased likelihood of physical health problems, such as cardiovascular disease and obesity, but not mental health problems. Depression becomes more of an issue in old age. The pressure to withdraw, first for physical and then emotional reasons, grows in age (Seltzer et al., 2011), but these pressures are universal among the elderly. In later years, the coresiding adult with I/DD may be able to aptly fill the role of supporter and confidant for the aging parent.

Siblings' Perspective

Siblings follow a wholly different path. Their family relationship with the brother or sister with I/DD is not initially rooted in authority and responsibility; they share an upbringing instead. In general, sibling support is the most enduring and evolved relationship their brothers/sisters with I/DD have (Heller & Schindler, 2009; Hodapp et al., 2010; Seltzer & Krauss, 2001), and both parties are enriched by the experience (Hodapp et al., 2010; McGraw & Walker, 2007; Seltzer, Greenberg, Orsmond, & Lounds, 2005). Siblings report that adjusting and responding to issues of I/DD in their formative years made them more empathetic, loving, and committed to social justice (Anderson et al., 2011; Dykens, 2005). The experience and its lessons vary widely, however.

Differences by Diagnosis

The influence and the quality of sibling relationships are developmental; the closer siblings are, both geographically and emotionally, the more consistently positive the experience (Freedman, Krauss, & Seltzer, 1997) and the better the outcome. Siblings of adults with Down syndrome have more contact with their siblings, are more positive about their sibling relationships, and are more optimistic about their siblings' futures (Orsmond & Seltzer, 2000) than are siblings with ASD. There is an emotional immediacy in persons with Down syndrome that is less accessible in ASD.

Siblings of children with Down syndrome growing up with a history of positive, engaged experiences report that their brother or sister had a deep influence on his or her identity, including making his or her choice in life partner and career decisions (Seltzer et al., 2005). Siblings of adults with ASD, on the other hand, grow into their acceptance of the sister/brother with ASD in adulthood. Early acceptance and engagement are improved when the caring sibling uses problem-focused coping skills and behavior challenges are minimized (Seltzer, Orsmond, & Esbensen, 2009) and the situation is not complicated by other mental health issues (Scltzer & Krauss, 2001).

Differences by Gender

The connections between siblings with and without I/DD are also influenced by the ages and genders of the sibling pairs. Older siblings, same gender pairs, and pairs in which the nondisabled siblings are sisters are more likely to have positive relationships (MassMutual, 2012). Brothers are less likely to have supportive relationships with sisters than brothers with I/DD (Seltzer et al., 2009; Seltzer & Krauss, 2001). Even if brothers do not have overtly supportive relationships with their sisters, they are often concerned about the financial futures of their siblings with I/DD (Orsmond & Seltzer, 2000).

Sisters are more relationally sensitive overall. They are more likely to visit, make regular phone contact (Seltzer et al., 2005), and engage the brother or sister in social outings (Seltzer & Krauss, 2001). This level of support extends daily physical and emotional supports to their sibling with I/DD as well (McGraw & Walker, 2007). Sisters actively redefine their siblings' disabilities by positively interpreting the disability and the effects of the disability on their families, focusing on their sibling's strengths and similarities to other people (McGraw & Walker, 2007). In addition to their positive interpretations, sisters are aware of the limitations of their siblings with I/DD. They often expect to fill their mother's gendered support-giving roles when their mothers are no longer able to provide necessary support (McGraw & Walker, 2007; Seltzer & Krauss, 2001).

Transition to Primary Supporter

Male and female siblings' support roles continue to evolve throughout the life of the family. The seminal event that redefines them is the slow retirement of the original parent from the role. Positive caring relationships tend to be sustained as siblings assume more authority and responsibility (Heller & Kramer, 2009; Seltzer & Krauss, 2001), but questions and conflict do arise in the transition. Parents may not see siblings as the ideal roommate for their adult children with I/DD (Anderson et al., 2011). Siblings believe they are more attuned to their brother's or sister's circumstances and should have more voice in decision making (see Arnold et al., 2012). However, the siblings wrestle with financial (MassMutual, 2012) burden and logistics. Few, even among committed supporters, wish to coreside with their sibling with I/DD (Heller & Kramer, 2009; Seltzer et al., 2005), and so planning for support is crucial at this stage. Beyond residence, planning must confront the diminishing capacities of some persons with I/DD themselves. Alzheimer's disease in adults with Down syndrome (Stancliffe et al., 2012; Zigman, Schupf, Haveman, & Silverman, 1997) and a host of physical health complications (Havercamp, Scandlin, & Roth, 2004) are common to I/DD and become the issues that frame the later years of sibling support.

ENVIRONMENTAL RESOURCES

Family support for loved ones with I/DD is embedded in the environmental resources that are available to them. Environmental resources such as modifications in the physical environment and services enhance the independence of adults with I/DD and reduce family support-giving demands.

Physical Environment

Assistive technology, adaptive equipment, and accommodations are the physical means of maximizing individual independence in self-care, home/daily living, employment, and/or community life, and minimizing the demand on family members

(Johnson & Kastner, 2005). These resources can range from the very low- to high-tech solutions across a variety of activities. Photo checklists posted in strategic locations remind the person about steps required to complete a task (e.g., setting the table for dinner). Color-coded systems make it easier to match items that belong together (e.g., cleaning supplies vs. toiletries in the bathroom). Communication boards help express simple commands, requests, ideas, and emotions without written or spoken language. Personal data devices such as laptops, smart phones, iPods, or iPads have become the platform for a burgeoning number of applications that support learning and memory, facilitate organization, and enhance both verbal and written communication (Boone, Burke, Fore, & Spencer, 2006; Forgrave, 2002; Mazzotti, Test, Wood, & Richter, 2010; Stock, Davies, Secor, & Wehmeyer, 2003). Augmentative and alternative communication (AAC) devices are particularly important for adults with I/DD who have difficulty communicating through speech (van der Meer, Sigafoos, O'Reilly, & Lancioni, 2011). Adults with I/DD may require mobility accommodations and environmental modifications such as walkers, wheelchairs, ramps, grab bars, walk-in showers, modified vehicles, expanded doorways, lowered countertops, and for some even the installation of elevators at home (Pynoos & Nishita, 2003).

Services

Like modifications to the physical environment, services include those available to all adults and those specific to adults with I/DD. Services are provided by businesses (e.g., employee training, Employee Assistance Program [EAP]) and the government (e.g., SSI, para-transit accessible buses; Wehman & Bricout, 2001). Communities offer adaptive recreation (e.g., adaptive aquatics programs at local park districts) and advocacy groups provide services, including sports programs (e.g., Special Olympics). Schools and adult service agencies provide services to support transition from school to adult life, employment, postsecondary education, and independent and supported living.

Transition Services

Beginning at age 16, school district personnel work with young adults with disabilities, their families, and relevant adult service providers to plan for and begin moving toward the young adults' transition into their adult lives (Individuals with Disabilities Education Act [IDEA], 2004). Transition plans focus on all aspects of adult life (e.g., employment, postsecondary education, independent living, community and social life). The planning and action processes assist young adults and their families as they move from one service system to another. Early experiential activities explore vocational and avocational themes in anticipation of subsequent and formal vocational and independent living assessments and plans. Emphasis at transition is on applied knowledge, skill, and accommodations around such activities as grocery shopping, navigating mass transit, cooking classes, volunteer work, and paid work supported by school staff (Johnson, Stodden, Emanuel, Mack, & Luecking, 2002; Kohler & Field, 2003). As the young adult ages out of the school system, support plans shift to adult services, including VR.

Vocational Rehabilitation

Rehabilitation counselors generally engage the family on, or near, this transitional stage between school and work through the VR system. As the name suggests, VR concentrates on maximizing community inclusion through full and competitive employment. Optimally, families have received some orientation regarding VR services during the transition years and are collaborating in the implementation and planning of the next stage of the young person's path to adulthood from the introductions forward. Service resources include vocational evaluation, job skills training and career-related education, job development and placement, and job coaching. VR counselors can also help adults with I/DD understand the job market and employers' job openings in a given geographic area, ensure that ADA requirements are applied to employment situations, and help obtain adaptive equipment and modifications. Early engagement is best. Obtaining paid employment before school exit enhances planning for long-term support services to help adults with I/DD maintain employment once school and VR funding supports are no longer available (Johnson et al., 2002; Test et al., 2009).

Postsecondary Education

Any postsecondary education in areas of interest, regardless of credit standing, tend to improved employment outcomes for people with I/DD (Neece, Kraemer, & Blacher, 2009). This is a relatively new innovation in I/DD policy and something well supported by families (Anderson et al., 2011). For young adults with disabilities who want to attend college, IDEA funding can be utilized to support dual enrollment in both high school and college and/or to provide personnel, such as a teacher or educational assistant, to help the young adults attend college-level classes. Postsecondary education programs also include career and technical training, union apprenticeships, and student disability services on college campuses (Collet-Klingenberg & Hanley-Maxwell, 2012). Programs (see Cutting-Edge Program, 2010; REACH, 2010) provide opportunities for adults with I/DD to get college-level experiences and education, including living in residence halls, preparing them for a variety of adult roles. These programs often include instruction in social and independent living skills in conjunction with academic coursework (Hart, 2006).

Independent and Supported Living

Individuals with I/DD choose to live in a range of housing options. Decisions of where, how, and with whom to live are often negotiated with family and formal support stakeholders, and mediated by client need, resource availability, and cost. Maximizing choice and independence in living arrangements is encouraged through individualized planning and support. From independent residence to full-time support in subsidized group home settings, service and accommodations are based on individual barriers to participation and personal preference (Anderson et al., 2011). Supports include adaptive equipment and technology to enhance independence and safety. Home living support integrates in-home training in daily living activities and community participation, personal support services, and supported living arrangements (e.g., supported apartments, group homes). A home support coordinator typically maintains communication with and between the individual and family and acts as point of contact for service coordination and supervision.

Long-Term Supports Services

Long-term supports services (LTSS) are provided in work, home, community, and transportations settings. LTSS is coordinated by a qualified professional (often a rehabilitation counselor) specializing in evaluation, planning, and implementation of long-term support. This is metalevel service that provides connections between services in the present and seeks seamless support over the life span. Although the majority of individuals who experience I/DD and their families desire and are qualified to receive long-term support services (Certo et al., 2008), accessing them can be a challenge in itself. Waiting lists and lack of providers complicate obtaining resources for transportation; employment; personal support at home, if necessary; and support for recreational activities. The implementation of LTSS is complicated. At age 18, regardless of disability diagnosis or length of time individuals with I/DD have received special education services, families and young adults must seek redetermination of disability status in order to begin or maintain public benefits and to apply for LTSS. The process and the accessibility of service providers vary from state to state. The process may also be complicated by guardianship issues related to the disability determination. If guardianship is required, family members, typically parents, must determine the appropriate type and extent of guardianship that will supply the decision making and consent supports needed by the adults with I/DD while allowing them to maintain responsibility and control over as many aspects of their own lives as possible. Often, LTSS and guardianship are topics covered by the IEP team during transition planning. However, these are topics rehabilitation counselors should also discuss with families and adults with I/DD to ensure they are aware of the range of options so they can make informed decisions (Parish & Lutwick, 2005). Most families require support to help them understand the process for obtaining LTSS, the availability of services, waiting lists, and alternatives, if applicable; navigate the service systems; and advocate for additional services, greater funding, and shorter waiting times (Anderson et al., 2011; Seltzer & Krauss, 2001).

Supports for Families

Support for the person with I/DD is, or at least should be, an indirect support for the family. His or her needs and lives are intertwined; what makes life more inclusive for the individual fulfills the wishes of the family. But the family is also tasked in the delivery of these resources and services. The success of these services is based in large part on an expectation that the family will trade in its own resources to make them work and on an assumption that the family has the prerequisite resources expected in the trade. True to the systems perspective, direct services to people with I/DD will require direct services to the family to be ultimately effective.

Information

The foundation of all empowering support is the translation of knowledge into skill. Families want to understand financial planning, legal issues, and the various support systems they must engage to help them plan for the future and address present demands. They want to be conversant in technological supports and know how to access recreational, transportation, and respite services. Siblings want information about housing and transition of guardianship. Siblings would like to be able to access online resources and support groups (Arnold et al., 2012). Siblings want workshops or training events provided by VR and other social service providers in their community (Arnold et al., 2012). They all want supports to help them learn how to become effective advocates for more services (Anderson et al., 2011).

Community

The search for an empowered sense of competence and efficacy in the bewildering morass of the support system has lead families to each other. The need for peer support created The Arc, a well-known advocacy and support organization for persons with I/DD and their families. The Arc provides information, services, and supports through local and state chapters. Services offered vary by chapter, but may include information, referral, advocacy for and by individuals, respite care, transportation, and medical, dental, OT, PT, speech and language, and behavior management. Local chapters may also offer supports for home and community living, transition planning, and families; case management; and leisure/recreation and employment programs, including supported employment and job training. State chapters support local chapters and engage in policy advocacy, and some provide assistance in case coordination and planning special needs trusts. In addition to these supports and services, The Arc also sponsors self-advocacy projects; a national sibling council; Autism Now, information and resources related to ASD; and a variety of other projects designed to support individuals with I/DD and their families (The Arc, 2013a). Other resources are available through local and online networks, such as the Sibling

Leadership Network (http://siblingleadership.org) and the Sibling Support Project (http://www.siblingsupport.org) and SibNet (on Yahoogroups and Facebook). Finally, supports and other resources are available through the University Centers for Excellence in Developmental Disabilities funded through the Developmental Disabilities Assistance and Bill of Rights Act (2000, PL 104-183).

Financial

Many of the external supports required by adults with I/DD and their families are funded through state and federal government programs, including Social Security's Plans for Achieving Self-Support (PASS) and HCBS waiver initiatives (see Arnold et al., 2012; Heller et al., 1999; Rizzolo et al., 2009), VR (e.g., vocational counseling, One-Stop Job Centers, literacy), Developmental Disabilities Assistance and Bill of Rights Act state grants (e.g., long-term supports, community training, case management), Carl D. Perkins Vocational and Technical Education Act of 2006 programs (career and technical training), and local and state-funded initiatives. Mental health, occupational therapy, physical therapy, and speech therapy services may be funded through private insurance and/or Medicaid (Anderson et al., 2011). Sometimes the state or local Arc chapters provide these services (The Arc, 2013a) as well.

In addition to publicly funded services, adults with I/DD are often eligible for income supports through SSI and/or SSDI. Additionally, if they receive income support from either source, they are eligible for Medicaid or Medicare, on the basis of their ages. To be eligible for SSI, adults with I/DD must have long-term and severe (physical and/or cognitive) functional limitations, incomes equal to or less than $1,040 a month in 2013, and a parent who has paid into social security. At age 18, adults who may or may not have received SSI benefits as children (due to parental income), may become eligible for SSI benefits; they may also be eligible for SSDI benefits if they meet the SSI criteria and if they have a parent who is receiving retirement or disability benefits, or is dead (Social Security Administration, 2013).

IMPLICATIONS FOR REHABILITATION COUNSELORS

Establishing working alliances with families that support a loved one with I/DD begins by listening. The family's major challenges are less likely to be a direct result of the presence of an intellectual impairment or its sequelae and more likely to be due to the underwhelming, poorly matched, uncoordinated, and potentially adversarial response of the various services systems that they have encountered over the years. It is the rehabilitation counselor who walks into the relationship with a potentially spoiled identity. He or she must first seek to find out what the family expects from him or her and deal positively and aggressively with those expectations.

Establishing trust begins with a validation of family concerns, a frank appraisal of the rehabilitation counseling role, and an immediate inculcation of the family's authority over the process. The rehabilitation counselor does not lead, but facilitates the group process, finding the client at the center, encouraging communication, and most importantly bringing useful information into the mix. It is the counselor's first task to uncover what information is needed and deliver it when, where, how, in the form that it can best serve the family. It is the counselor's second task to link the family directly to sources of information it can use without mediation. And third, the counselor links to people, services, and all other resources that can inform the emerging plan and empower the family within it.

In short, the most effective means of building a working alliance is through good case management. This is case management informed by strengths-based planning (Russo, 1999) that dwells in the positive and the possible, that eschews the pathologic, builds resilience through action, and seeks strength through community (Saleeby, 1996). Even toxic relationships with past service providers can be recast as experiences to be mined for the lessons learned and skills developed. It is through this process that the family practices articulating its needs (Hayden & Heller, 1997), making concrete plans for the future (Heller & Schindler, 2009), and exploring the challenging issues that await it there (Arnold et al., 2012). Among these concerns are issues of health, transportation, communication, and daily living.

Health Issues

Adults with I/DD are four to five times more likely to have chronic health problems than are adults without disabilities (Havercamp et al., 2004) and less likely to receive regular health support (Seltzer & Krauss, 2001). Coexisting physical disabilities, such as cerebral palsy, complicate transient health treatment and require extensive medical care for ongoing health issues such as swallowing difficulties, muscle atrophy, and decubitus ulcers. Coexisting psychiatric diagnoses pose similar challenges in finding dually qualified practitioners in an already fragmented mental health service system (Seltzer et al., 2001). Families frequently remain involved in client's medical decisions (Green, 2007) over the life span, especially if their history reflects inadequate professional support (Krahn, Hammond, & Turner, 2006). Families often require assistance to find health care providers who have the knowledge and experience to meet their adult children's needs (Geenen, Powers, & Sells, 2003), manage paperwork, and communicate with health care providers (Krahn et al., 2006).

Family members may also require help in securing services to address their own physical and mental health challenges. Support giving can be exhausting work, and unremitting vigilance takes a physical and psychological toll. Over time, chronic stress translates to illness (White et al., 2012) and substantial health problems increase with age (Dillenburger & McKerr, 2011). Support givers may need assistance in managing their personal health, counseling support, but most of all, respite and home-based assistance (Berry & Hardman, 1998).

Transportation

Transportation is an issue that complicates nearly every other aspect of community inclusion. Access to work, school, marketplace, and health care is often dependent on a reliable and affordable means of moving between them. Support givers report that family members provide transportation support for 88% of adults with I/DD, and approximately 50% identify transportation as a critical support/service (Anderson et al., 2011). Consequently, rehabilitation counselors should help family members identify available options and financial supports, securing and arranging transportation supports and services and negotiating the problems associated with transportation supports (e.g., unreliable services; Freedman & Boyer, 2000; Hammel et al., 2008). Rehabilitation counselors may also need to help secure the required training services and supports for adults who can learn to use transportation options independently.

Communication

When working with individuals who use AAC to communicate, rehabilitation counselors may have to support families in a variety of ways, including helping family members negotiate the processes of identifying and securing communication supports. This assistance may include helping family members connect with specialists, interpret recommendations and select most appropriate devices, and secure funding. Families may also require assistance in learning how to use and sometimes require encouragement to use the communication software and/or devices (Scherer & Glueckauf, 2005).

Daily Living

Whether or not family members coreside with adults with I/DD, meeting daily support challenges can be difficult. Rehabilitation counselors helping families create these support plans should develop deep understandings of how families function as a unit and the relationships between and among individual family members. Effective support planning is person centered and strengths based (Claes, Van Hove, Vandevelde, van Loon, & Schalock, 2010).

Concluding Considerations

The official determination of I/DD is typically done to assist individuals and their families in obtaining services through schools and agencies that provide specialized supports (Howlin, 2000; Simeonsson et al., 2003). Disability determination and accompanying services usually extend to home and community waiver services, Social Security administration benefits, and rehabilitation services as individuals move into their adulthoods (Kane, Kane, & Ladd, 1998). Throughout their lives, individuals with I/DD, such as Anna and Bill, along with their families, require a variety of supports and services to meet their unique needs and achieve desired outcomes, taking family assets and struggles into consideration as well (Mansell, 2010). Ongoing collaboration among professionals and individuals with I/DD and their family members is an essential component of quality supports.

Individuals with I/DD and their families are complex systems like other families; they have a range of ways to interact with one another, problem solve, cope (Magill-Evans, Darrah, Pain, Adkins, & Kratochvil, 2001; Seligman & Darling, 2009), and change over the life cycle of the family. As a result, it is important for disability services to be dynamic rather than static and flexible rather than rigid in the creation and delivery of supports (Magill-Evans et al., 2001; Schneider, Wedgewood, Llewellyn, & McConnell, 2006). As individuals grow and age, family structures and support systems are likely to shift (Seligman & Darling, 2009). Bill's story provides a good example of someone with autism whose daily challenges had to be met outside of the family home with the onset of puberty. In other families, and under different circumstances (e.g., the availability of respite and in-home supports), families may have made different decisions. In other words, disability services should be tailored to the lives of individuals with I/DD and their families. They should be designed to facilitate optimal outcomes for each individual and his or her family. That means service providers, including rehabilitation counselors, should welcome and support family contributions in the lives of the family members with I/DD (Blue-Banning, Summers, Frankland, Nelson, & Beegle, 2004; Turnbull, Turnbull, Erwin, & Soodak, 2006). Families want rehabilitation counselors to acknowledge and enhance family members' support-giving roles and the natural supports they provide, and to help adults with I/DD and their families create fulfilling lives for these adults while ensuring safety nets are in place.

REFERENCES

American Association on Intellectual & Developmental Disabilities. (2011). *Intellectual disability: Definition, classification, and systems of supports* (11th ed.). Washington, DC: Author.

Anderson, L. L., Larson, S. A., & Wuorio, A. (2011). *2010 FINDS national survey technical report part 1: Family caregiver survey.* Minneapolis: University of Minnesota, Research and Training Center on Community Living.

Arnold, C. K., Heller, T., & Kramer, J. (2012). Support needs of siblings of people with developmental disabilities. *Intellectual and Developmental Disabilities, 50*(5), 373–382.

Baumrind, D. (1991). Effective parenting during the early adolescent transition. In P. A. Cowan & E. M. Hetherington (Eds.), *Family transitions: Advances in family research series* (pp. 111–163). Hillsdale, NJ: Lawrence Erlbaum.

Berry, J. O., & Hardman, M. L. (1998). *Lifespan perspectives on the family and disability.* Boston, MA: Allyn & Bacon.

Bianco, M., Garrison-Wade, D. F., Tobin, R., & Lehmann, J. P. (2009). Parents' perceptions of postschool years for young adults with developmental disabilities. *Intellectual and Developmental Disabilities, 3*(47), 186–196.

Birditt, K. S., Miller, L. M., Fingerman, K. L., & Lefkowitz, E. S. (2009). Tensions in the parent and adult child relationship: Links to solidarity and ambivalence. *Psychology and Aging, 24,* 287–295.

Blacher, J., Neece, C. L., & Paczkowski, E. (2005). Families and intellectual disability. *Current Opinions in Psychiatry, 18,* 507–513.

Blue-Banning, M., Summers, J. A., Frankland, H. C., Nelson, L. L., & Beegle, G. (2004). Dimensions of family and professional partnerships: Constructive guidelines for collaboration. *Exceptional children, 70*(2), 167–184.

Boone, R. T., Burke, M. D., Fore, C., III, & Spencer, V. G. (2006). The impact of cognitive organizers and technology-based practices on student success in secondary social studies classrooms. *Journal of Special Education Technology, 21*(1), 5–15.

Boyle, C. A., Boulet, S., Schieve, L., Cohen, R. A., Blumberg, S. J., Yeargin-Allsopp, M., . . . Kogan, M. D. (2011). Trends in the prevalence of developmental disabilities in US children, 1997–2008. *Pediatrics, 127*(6), 1034–1042.

Center for Disease Control. (2013). *Developmental disabilities. Facts about developmental disabilities.* Retrieved from http://www.cdc.gov/ncbddd/developmentaldisabilities/facts.html

Certo, N. J., Brown, L., Courey, S., Belanger, D., Luecking, R. G., & Murphy, S. (2008). Seamless transition and longterm support for individuals with severe intellectual disabilities. *Research & Practice for Persons with Severe Disabilities, 33*(3), 85–95.

Claes, C., Van Hove, G., Vandevelde, S., van Loon, J., & Schalock, R. L. (2010). Person-centered planning: Analysis of research and effectiveness. *Intellectual and Developmental Disabilities, 48,* 432–453.

Collet-Klingenberg, L., & Hanley-Maxwell, C. (2012). The history of disability and education: Moving from exclusion to inclusion. In C. Hanley-Maxwell & L. Collet-Klingenberg (Eds.), *SAGE reference series on disability: Volume 2, education.* Thousand Oaks, CA: SAGE.

Collins, W. A., & Russell, G. (1991). Mother–child and father–child relationships in middle childhood and adolescence: A developmental analysis. *Developmental Review, 11,* 99–136.

Cutting-Edge Program. (2010). Retrieved from http://www.edgewood.edu/Prospective-Students/Cutting-Edge

Developmental Disabilities Assistance and Bill of Rights Act. 42 USC 6000, et seq. (2000).

Dillenburger, K., & McKerr, L (2011). "How long are we able to go on?" Issues faced by older family caregivers of adults with disabilities. *British Journal of Learning Disabilities, 39,* 29–38.

Doren, B., Gau, J., & Lindstrom, L. (2012). The relationship between parent expectations and post-school outcomes of adolescents with disabilities. *Exceptional Children, 79*(1), 7–23.

Dykens, E. M. (2005). Happiness, well-being, and character strengths: Outcomes for families and siblings of persons with mental retardation. *Mental Retardation, 43*(5), 360–364.

Forgrave, K. E. (2002). Assistive technology: Empowering students with learning disabilities. *Assistive Technology, 73,* 122–126.

Freedman, R. I., & Boyer, N. C. (2000). The power to choose: Supports for families caring for individuals with developmental disabilities. *Health & Social Work, 25*(1), 59–68.

Freedman, R. I., Krauss, M. W., & Seltzer, M. M. (1997). Aging parents residential plans for adult children with mental retardation. *Mental Retardation, 35*(2), 114–123.

Fujiura, G. T. (2010). Aging families and the demographics if family financial support of adults with disabilities. *Journal of Disability Studies, 20*(4), 241–250.

Geenen, S. J., Powers, L. E., & Sells, W. (2003). Understanding the role of health care providers during the transition of adolescents with disabilities and special health care needs. *Journal of Adolescent Health, 32*(3), 225–233.

Green, S. E. (2007). "We're tired, not sad": Benefits and burdens of mothering a child with a disability. *Social Science and Medicine, 64*(1), 150–163.

Griffiths, D. L., & Unger, D. G. (1994). Views about permanency planning for families with adult children with mental retardation. *Family Relations, 43*, 221–227.

Hammel, J., Magasi, S., Heinemann, A., Whiteneck, G., Bogner, J., & Rodriguez, E. (2008). What does participation mean? An insider perspective from people with disabilities. *Disability and Rehabilitation, 30*(19), 1445–1460.

Hanley-Maxwell, C., Whitney-Thomas, J., & Pogoloff, S. (1995). The second shock: Parental perspectives of their child's transition from school to adult life. *Journal of the Association for Persons with Severe Handicaps, 20*, 3–16.

Hart, D. (2006). *Research to practice: Postsecondary education options for students with intellectual disabilities.* Boston: University of Massachusetts, Scholar Works.

Hartley, S., Barker, E., Seltzer, M. M., Floyd, F., Greenberg, J., Orsmond, G., & Bolt, D. (2010). The relative risk and timing of divorce in families of children with an autism spectrum disorder. *Journal of Family Psychology, 24*, 449–457.

Hatton, C., & Emerson, E. (2003). Families with a person with intellectual disabilities: Stress and impact. *Current Opinion in Psychiatry, 16*, 497–501.

Havercamp, S. M., Scandlin, D., & Roth, M. (2004). Health disparities among adults with developmental disabilities, adults with other disabilities, and adults not reporting disability in North Carolina. *Public Health Reports, 119*, 418–426.

Hayden, M. F., & Heller, T. (1997). Support, problem-solving/coping ability, and personal burden of younger and older caregivers of adults with mental retardation. *Mental Retardation, 35*(5), 364–372.

Hegar, R., & Scannapieco, M. (2000). Grandma's babies: The problem of welfare eligibility for children raised by relatives. *Journal of Sociology and Social Welfare, 27*, 153–171.

Heller, T., & Kramer, J. (2009). Involvement of adult siblings of persons with developmental disabilities in future planning. *Intellectual and Developmental Disabilities, 47*(3), 208–209.

Heller, T., Miller, A. B., & Hsieh, K. (1999). Impact of a consumer-directed family support program on adults with developmental disabilities and their family caregivers. *Family Relations, 48*, 419–427.

Heller, T., & Schindler, A. (2009). Family support interventions for families of adults with intellectual and developmental disabilities. In L. M. Glidden & M. M. Seltzer (Eds.), *International review of research in mental retardation* (Vol. 9, pp. 300–325) [Special issue on families]. New York, NY: Academic Press.

Hodapp, R. M., Urbano, R. C., & Burke, M. M. (2010). Adult female and male siblings of persons with developmental disabilities: Findings from a national survey. *Intellectual and Developmental Disabilities, 48*(1), 52–62.

Howlin, P. (2000). Autism and intellectual disability: Diagnostic and treatment issues. *Journal of the Royal Society of Medicine, 93*(7), 351.

Individuals with Disabilities Education Improvement Act, 20 U.S.C. §1400 et seq. (2004).

Johnson, C. P., & Kastner, T. A. (2005). Helping families raise children with special health care needs at home. *Pediatrics, 115*(2), 507–511.

Johnson, D. R., Stodden, R., Emanuel, E., Luecking, R., & Mack, M. (2002). Current challenges facing secondary education and transition services: What research tells us. *Exceptional Children, 68*(4), 519–531.

Kane, R. A., Kane, R. L., & Ladd, R. C. (1998). *The heart of long term care.* New York, NY: Oxford University Press.

Kohler, P. D., & Field, S. (2003). Transition-focused education foundation for the future. *Journal of Special Education, 37*(3), 174–183.

Krahn, G. L., Hammond, L., & Turner, A. (2006). A cascade of disparities: Health and health care access for people with intellectual disabilities. *Mental Retardation and Developmental Disabilities Research Reviews, 12*(1), 70–82.

Magill-Evans, J., Darrah, J., Pain, K., Adkins, R., & Kratochvil, M. (2001). Are families with adolescents and young adults with cerebral palsy the same as other families? *Developmental Medicine and Child Neurology, 43*(7), 466–472.

Mansell, J. (2010). Raising our sights: Services for adults with profound intellectual and multiple disabilities. *Tizard Learning Disability Review, 15*(3), 5–12.

MassMutual. (2012). *Caring for a sibling with a disability: Easter seals sibling study.* Retrieved from http://www.massmutual.com/mmfg/pdf/Sibling%20Study%20Key%20Findings_SC8200.pdf

Mazzotti, V. L., Test, D. W., Wood, C. L., & Richter, S. (2010). Effects of computer-assisted instruction on students' knowledge of postschool options. *Career Development for Exceptional Individuals, 33*(1), 25–40.

McCallion, P., & Toseland, R. W. (1993). Empowering families of adolescents and adults with developmental disabilities. *Families in Society, 74*, 579–587.

McGraw, L. A., & Walker, A. J. (2007). Meanings of sisterhood and developmental disabilities: Narratives from white nondisabled sisters. *Journal of Family Issues, 28*(4), 474–500.

Neece, C. L., Kraemer, B. R., & Blacher, J. (2009). Transition satisfaction and family well-being among parents of young adults with severe intellectual disability. *Intellectual and Developmental Disabilities, 47*, 31–43.

Orsmond, G., & Seltzer, M. (2000). Brothers and sisters of adults with mental retardation: Gendered nature of the sibling relationship. *American Journal on Mental Retardation, 105*, 486–508.

Parish, S. L., & Lutwick, Z. E. (2005). A critical analysis of the emerging crisis in long-term care for people with developmental disabilities. *Social Work, 50*(4), 345–354.

Parish, S. L., Seltzer, M. M., Greenberg, J. S., & Floyd, F. J. (2004). Economic implications of caregiving at midlife: Comparing parents with and without children who had developmental disabilities. *Mental Retardation, 42*, 413–426. [PubMed: 15516174]

Pruchno, R. A. (2003). Enmeshed lives: Adult children with developmental disabilities and their aging mothers. *Psychology and Aging, 18*, 851–857.

Pynoos, J., & Nishita, C. M. (2003). The cost and financing of home modifications in the United States. *Journal of Disability Policy Studies, 14*(2), 68–73.

REACH. (2010). *REACH: Reaching educational and career hopes.* Retrieved from http://www.education.uiowa.edu/reach/

Rizzolo, M. C., Hemp, R., Braddock, D., & Schindler, A. (2009). Family support services for person with intellectual and developmental disabilities: Recent national trends. *Intellectual and Developmental Disabilities, 47*(2), 152–155.

Rueda, R., Monzo, L., Shapiro, J., Gomez, J., & Blacher, J. (2005). Cultural models of transition: Latina mothers of young adults with developmental disabilities. *Exceptional Children, 71*(4), 401–414.

Russo, R. J. (1999). Applying a strengths-based practice approach in working with people developmental disabilities and their families. *Families in Society, 80,* 25–33.

Ryan, R. M., & Lynch, J. H. (1989). Emotional autonomy versus detachment: Revising the vicissitudes of adolescence and young adulthood. *Child Development, 60,* 340–346.

Saleeby, D. (1996). The strengths based perspective in social work practice: Extensions and cautions. *Social Work, 41*(3), 296–305.

Scherer, M. J., & Glueckauf, R. (2005). Assessing the benefits of assistive technologies for activities and participation. *Rehabilitation Psychology, 50*(2), 132.

Schneider, J., Wedgewood, N., Llewellyn, G., & McConnell, D. (2006). Families challenged by and accommodating to the adolescent years. *Journal of Intellectual Disability Research, 50*(12), 926–936.

Seligman, M., & Darling, R. B. (2009). *Ordinary families, special children: A system approach to childhood disability.* New York, NY: Guilford.

Seltzer, M. M., Floyd, F. J., Song, J., Greenberg, J. S., & Hong, J. (2011). Midlife and aging parents of adults with intellectual and developmental disabilities: Impacts of lifelong parenting. *American Journal of Developmental Disabilities, 11*(6), 479–499.

Seltzer, M. M., Greenberg, J. S., Floyd, F. J., Pettee, Y., & Hong, J. (2001). Life course impacts of parenting a child with a disability. *American Journal of Developmental Disabilities, 106*(3), 265–286.

Seltzer, M. M., Greenberg, J. S., Orsmond, G. I., & Lounds, J. (2005). Life course studies of siblings of individuals with developmental disabilities. *Mental Retardation, 43*(5), 354–359.

Seltzer, M. M., & Krauss, M. W. (2001). Quality of life of adults with mental retardation/developmental disabilities who live with family. *Mental Retardation and Developmental Disabilities Research Reviews, 7,* 105–114.

Seltzer, M. M., Orsmond, G. I., & Esbensen, A. J. (2009). Siblings of individuals with an autism spectrum disorder: Sibling relationships and wellbeing in adolescence and adulthood. *Autism, 13*(1), 59–80.

Simeonsson, R. J., Leonardi, M., Lollar, D., Bjorck-Akesson, E., Hollenweger, J., & Martinuzzi, A. (2003). Applying the International Classification of Functioning, Disability and Health (ICF) to measure childhood disability. *Disability & Rehabilitation, 25*(11–12), 602–610.

Social Security Administration. (2013, March). *Benefits for children with disabilities* (SSA Publication No. 05-10026, ICN 455360). Washington, DC: Author.

Stancliffe, R. J., Lakin, K. C., Larson, S., Engler, J., Taub, S., Fortune, J., & Berhadsky, J. (2012). Demographic characteristics, health conditions, and residential service use in adults with Down syndrome in 25 U.S. states. *Intellectual and Developmental Disabilities, 50*(2), 92–108.

Stewart, L. M. (2013). Family care responsibilities and employment: Exploring the impact of type of family care on work–family and family–work conflict. *Journal of Family Issues, 3*(1), 113–138.

Stock, S. E., Davies, D. K., Secor, R. R., & Wehmeyer, M. L. (2003). Self-directed career preference selection for individuals with intellectual disabilities: Using computer technology
to enhance self-determination. *Journal of Vocational Rehabilitation, 19,* 95–103.

Test, D. W., Mazzotti, V. L., Mustian, A. L., Fowler, C. H., Kortering, L., & Kohler, P. (2009).
Evidence-based secondary transition predictors for improving postschool outcomes for
students with disabilities. *Career Development for Exceptional Individuals, 32*(3), 160–181.

The Arc. (2013a). *What we do. Programs and services: Find help from The Arc.* Retrieved from
http://www.thearc.org/what-we-do/programs-and-services

The Arc. (2013b). *What we do. Resources. Introduction to intellectual disability. How does the DD
definition compare with the AAIDD definition of intellectual disability?* Retrieved from http://
www.thearc.org/page.aspx?pid=2448

Tichá, R., Lakin, K. C., Larson, S. A., Stancliffe, R. J., Taub, S., Engler, J., . . . Moseley, C. (2012).
Correlates of everyday choice and support-related choice for 8,892 randomly sampled
adults with intellectual and developmental disabilities in 19 states. *Intellectual and Developmental Disabilities, 50*(6), 486–504.

Turnbull, A. P., Turnbull, H. R., Erwin, E., & Soodak, L. (2006). *Families, professionals, and excep-
tionality.* Upper Saddle River, NJ: Merrill/Prentice Hall.

Valentine, D. P., McDermott, S., & Anderson, D. (1998). Mothers of adults with mental retardation: Is race a factor in perceptions of burdens or gratifications? *Families in Society,
79*(6), 577–584.

van der Meer, L., Sigafoos, J., O'Reilly, M. F., & Lancioni, G. (2011). Assessing preferences for
AAC options in communication interventions for individuals with developmental disabilities: A review of the literature. *Research in Developmental Disabilities, 32,* 1422–1431.

Van Naarden Braun, K., Yeargin-Allsopp, M., & Lollar, D. (2009). Activity limitations among
young adults with developmental disabilities: A population based follow-up study.
Research in Developmental Disabilities, 30, 179–191.

Wehman, P., & Bricout, J. (2001). Supported employment: New directions for the new mil-
lennium. In P. Wehman (Ed.), *Supported employment in business: Expanding the capacity of
workers with disabilities* (pp. 3–22). St. Augustine, FL: TRN.

White, S. E., McMorris, C., Weiss, J. A., & Lunsky, Y. (2012). The experience of crisis in families
of individuals with autism spectrum disorder across the lifespan. *Journal of Child and
Family Studies, 21,* 457–465.

Widmer, E. D., Kempf, N., Sapin, M., & Galli-Carminate, G. (2013). Family beyond parents?
An exploration of family configurations and psychological adjustment in young adults
with intellectual disabilities. *Research in Developmental Disabilities, 34,* 207–217.

World Health Organization. (2001). *International classification of functioning, disability, and health.*
Geneva, Switzerland: Author.

Yamaki, K., & Fujiura, G. T. (2002). Employment and income status of adults with developmental disabilities living in the community. *Mental Retardation, 40,* 132–141.

Yoong, A., & Koritsas, S. (2012). The impact of caring for adults with intellectual disability
on the quality of life of parents. *Journal of Intellectual Disability Research, 56*(60), 609–619.

Zigman, W., Schupf, N., Haveman, M., & Silverman, W. (1997). The epidemiology of Alzheimer's disease in mental retardation: Results and recommendations from an international
conference. *Journal of Intellectual Disability Research, 41*(1), 76–80.

CHAPTER 7

Recovery, Families, and Psychiatric Disabilities

Lynda R. Matthews, Marianne Farkas, Michelle Medway, and Natalie Taylor

Families of people with psychiatric disabilities can be credited with a paradigmatic shift in their treatment and care. Before the notion of recovery, mental health professionals believed that a prognosis of serious mental illness was one of inevitable decline into a life devoid of meaning and hope and defined care and treatment accordingly (Farkas, Gagne, Anthony, & Chamberlin, 2005; Harrison et al., 2001). Reports of exploitation of people with mental disorders and a lack of voice to advocate change led people with psychiatric disabilities and their families to organize in defiance of existing medical assumptions that locked people into sick roles, devalued their input into life decisions and medical care, and emphasized isolation and medication (Anthony, Cohen, Farkas, & Gagne, 2002). The resulting consumer and family support groups promoted self-definition, self-determination, rights protection, and advocacy (Anthony et al., 2002). Since then, personal experiences of recovery that have underpinned an alternative vision of mental illness (Deegan, 1988), together with longitudinal evidence of improved functioning in people with serious mental illness (Harrison et al., 2001), have identified recovery as desirable and possible (Farkas & Anthony, 2010).

The vision of recovery for individuals with psychiatric disabilities is based on values of hope, self-determination, choice, partnership, and respect for the human being involved (Farkas, 2007). Supporting this orientation, psychiatric rehabilitation includes "systematic efforts to help adults with psychiatric disabilities move forward in their recovery process" (Corrigan, Mueser, Bond, Drake, & Solomon, 2008, p. 52). With its focus on empowerment, recovery, and the achievement of a meaningful life, psychiatric rehabilitation interventions help people gain or regain valued roles in valued community settings by improving skills and providing environmental supports (Anthony et al., 2002). While acknowledging the importance of treatment interventions that focus on symptom reduction, its approach targets the

International Classification of Functioning (ICF) dimensions of activity, participation, and environment to improve functional ability and facilitate recovery in people with psychiatric disabilities (Farkas & Anthony, 2010). Several of these approaches are discussed in this chapter through the case studies provided.

Among individuals with disabilities, mental illnesses are the single most common cause of long-term disability (Mathers & Loncar, 2006). The impact of psychiatric disability on individuals, their families, and society is devastating. According to the World Health Organization, psychiatric disorders account for 14% of all disease-adjusted life years (DALYs: years with disease plus years of life lost), and 28% of DALYs due to noncommunicable diseases such as AIDS (World Health Organization [WHO], 2008). In addition to the symptoms of mental illness, people with psychiatric disabilities and their families also have to deal with the stigma and discrimination that surrounds mental illness. Stigma and discrimination lead to avoidance and stereotyping and at times present greater barriers to recovery and participation than the clinical features of the illness (Watson & Eack, 2011). Consequently, the family experience of serious mental illness takes place as an ongoing effort to gain and maintain a proper place in the community for the family member, as well as coping with its effects on the family.

The family experience of providing support and care is discussed herein from a recovery point of view using case studies of families living with the two most prominent diagnoses, schizophrenia and major depressive disorder (MDD). Specific profiles of function for each disorder are provided and implications for activities and participation for individuals and families are discussed.

PSYCHIATRIC DISABILITIES: FUNCTION AND STIGMA

Various definitions of serious psychiatric disability share common elements: a diagnosis of mental illness, prolonged duration, with functional or role incapacity (Jans, Stoddard, & Kraus, 2004). Whether the target population is defined using medical, rehabilitation, mental health, or empirically derived criteria, all definitions coalesce around the description of a disability with resulting functional impairment that substantially limits one or more major life activities (Goldman, Gattozzi, & Taube, 1981).

The nature of an individual's symptoms and level of function, together with the stigma associated with mental illness, increases the potential for people with mental illnesses to experience psychiatric disabilities. One of the defining features of psychiatric disability is the difficulty that a person has achieving typical, age-appropriate goals because of his or her mental illness (Corrigan et al., 2008). Having a psychiatric disability in the absence of effective rehabilitation, therefore, has the potential to significantly influence a wide range of opportunities and life choices as demonstrated in the following sections and their case studies.

Schizophrenia

Schizophrenia can be viewed as a biological disorder that is marked by periods of false perceptions (hallucinations) and false beliefs (delusions) that usually are not continuous. Deficiencies or imbalances in neurotransmitters such as dopamine, serotonin, glutamate, and GABA interfere with the transmission of messages between parts of the brain and this gives rise to the positive, negative, and cognitive symptoms of schizophrenia (Chen et al., 2012; Dissanayake, Mason, & Marsden, 2013). Primarily the frontal and temporal lobes are most affected with the parietal and occipital lobes affected to a lesser extent (Antonius et al., 2011). The frontal lobes are responsible for attention, working memory, language skills, and executive functioning and have been shown to progressively deteriorate after onset of schizophrenia, particularly during the acute phase of the illness (Cobia, Smith, Wang, & Csernansky, 2012). Underactivity in this area results in both the negative symptoms of schizophrenia—a blunted affect leading to altered emotional reactivity, anhedonia, apathy, and alogia—and the cognitive impairment associated with schizophrenia—memory impairment, difficulties with attention and concentration, reduced executive functioning and psychomotor speed, and difficulty with learning (Mueser & McGurk, 2004).

The temporal and parietal lobes play an important role in sensory input, auditory perception, language and speech production, and memory formation. Overactivity in these areas has been associated with the positive symptoms of schizophrenia such as hallucinations, delusions, and excessive internal stimulation (Pratt, Gill, Varrett, & Roberts, 2007). Positive symptoms, which are episodic in nature, are most likely to bring people with schizophrenia to the attention of health services and often lead to periods of hospitalization, whereas cognitive and negative symptoms strongly influence a person's ability to function on a day-to-day basis (Mueser, Deavers, Penn, & Cassisi, 2013).

CASE STUDY

My daughter Sally was 20 when she was diagnosed with schizophrenia. I know she has always had difficulty making friends and she struggled at school, but at the time I never thought that it was anything serious. We were happy for her when she got a part-time job in a large diner after finishing school. However, a few months after starting work things began to go wrong. She lost her job because she got the orders mixed up and had begun talking strangely to customers. Her brothers said that people in town were talking about her, saying she was "odd," and they had heard she was using marijuana pretty regularly. Thinking this was the problem we tried to talk with her so we could find out how we could help but she was very suspicious of us, got quite angry, and she refused outright to see our doctor or the local drug and alcohol worker to get help. She became increasingly confused and agitated; she spent hours in her bedroom; she talked to herself and wouldn't watch television. It became obvious that this behavior wasn't a result of the marijuana, so after talking with our doctor again, Tom and I took her to the local hospital.

They told us she had a psychotic illness. She was hearing voices that told her if she did not do as they said terrible harm would come to the people in her family. She was paranoid about other people and believed people were purposefully trying to make her life miserable. She was hospitalized and started on medication. Sally was assigned a case worker at the local community mental health center, but she only went once and before long we noticed that she was becoming agitated again. It followed another visit to the doctors, more medication, another referral … I think you get the idea. Sally has been rehospitalized four times in the last few years. Sometimes she disappears for days on end. The police find her and bring her home. It's been an incredibly tense time, and there have been so many family arguments. It seems we just get her going well and then she goes off her medication and ends up sick again.

After Sally's last discharge from hospital, we met with the mental health team to talk about ways to help Sally remember to take her medication. Given the amount of time Sally had been spending on the streets and in hospital, they suggested a referral to a community treatment program where Sally could get support with taking her medication as well as get treatment for her drug use, and possibly get a job. Sally seemed to like the idea of moving out into an apartment and I certainly didn't want to see her back in hospital again or on the streets. Yet, we were pretty anxious about the care she might get; we'd heard awful stories about the treatment people get by some professionals and we weren't too keen to place our trust in the system. However, Sally and Jessica, her worker, keep us informed of what's happening. We chat with Sally on the phone regularly and still have the usual family get-togethers. Sally recently told us that she's been talking with a case worker who is going to help her to get a job. I'm not sure that's going to be good for Sally but she seems determined.

How have things been for the family? Well it seems like our lives have been in chaos for many years and to some degree we are still trying to understand what's happened and how our lives have changed. It's such a steep learning curve and we've experienced such a range of emotions that it's difficult to know which way is up sometimes. While the mental health team provided us with some initial support and information about schizophrenia, it wasn't until Tom and I went to a program for families that was run by parents who'd experienced the same thing as us that we realized that other people were going through the same emotions, disruptions, financial problems, fatigue, and isolation that we had. Our sons have been affected too even though we tried as much as possible to stop Sally's illness from disrupting their lives. The eldest two had already moved out of home when she was diagnosed but they had lived with her illness and people's comments prior to the diagnosis. And our youngest recently told me that his friends asked him why he didn't do more to keep Sally on track. It hurts me to hear that. Yet they continue to support Sally in their own ways, and to some degree we're a little bit closer as a family because of it.

Major Depressive Disorder

MDD affects areas such as the hippocampus, amygdala, and the prefrontal cortex. These areas of the brain coordinate memory, attention, emotional regulation, as well as cognitive processes and sensory perception (Palazidou, 2012). People with MDD, therefore, have a diminished ability to think or concentrate, and thought processes tend to include rumination and ideas of worthlessness and negative self-judgments (Rimes & Watkins, 2005). In the vast majority of cases, depression is associated with a deficiency in monoamines in the brain, such as serotonin, dopamine, and adrenaline. Balance among these brain chemicals helps to control body processes such as energy, appetite, sleep, and sex drive (Willner, Scheel-Krüger, & Belzung, 2013). Symptoms therefore include sad mood, loss of appetite and libido, feelings of despair and guilt, insomnia, psychomotor retardation, and suicidal thoughts. Objectively, people with MDD show some level of interpersonal impairment, such as poor posture and decreased facial expressions, and are more likely to make directly negative statements during conversation (Segrin, 2000). Primarily, MDD is characterized by depressed affect and anhedonia (Ball, Manicavasagar, & Mitchell, 2011).

CASE STUDY

Rhys is a 40-year-old chemical engineer who was diagnosed with MDD 2 years ago. It's been a long, tough haul over the past few years for him and his wife, Kate. Managing his illness, coping with hospitalizations, and trying to find a way forward have had their toll, but his recent return to part-time work has signaled the next phase in his rehabilitation and a move closer toward his recovery.

Rhys admits that he was reluctant to get help for depression in the early years because he feared people's reactions to him having a mental illness. It wasn't long after his daughter's birth, however, that he began to feel very empty and despairing. His own disruptive childhood was replaying in his head. Kate agrees that he repeatedly told her about the guilt he felt about not being a good father to Ally, but Kate put his feelings down to general apprehension that comes with being a new dad. She noticed that he was drinking more than usual and not taking as much care with his personal appearance, but she was more annoyed with the fact that he was just lazing around and not helping her with work around the house. It was when she realized he was barely sleeping more than a few hours each night that she realized something was wrong. She took Rhys to the doctors and they prescribed sleeping tablets for his insomnia. These helped for a while. However, it wasn't long before his declining performance at work was noted by his employer who subsequently issued him a warning. A few days later, Kate found Rhys in a semiconscious state when she arrived home from work; Rhys had been drinking and taken sleeping tablets afterward to help him sleep. At the hospital, he denied suicidal thoughts but he did tell his doctor that he felt as if his life was not worth living. Rhys was diagnosed with major depression. He was prescribed antidepressants and started in counseling.

Kate admits she didn't know what to do or how to manage Rhys's changing behavior. At the time she thought he was reacting to having a new baby, she put it down to stress from the restructure at work. She recalls it as a very worrying, at times overwhelming, time in her life and she considered leaving him on more than one occasion just to escape the stress. While things are looking up, she is still very concerned about his use of alcohol and the effect it has on his medication. Kate notes that she's lucky that her mother has always been there to help and support her and Rhys as needed and that Rhys's brother Jake has been dropping around more to see them, often taking Rhys out to visit old schoolmates or to football. She recalls that they used to have a good group of friends but they haven't been able to go out with the group for a while, and Kate has noticed they don't drop around much anymore. She misses the comfort and familiarity that comes with the close friendships they had. One of the better things that have happened since Rhys's hospitalization has been meeting Steve, his peer-support worker. Being able to share their experiences with Steve and learning about how to move forward has been good for them both. And Rhys's recent return to work is another step closer to getting back to normal routine, even though she knows he worries about whether he can perform at the level his employers expect of him. Nevertheless, she indicates that she is starting to feel hopeful for the future.

SUPPORTING ACTIVITY AND PARTICIPATION

Supportive relationships with friends, family, or health professionals have the potential to influence the way a person adjusts to having a psychiatric disability, to his or her rehabilitation, and his or her recovery (Topor et al., 2006). The shift from institutionalization to community-based care and community integration means that family members are more likely to become the primary support system for their relative with mental illness (Stein, Aguirre, & Hunt, 2013). In a mobile society, families can include anyone (i.e., friends, community leaders, partners and relatives). Between 50% and 90% of people who have received treatment live with a relative (Schulze & Rossler, 2005), and about 85% have some form of ongoing contact with family (Lehman & Steinwachs, 1998). When family is available, spouses are most likely to provide support for their partners with MDD due to its typical onset in adulthood. Parents are typical providers of support for their children with schizophrenia, given its earlier onset in adolescence (Wijngaarden et al., 2009). However, for some, family members are no longer available or support available from the family changes, and in these situations family may be trusted case workers, close friends, or peer-support workers.

The following sections provide an overview of some of the challenges people with psychiatric disabilities face, the interventions that have been developed to help address the issues, and the common ways that families participate in these interventions. Given the importance of support to rehabilitation outcomes, the engagement of family in the early stages of recovery is critical.

Health and Wellness

People living with schizophrenia or MDD have to deal not only with their symptoms but also with the high risk of physical health concerns that arise from poor health behaviors, the side effects of medication, and inadequate medical care. Sally and others living with schizophrenia have an increased risk of cardiovascular disease, metabolic syndrome, and cancer and a decreased life expectancy of 13 to 25 years when compared with the general population (Nielsen, Uggerby, Jensen, & McGrath, 2013). People like Rhys who live with MDD may also have a serious physical condition such as cancer, HIV/AIDS, and Parkinson's disease, and in these situations people tend to experience more severe symptoms in both disorders (Cassano & Fava, 2002). They are also at greater risk of cardiac mortality with the relationship strengthening with the severity of the depressive episode (Lespérance, Frasure-Smith, Talajic, & Bourassa, 2002). This association extends to all-cause mortality, where the potential for death nearly doubles in individuals with clinical depression (Almeida, Alfonso, Hankey, & Flicker, 2010). People with severe mental illnesses have significantly increased rates of suicide. Depression is the single greatest risk factor for suicide, and people with MDD are more than 25 times more likely to commit suicide than the general population (Osby, Brandt, Correia, Ekbom, & Sparen, 2001).

Screening for physical illness and implementation of prevention strategies for people in Sally's and Rhys's situation is significantly lacking (Stanley & Laugharne, 2011), often due to difficulty ascertaining who is responsible for the detection, monitoring, and management of these physical health concerns (Stanley & Laugharne, 2011). The stigma of mental illness often makes providers hesitant to serve those with psychiatric conditions. Unless prompted by family, friends, or support workers, people with serious mental illnesses rarely engage with medical services, and when they do, often the phenomenon of "diagnostic overshadowing" complicates treatment, that is, attributing reported physical symptoms to a mental illness (Robson & Gray, 2007). Contributing to the undiagnosed physical health problems is the fact that many psychiatrists are inadequately trained to detect health problems (Leucht, Burkard, Henderson, Maj, & Sartorius, 2007). Family involvement in physical health is therefore often likely to be one of monitoring ongoing physical health and encouraging practical steps to improve health in common problem areas such as inactivity, poor diet, and smoking cessation (Corrigan et al., 2008).

Substance Use Disorders

The prevalence of coexisting substance abuse may further complicate the functioning of people with mental illnesses (Matthews, Harris, Jaworski, Alam, & Bozdag, 2013). Individuals living with psychiatric conditions (particularly young adults) can find the use of alcohol or drugs to be a way of fitting in socially, a method of self-medication to calm anxieties or help with common bouts of sleeplessness (NAMI, 2013). Nearly half of all people living with serious mental illnesses will develop a substance use disorder that can have detrimental effects on their recovery (Mueser & Gingerich, 2013). Increased hospitalizations; more medical, legal, and financial problems; increased risk of homelessness and suicidality; poorer social connections; and lack of engagement in treatment are more likely to occur in a person living with schizophrenia or MDD and a coexisting substance use disorder (Lechner et al., 2013; Mueser & Gingerich, 2013). The nature of the treatment he or she receives will significantly affect outcomes. Sally, who has been receiving integrated dual disorder treatment—a comprehensive, coordinated mental health and substance abuse treatment program run by the same practitioner—has had a notable improvement in her marijuana use. Rhys, on the other hand, has been attending separate substance use and mental health treatment interventions. Evidence suggests that it is unlikely that he will achieve the same positive outcomes as Sally, given that each intervention has not been individually tailored and coordinated for his situation (Drake, Mueser, Brunette, & McHugo, 2004).

There are a number of ways that families can support relatives with coexisting conditions. Discussing the matter with their relative provides a better understanding of the reasons why he or she is using substances and what needs are being met. Families can be active in identifying strategies to help reduce use or to promote abstinence, or guard against relapses. Depending on the nature of their relationship with their relative's treatment provider, they may be well placed to monitor and share information about the substance use with health professionals (Mueser & Fox, 1998).

Self-Care Issues and Activities of Daily Living

The impact that schizophrenia and MDD have on a person's ability to function and care for him- or herself is considerable. Many people living with a serious mental disorder lose or fail to develop the critical skills needed to live safely in their community, including those required for maintaining personal hygiene, attending appointments, taking medication, seeking support, and building and maintaining relationships (Judd et al., 2000; Mueser et al., 2013). These everyday tasks can have huge consequences, including social and health needs not being met, the ability to earn an income and be self-sufficient being compromised, and the ability to seek and participate in rehabilitation being impaired (Mueser et al., 2013). This is especially the case for people living with schizophrenia in that its onset in adolescence means that mastery of adult social roles and skills such as adult relationships, sexual behaviors, and work-related skills is interrupted (Bellack, 2004).

The loss of skills that affect functioning and productivity increases overall dependence on family, which is often required to help with personal care, transportation, meal preparation, housework, continuous supervision, budgeting, and financial assistance (Corrigan et al., 2008). Many family members provide direct material assistance such as food, money, and clothing even when they do not live with their relative with mental disorder (Intagliata, Willer, & Egri, 1986). Providing social skills and independent living training programs that are focused on meeting specific roles that the individual wants to achieve (e.g., part-time work, tenant in an apartment, student, boyfriend) increases the motivation that individuals have for learning a range of skills, including the basic ones such as activities of daily living. When these skills are maintained over time, they tend to improve the quality of social and leisure functioning (Bellack, 2004; Farkas & Anthony, 2010; Lyman, Kurtz, Farkas, George, & Dougherty, 2014).

Cognitive Function

Cognitive impairment is a central feature of schizophrenia and MDD. If Sally or Rhys were to achieve clinical recovery, research suggests that they would likely experience residual cognitive difficulties, particularly in memory, problem solving, and social functioning, demonstrating the profound impact that the longitudinal course of schizophrenia and MDD has on an individual's quality of life (Gold, 2004; Lépine & Briley, 2011). The antipsychotic medication that Sally takes, for example, has been effective over time in reducing psychotic symptoms but has been less effective in addressing the problems she has with social cognition and executive processing (Lindenmayer, Nasrallah, Pucci, James, & Citrome, 2013). While the social skills training Sally received has helped with general psychosocial function, she still has particular difficulty with social perception, memory, and attention. As Sally has set a rehabilitation goal of returning to work, Jessica and Sally have been talking about an integrated cognitive remediation program that will help address these skill deficits. Jessica knows that improved function in these areas would mean that Sally could better enjoy her social relationships (Kurtz & Richardson, 2012) and improve skills needed for rehabilitation outcomes such as employment (McGurk & Wykes, 2008).

Interventions to Improve Function and Participation

ICF environmental factors "make up the physical, social and attitudinal environment in which people live and conduct their lives" (World Health Organisation, 2001, p. 10). The degree to which these factors improve or impede function, activity, and participation are of central importance to a person's recovery, community integration, and quality of life. A number of rehabilitation interventions that include skill development to improve function have already been mentioned in this chapter (i.e., integrated dual disorder treatment, social skills training, and cognitive remediation).

Medication and Illness Self-Management

Medication is the main intervention used to improve body function in people with serious mental illnesses. Recent large-scale studies have consistently shown that medication is effective but only in a limited way as it may control some symptoms, for some periods of time, for some people, and does not, by itself, improve community functioning (Swartz et al., 2007). A later summary of the studies concluded that antipsychotic drugs have been proven an effective treatment of schizophrenia, but have substantial limitations in their efficacy and safety; individual patient response to antipsychotic drugs varies widely with substantial impact on recovery (Lieberman & Stroop, 2011). In addition to the limits of the treatment itself, symptoms of the disorder and related stigma can often prevent people from seeking treatment (Kurtz, Olfson, & Rose, 2013). For this reason, family members are frequently responsible for seeking medical treatment, as seen in both Sally's and Rhys's situation. The value of medication in reducing symptoms and helping prevent relapses, however, is only achieved with adherence to a medication regimen, and in the case of mental disorders nonadherence may be 50% or higher (Fenton, Blyler, & Heinssen, 1997). A combination of factors affects consistency in taking medication. The more common factors include ineffective symptom relief that results from incorrect prescribing, the unpleasant side effects of medication, cognitive difficulties, and environmental issues such as unstable housing (Mueser et al., 2002).

Evidence suggests that gaining the ability to self-manage mental illnesses improves medication adherence (Dolder, Lacro, Leckband, & Jeste, 2003). The idea behind illness self-management is that providing people with psychiatric disabilities information about their illness, about knowing how to effectively use medication, being able to identify events that lead to relapses, and planning ahead for potential crises, helps them to deal more effectively with their disorder. After attending illness self-management sessions with his wife, Rhys learned about a number of practical strategies for improving his medication-taking routine, including co-locating his medication with his toothbrush and talking with his doctor about the possibility of reducing the number of times he takes his medication from twice to once a day (Fardig, Lewander, Melin, Folke, & Fredriksson, 2011). Involving families in illness self-management programs (e.g., Whitley, Gingerich, Lutz, & Mueser, 2009) is an important step toward gaining their support because family support has been shown to result in better self-management, improved control of their disorder, and lower hospitalization rates (Corrigan et al., 2008).

Assertive Community Treatment

Many like Sally with more severe and persistent conditions have difficulty sustaining community living and are at a high risk of relapse and hospitalization. Programs of assertive community treatment (PACT) are an effective way to engage people in treatment and rehabilitation services (Rice, 2011). Providing outreach, intensive, and comprehensive community-based treatment and services by a multidisciplinary team that is available 24 hours a day increases housing stability, improves employment, and reduces symptoms and the need for hospitalization (Bond, Drake, Mueser, & Latimer, 2001). The low staff-to-people ratio means that PACT workers have time to provide assistance in ways such as supporting individuals in taking medication, getting to appointments, talking to housing providers and welfare agencies as well as families and employers (Tschopp, Berven, & Chan, 2011).

Vocational Rehabilitation

Employment rates are low for people with psychiatric disabilities, and people living with schizophrenia generally have lower employment rates than people living with MDD (King et al., 2006). Low employment rates have been explained in terms of barriers arising from psychiatric symptoms, work performance, neurocognitive impairment (Tsang, Leung, Chung, Bell, & Cheung, 2010), comorbid substance use (Biegel, Stevenson, Beimers, Ronis, & Boyle, 2010), and physical health problems (Waghorn, Lloyd, Abraham, Silvester, & Chant, 2008). Structural aspects of care, such as income-support guidelines can create a disincentive to work. The lack of communication and coordination between services, limited funding for vocational rehabilitation (VR), and stigma among employers further complicate employment efforts (King et al., 2006). Providers contribute to the person's fear of employment by focusing on deficits in their planning consultation. Sometimes service providers resort to professional coercion (Rapp & Goscha, 2006) because they believe that work is too stressful (Marwaha, Balachandra, & Johnson, 2008), despite abundant evidence to the contrary (Kukla, Bond, & Xie, 2012). These negative factors undermine individuals' hopes and dreams that work and recovery are possible and discourage people from pursuing employment and enrollment in vocational programs. Negative attitudes about work among family members, related to concerns about stress or the loss of benefits, also have similar discouraging effects (Mueser & Gingerich, 2006). Providing families with information about the value of work, the components of good VR programs, and how to encourage job seeking will help to secure the family support needed to achieve a good work outcome (Bond, Becker, et al., 2001).

Despite the barriers, many people living with psychiatric disabilities want meaningful work, and a variety of VR interventions are available (e.g., clubhouse programs, social firms, and supported employment) to provide support for people to do "real work for real pay" (Farkas & Anthony, 2010, p. 121). For people who want to work, supported employment programs such as Individual Placement and Support (IPS; Becker & Drake, 1994) and the Choose-Get-Keep-Leave approaches (Danley & Anthony, 1987) achieve better employment outcomes than other VR programs (Bond, Drake, & Becker, 2008).

One of the main predictors of work success is previous work history. Rhys and other individuals with later-onset mental illnesses who have had the opportunity to develop social and employment-related skills generally fare better than Sally whose early onset of mental illness has inhibited work and other formative experiences. The integration of mental health and VR services with the open-ended, individualized support of IPS can help Sally and others living with schizophrenia "to become employed in jobs that match their skills, interests, and preferences and provides whatever supports are needed to ensure success and satisfaction" (Pratt et al., 2007, p. 270).

Family Psychoeducation

Many families have strengths and demonstrate resilience in their support of their relative over time, but many also experience the stress that psychiatric disability can place on families. Interventions that help address the information and support needs of families increase their ability to improve the outcomes of family members with psychiatric disabilities (Pratt et al., 2007). Professional family psychoeducation programs provide information about mental illness and treatment and deliver skills in problem solving, coping, and communication to individuals with psychiatric disabilities and their families. They are effective in reducing relapses and hospitalizations, increasing knowledge about mental illness and treatments, reducing family burden, and improving family functioning and family relationships when provided as part of the family member's treatment (Cuijpers, 1999; Pharoah, Mari, Rathbone, & Wong, 2010). Not all people with psychiatric disabilities receive treatment, which means that many families do not have access to professionally conducted programs. Many families have had poor experiences with mental health professionals and do not want to engage in formal programs (Corrigan et al., 2008). For these families, education and support programs run by peers may provide a useful source of support, encouragement, and hope (Davidson, Chinman, Sells, & Rowe, 2006).

Peer-Support Services

Formal and informal peer support is increasingly recognized as having an important role in recovery for people with psychiatric disabilities. Peer support involves people "who have a history of mental illness and who have experienced significant improvement in their psychiatric condition offering services and/or supports to other people with serious mental illness who are considered to be not as far along in their own recovery process" (Davidson et al., 2006, p. 444). Peer services are available for both the individuals with psychiatric disability and their families through mutual support groups, self-help organizations, and peer-operated services. As seen in Rhys's situation, being able to share challenges and develop a friendship with a peer worker can be instrumental in developing a sense of future and recovery. Family-led interventions that provide practical advice, information, and support for families on how to successfully manage a psychiatric disability are effective for improving the family's knowledge about psychiatric disability, for increasing families' sense of empowerment and self-care, and reducing subjective burden

(Dixon et al., 2004). They are particularly important for families of relatives who are not in treatment and who would otherwise have limited access to support services (Murray-Swank & Dixon, 2004).

SUPPORTING FAMILIES IN RECOVERY

A diagnosis of mental illness triggers major role changes in families for which they are little prepared. At the time of their relative's diagnosis, families experience feelings of grief and loss (Stein et al., 2013) and regularly report strong feelings of guilt, embarrassment, and self-blame (Karnieli-Miller et al., 2013). Spaniol and Nelson (2013) have suggested that families go through their own process of recovery. They have identified the following stages in family recovery: shock, discovery, denial; recognition and acceptance; coping; and personal and political advocacy. They suggest that each phase requires different kinds of support from other family members and providers. For example, when families are in shock about the diagnosis of their loved one, information about the phases of family recovery, information about family coping strategies, support from others who are further along in their journey are all helpful. On the other hand, when families are in the phase of recognition and acceptance, information about the condition, medication benefits and limitations, resources, and crisis-intervention techniques have been found to be more useful.

Adjustment to these changes is often very long and difficult. While supporting a family member living with mental illness, families will often experience a mixture of emotions such as fear, anxiety, guilt, and sadness, which are particularly noticeable during times of high stress related to their support role (Panayiotopoulos, Pavlakis, & Apostolou, 2013). Contact with families early in the recovery process by people who are sensitive to their experiences and who provide information, appropriate expectations, and where to get support via professionally conducted family psychoeducation or family-led education programs goes a long way toward meeting families' needs at that time (Pickett-Schenk, Lippincott, Bennett, & Steigman, 2008).

Providing support for people with psychiatric disabilities may have an impact on people's emotional, social, and physical function (Heru, Ryan, & Vlastos, 2004). Inadequate social support from professionals and problems experienced with mental health services also contribute to poor health (Moller, Gudde, Folden, & Linaker, 2009). In situations where there is family dysfunction and little help is received from other relatives, family members providing support are more likely to report lower levels of vitality, health, and quality of life (Lépine & Briley, 2011; Wijngaarden et al., 2009). Family members also fear how their situation may influence social relationships with friends and the wider community (Phelan, Bromet, & Link, 1998). Social isolation is a common consequence arising from stigma and discrimination (Larson & Corrigan, 2008) and while support from friends and other family members is known to be positively related to psychological well-being for people with psychiatric disabilities and their support person, they receive less support and have fewer social contacts with other people than those supporting a family member with a physical condition (Stein et al., 2013). In these situations, families may benefit from participating in a self-help or advocacy group or in education activities organized by groups such as NAMI to improve their access to social support. Provision of information, skills, and social contact may help to reduce the sense of isolation and loneliness that often accompanies families of people with mental illnesses.

Families also report strengths and positive aspects to supporting people with psychiatric disabilities. For example, personal esteem and satisfaction and the ability to find or make meaning through providing support have been reported as positive aspects (Hunt, 2003). Others have reported increased resilience, adaptation, and coping; improved familial bonds; and stronger commitments to each other (Mannion, 1996; Marsh et al., 1996). Identifying resilience in individuals and families and the positive aspects of providing support, including satisfaction and quality-of-life gains, is an important way of acknowledging this valuable way of family coping (Panayiotopoulos et al., 2013).

Implications for Rehabilitation Counseling

Given the focus of psychiatric rehabilitation on community-based services, integrated settings, and environmental supports, involving families in a genuine working relationship is critical to the provision of normalized services for people with psychiatric disabilities (Pratt et al., 2007). Families provide in-depth longitudinal information about their loved ones with mental illnesses that informs successful case management and rehabilitation interventions. They help motivate and support their relative in taking his or her medication and continuing the treatment plan. Acutely aware of the importance of timing in crisis intervention, families often recognize the early signs of crisis or relapse and seek assistance from the relevant crisis-intervention supports (Intagliata et al., 1986).

Engaging families as partners in rehabilitation may appear to be a relatively straightforward component of rehabilitation counseling service and resource coordination. Some families, however, may be cautious about and reluctant to participate in any partnership due to previous encounters with health professionals that have left them feeling ignored and blamed for their relative's illness (Kaas, Lee, & Peitzman, 2003). Listening to families with understanding and compassion rather than defensiveness, pointing out their strengths and resilience in dealing with the long-term situation, and acknowledging the contributions that they already make in regard to the treatment, rehabilitation, and recovery of their relative are important components that help to forge a strong working alliance with families (Intagliata et al., 1986).

Asking about families' expectations of rehabilitation can also provide opportunities to discuss the rehabilitation process and the ways that a partnership with families can further influence the positive progress of their relative's rehabilitation and recovery. Importantly, making sure you have up-to-date information about psychiatric disabilities, psychiatric rehabilitation, and recovery, as well as examining and challenging personal beliefs and attitudes about stigma, will help to reduce the potential to perpetuate stigma and discrimination against people with psychiatric disabilities and promote confidence in the families we wish to engage (Horsfall, Cleary, & Hunt, 2010).

It is important to find out about the cultural beliefs families have in regard to mental illness and the goals of recovery (a meaningful life) and to determine what "meaning" means within their cultural background. Finding out how families are dealing with feelings of loss and grief about their expectations for their family member and how they see their role now helps to identify the nature of support that can be provided. Their new awareness about what mental illnesses are and what the future may hold can create a crisis in meaning for the family members, depending on what roles they were used to playing with their relative with mental illness. Questions about oneself; about one's relationships to others; to one's living, learning, and work communities; and to meaning and purpose in life become important to explore and important for providers to hear.

Family members cope with the disruption in normal family life, recurrent crises, the persistence of the illness, the loss of faith in professionals and the mental health system, and the aspirations of their family member with a mental illness. Family members may become more angry and assertive when they are first learning to cope and demand more services or better services as they begin to understand the implications of what is needed and what is actually available. Providers need to accept the anger as a normal, common reaction to the very real situation of a lack of appropriate resources, which exists in most communities.

When surveyed, families indicated that they want workers who will treat them with "more respect" and appreciate "just how far a little kindness goes" (Hocking, 2003, p. 47). Respectful, recovery-oriented services to people with psychiatric disabilities and their families are provided by rehabilitation counselors who embrace the values, attitudes, knowledge, and skills of psychiatric rehabilitation. Appropriate values include a holistic person-centered orientation that focuses on strengths and abilities rather than deficits, inclusion of people in the planning and delivery of their services ("nothing about us without us"), supporting self-determination and choice and allowing people to make informed decisions about their own lives, appreciating the potential for growth, and creating and maintaining hope for the future, and support from a recovery point of view (Farkas, 2007, pp. 71–72). The knowledge, attitudes, and skills required to work competently with people with psychiatric disabilities and their families reflect the goals and values of psychiatric rehabilitation (Pratt et al., 2007). Of the 12 competency sets identified by an expert panel of health and rehabilitation professionals, people with psychiatric disabilities, and family members (Coursey et al., 2000), those specific to working with families are detailed in Table 7.1. They focus on understanding the family experience, engaging

TABLE 7.1 Specific Attitudes, Knowledge, Behavior, and Skills for Working Competently With Families of People With Psychiatric Disabilities

Competency set: Where relevant, include family members and caring others in all aspects of service planning, delivery, and evaluation

A. Understand the unique issues facing family members. Consider the particular issues of parents, spouses, siblings, offspring, and caring others:
- Identify the impact of mental illness on family relationships and dynamics that can put family members at psychological and physical risk

B. Engage families in the treatment and rehabilitation process:
- Approach families with tolerance, respect, and compassion
- Acknowledge the strengths, expertise, and contributions of family members
- Communicate effectively with families
- Invite and foster expression of family concerns, needs, and questions
- Value family involvement in all phases of treatment and rehabilitation
- Educate families and prepare family members to effectively participate in treatment and rehabilitation
- Solicit family input and collaboration in service planning and support activities
- Provide support and resources as needed to facilitate involvement (e.g., child care, transportation)
- Develop strategies for resolving problems related to confidentiality

C. Become knowledgeable about family support resources and intervention strategies:
- Identify local, regional, statewide, and national family support services, such as NAMI and its affiliates
- Make appropriate referrals to family support resources such as respite care
- Acquire information about effective family interventions
- Provides family interventions or makes referrals to qualified professionals

D. Address the expressed needs of individual families:
- Conduct a family assessment
- Develop an individual family service plan
- Provide information about mental disorders and treatment
- Promote the development of effective coping skills, including stress management, communication, illness management, wellness maintenance, problem solving, conflict resolution, and assertiveness skills
- Assist families in meeting their own immediate and long-term needs for information, skills, support, and services
- Address the unique needs of parents with psychiatric disabilities who are raising their children and, if needed, provide preventative interventions for their children or provide referral and linkage services

Source: Coursey et al. (2000), pp. 381–382.

families in rehabilitation, and knowing about family needs, support resources, and interventions.

Finally, as family members move into the last phases of the recovery process, they gradually come to a new awareness of themselves. This awareness can include a greater level of personal and political advocacy and increased assertiveness and confidence, which rehabilitation counselors need to support rather than block. Sometimes, the level of professional competency in the community is inadequate. Sometimes very talented individuals with mental illnesses are given services intended for those with less intelligence or fewer aspirations. Family members range from despair to anger in their response to such treatment. Rehabilitation providers need to build on their alliance with families to help develop new resources and to recognize the realities of what is available. They must also be prepared to work with and on behalf of people with psychiatric disabilities and their families in action against any forms of individual, public, or structural stigma that limits their life choices.

CONCLUSION

People with psychiatric disabilities experience functional and role incapacities that substantially limit their activity in one or more major life activities. Psychiatric rehabilitation, with its focus on empowerment and recovery, helps people gain or regain valued roles in valued community settings by improving skills and providing environmental supports. Families are most likely to be the primary support system for their loved ones with mental illnesses, and given the importance of this support to rehabilitation outcomes, families need to be engaged as active partners in rehabilitation in the early stages of recovery. Rehabilitation counselors need to acknowledge the scope of support that families provide to their relatives, the major role changes families may experience, and the long and difficult adjustment that follows a diagnosis of mental illness. Ensuring families have the relevant information, support, and services they need at the right time will help promote family recovery. Services and interventions that are supported by an evidence base and delivered by practitioners who embrace the values that support the recovery process will help individuals with mental illnesses and their families achieve a meaningful life.

REFERENCES

Almeida, O. P., Alfonso, H., Hankey, G. J., & Flicker, L. (2010). Depression, antidepressant use and mortality in later life: The health in men study. *PLoS One, 5*(6), e11266.

Anthony, W. A., Cohen, M., Farkas, M., & Gagne, C. (2002). *Psychiatric rehabilitation* (2nd ed.). Boston, MA: Boston University Centre for Psychiatric Rehabilitation.

Antonius, D., Prudent, V., Rebani, Y., D'Angelo, D., Ardekani, B. A., Malaspina, D., & Hoptman, M. J. (2011). White matter integrity and lack of insight in schizophrenia and schizoaffective disorder. *Schizophrenia Research, 128*(1–3), 76–82. doi:10.1016/j.schres.2011.02.020

Ball, J. R., Manicavasagar, V. L., & Mitchell, P. B. (2011). Mood disorders: An Australasian focus. In E. Rieger (Ed.), *Abnormal psychology: Leading researcher perspectives*, (2nd ed; pp. 91–132). Australia: McGraw Hill.

Becker, D. R., & Drake, R. E. (1994). Individual placement and support: A community mentalhealth center approach to vocational rehabilitation. *Community Mental Health Journal, 30*, 193–206.

Bellack, A. S. (2004). Skills training for people with severe mental illness. *Psychiatric Rehabilitation Journal, 27*, 375–391.

Biegel, D. E., Stevenson, L. D., Beimers, D., Ronis, R. J., & Boyle, P. (2010). Predictors of competitive employment among consumers with co-occuring mental and substance use disorders. *Research on Social Work Practice, 20*, 191–201.

Bond, G. R., Becker, D. R., Drake, R. E., Rapp, C. A., Meisler, N., Lehman, A. F., . . . Blyler, C. R. (2001). Implementing supported employment as an evidence-based practice. *Psychiatric Services, 52*, 313–322.

Bond, G. R., Drake, R. E., & Becker, D. R. (2008). An update on randomized controlled trials of evidence-based supported employment. *Psychiatric Rehabilitation Journal, 31*, 280–290.

Bond, G. R., Drake, R. E., Mueser, K. T., & Latimer, E. (2001). Assertive community treatment for people with severe mental illness: Critical ingredients and impact on clients. *Disease Management and Health Outcomes, 9*, 141–159.

Cassano, P., & Fava, M. (2002). Depression and public health, an overview. *Journal of Psychosomatic Research, 53*, 849–857.

Chen, J., Calhoun, V. D., Pearlson, G. D., Ehrlich, S., Turner, J. A., Ho, B.-C., . . . Liu, J. (2012). Multifaceted genomic risk for brain function in schizophrenia. *Neuroimage, 61*(4), 866–875. doi:10.1016/j.neuroimage.2012.03.022

Cobia, D. J., Smith, M. J., Wang, L., & Csernansky, J. G. (2012). Longitudinal progression of frontal and temporal lobe changes in schizophrenia. *Schizophrenia Research, 139*(1–3), 1–6. doi:10.1016/j.schres.2012.05.002

Corrigan, P. W., Mueser, K. T., Bond, G. R., Drake, R. E., & Solomon, P. (2008). *Principles and practice of psychiatric rehabilitation: An empirical approach.* New York, NY: Guilford.

Coursey, R. D., Curtis, L., Marsh, D., Campbell, J., Harding, C., Spaniol, L., . . . Zahniser, J. (2000). Competencies for direct service staff members who work with adults with severe mental illnesses: Specific knowledge, attitudes, skills, and bibliography. *Psychiatric Rehabilitation Journal, 23*, 378–392.

Cuijpers, P. (1999). The effects of family interventions on relatives' burden: A meta-analysis. *Journal of Mental Health, 8*, 275–285.

Danley, K. S., & Anthony, W. A. (1987). The choose get keep approach to supported employment. *American Rehabilitation, 13*, 6–9, 27–29.

Davidson, L., Chinman, M., Sells, D., & Rowe, M. (2006). Peer support among adults with serious mental illness: A report from the field. *Schizophrenia Bulletin, 32*, 443–450.

Deegan, P. E. (1988). Recovery: The lived experience of rehabilitation. *Psychosocial Rehabilitation Journal, 11*, 11–19.

Dissanayake, D. W. N., Mason, R., & Marsden, C. A. (2013). Sensory gating, cannabinoids and schizophrenia. *Neuropharmacology, 67*, 66–77. doi:10.1016/j.neuropharm.2012.10.011

Dixon, L. B., Lucksted, A., Stewart, B., Burland, J., Brown, C., Postrado, L., . . . Hoffman, M. (2004). Outcomes of the peer-taught 12-week family-to-family education program for severe mental illness. *Acta Psychiatrica Scandinavica, 109*, 207–215.

Dolder, C. R., Lacro, J. P., Leckband, S., & Jeste, D. V. (2003). Interventions to improve antipsychotic medication adherence: Review of recent literature. *Journal of Clinical Psychopharmacology, 23*, 389–399.

Drake, R. E., Mueser, K. T., Brunette, M., & McHugo, G. J. (2004). A review of treatments for people with severe mental illness and co-occurring substance use disorder. *Psychiatric Rehabilitation Journal, 27*, 360–374.

Fardig, R., Lewander, T., Melin, L., Folke, F., & Fredriksson, A. (2011). A randomized controlled trial of the illnes management and recovery program for persons with schizophrenia. *Psychiatric Services, 62*, 606–612.

Farkas, M. (2007). The vision of recovery today: What it is and what it means for services. *World Psychiatry, 6*, 68–74.

Farkas, M., & Anthony, W. A. (2010). Psychiatric rehabilitation interventions: A review. *International Review of Psychiatry, 22*, 114–129.

Farkas, M., Gagne, C., Anthony, W. A., & Chamberlin, J. (2005). Implementing recovery oriented evidence based programs: Identifying the critical dimensions. *Community Mental Health Journal, 41*, 141–158.

Fenton, W. S., Blyler, C. R., & Heinssen, R. K. (1997). Determinants of medication compliance in schizophrenia: Empirical and clinical findings. *Schizophrenia Bulletin, 23*, 637–651.

Gold, J. M. (2004). Cognitive deficits as treatment targets in schizophrenia. *Schizophrenia Research, 72*, 21–28.

Goldman, H. H., Gattozzi, A. A., & Taube, C. A. (1981). Defining and counting the chronically mentally ill. *Hospital and Community Psychiatry, 32*, 21–27.

Harrison, G., Hopper, K., Craig, T., Laska, E., Siegel, C., Wanderling, J., . . . Wiersma, D. (2001). Recovery from psychotic illness: A 15-and 25-year international follow-up study. *British Journal of Psychiatry, 178*, 506–517. doi:10.1192/bjp.178.6.506

Heru, A., Ryan, C., & Vlastos, K. (2004). Quality of life and family functioning in caregivers of relatives with mood disorders. *Psychiatric Rehabilitation Journal, 28*, 67–71.

Hocking, B. (2003). Reducingmental illness stigma and discrimination. *Medical Journal of Australia, 178*, 47–48.

Horsfall, J., Cleary, M., & Hunt, G. E. (2010). Stigma in mental health: Clients and professionals. *Issues in Mental Health Nursing, 31*, 450–455.

Hunt, C. (2003). Concepts in caregiver research. *Journal of Nursing Scholarship, 35*, 27–32.

Intagliata, J., Willer, B., & Egri, G. (1986). Role of the family in case management of the mentally ill. *Schizophrenia Bulletin, 12*, 699–708.

Jans, L., Stoddard, S., & Kraus, L. (2004). *Chartbook on mental health and disability.* Washington, DC: U.S. Department of Education, National Institute on Disability and Rehabilitation Research.

Judd, L. L., Akiskal, H. S., Zeller, P. J., Paulus, M., Leon, A. C., Maser, J. D., . . . Mueller, T. I. (2000). Psychosocial disability during the long-term course of unipolar major depressive disorder. *Archives of General Psychiatry, 57*(4), 375.

Kaas, M., Lee, S., & Peitzman, C. (2003). Barriers to collaboration between mental health professionals and families in the care of persons with severe mental illness. *Issues in Mental Health Nursing, 24*, 741–756.

Karnieli-Miller, O., Perlick, D. A., Nelson, A., Mattias, K., Corrigan, P., & Roe, D. (2013). Family members' of persons living with a serious mental illness: Experiences and efforts to cope with stigma. *Journal of Mental Health, 22*(3), 254–262. doi:10.3109/09638237.2013.779368

King, R., Waghorn, G., Lloyd, C., McLeod, P., McMah, T., & Leong, C. (2006). Enhancing employment services for people with severe mental illness: The challenge of the Australian service environment. *Australian and New Zealand Journal of Psychiatry, 40*, 471–477.

Kukla, M., Bond, G. R., & Xie, H. (2012). A prospective investigation of work and nonvocational outcomes in adults with severe mental illness. *Journal of Nervous and Mental Disease, 200*, 214–222.

Kurtz, M. M., & Richardson, C. L. (2012). Social cognitive training for schizophrenia: A meta-analytic investigation of controlled research. *Schizophrenia Bulletin, 38*, 1092–1104.

Kurtz, M. M., Olfson, R. H., & Rose, J. (2013). Self-efficacy and functional status in schizophrenia: Relationship to insight, cognition and negative symptoms. *Schizophrenia Research, 145*(1–3), 69–74. doi:10.1016/j.schres.2012.12.030

Larson, J. E., & Corrigan, P. W. (2008). The stigma of families with mental illness. *Academic Psychiatry, 32*, 87–91.

Lechner, W. V., Dahne, J., Chen, K. W., Pickover, A., Richards, J. M., Daughters, S. B., & Lejuez, C. W. (2013). The prevalence of substance use disorders and psychiatric disorders as a function of psychotic symptoms. *Drug and Alcohol Dependence, 131*(1–2), 78–84.

Lehman, F., & Steinwachs, D. M. (1998). Patterns of usual care for schizophrenia: Initial results from the Schizophrenia Patient Outcomes Research Team (PORT) client survey. *Schizophrenia Bulletin, 24*, 11–20.

Lépine, J.-P., & Briley, M. (2011). The increasing burden of depression. *Neuropsychiatric disease and treatment, 7*(Suppl. 1), 3.

Lespérance, F., Frasure-Smith, N., Talajic, M., & Bourassa, M. G. (2002). Five-year risk of cardiac mortality in relation to initial severity and one-year changes in depression symptoms after myocardial infarction. *Circulation, 105*(9), 1049–1053.

Leucht, S., Burkard, T., Henderson, J., Maj, M., & Sartorius, N. (2007). Physical illness and schizophrenia: A review of the literature. *Acta Psychiatrica Scandinavica, 116*, 317–333.

Lieberman, J. A., & Stroop, T. S. (2011). The NIMH-CATIE schizophrenia dtudy: What did we learn? *Amerian Journal of Psychiatry, 168*, 770–775.

Lindenmayer, J. P., Nasrallah, H., Pucci, M., James, S., & Citrome, L. (2013). A systematic review of psychostimulant treatment of negative symptoms of schizophrenia: Challenges and therapeutic opportunities. *Schizophrenia Research, 147*, 241–252.

Lyman, R., Kurtz, M. M., Farkas, M., George, P., & Dougherty, R. (2014). Skill building: Assessing the evidence. *Psychiatric Services, 65*, 727–738.

Mannion, E. (1996). Resilience and burden in spouses of people with mental illness. *Psychiatric Rehabilitation Journal, 20*, 13–23.

Marsh, D., Lefley, H., Evans-Rhodes, D., Ansell, V., Doerzbacher, B., LaBarbera, L., & Paluzzi, J. E. (1996). The family experience of mental illness: Evidence for resilience. *Psychiatric Rehabilitation Journal, 20*, 3–12.

Marwaha, S., Balachandra, S., & Johnson, S. (2008). Clinicians' attitudes to the employment of people with psychosis. *Social Psychiatry and Psychiatric Epidemiology, 44*, 349–360.

Mathers, C. D., & Loncar, D. (2006). Projections of global mortality and burden of disease from 2002 to 2030. *PLoS Medicine, 3*, e422.

Matthews, L. R., Harris, L. M., Jaworski, A., Alam, A., & Bozdag, G. (2013). Function in job seekers with mental health and drug and alcohol problems who access community based disability employment services. *Disability and Rehabilitation, 35*(6), 460–467. doi:10 .3109/09638288.2012.699583

McGurk, S. R., & Wykes, T. (2008). Cognitive remediation and vocational rehabilitation. *Psychiatric Rehabilitation Journal, 31*, 350–359.

Moller, T., Gudde, C. B., Folden, G. E., & Linaker, O. M. (2009). The experience of caring in relatives to patients with serious mental illness: Gender differences, health and functioning. *Scandinavian Journal of Caring Science, 23*, 153–160.

Mueser, K. T., & Fox, L. (1998). Dual diagnosis: How families can help. *Journal of the California Alliance for the Mentally Ill, 9*, 53–55.

Mueser, K. T., & Gingerich, S. (2006). *The complete family guide to schizophrenia: Helping your loved one get the most out of life*. New York, NY: Guilford.

Mueser, K. T., & Gingerich, S. (2013). Treatment of co-occurring psychotic and substance use disorders. *Social Work in Public Health, 28*(3–4), 424–439. doi:10.1080/19371918.2013.774676

Mueser, K. T., & McGurk, S. R. (2004). Schizophrenia. *Lancet, 363*(9426), 2063–2072. doi:10.1016/ s0140-6736(04)16458-1

Mueser, K. T., Corrigan, P. W., Hilton, D. W., Tanzman, B., Schaub, A., Gingerich, S., . . . Herz, M. I. (2002). Illness management and recovery: A review of the research. *Psychiatric Services, 53*, 1272–1284.

Mueser, K. T., Deavers, F., Penn, D. L., & Cassisi, J. E. (2013). Psychosocial treatments for schizophrenia. *Annual Review of Clinical Psychology, 9*, 465–497. doi:10.1146/ annurev-clinpsy-050212-185620

Murray-Swank, A. B., & Dixon, L. B. (2004). Family psychoeducation as an evidence-based practice. *CNS Spectrums, 9*, 905–912.

NAMI. (2013). *Dual diagnosis and mental illnesses*. Retrieved from https://www.nami.org/Template.cfm?Section=By_Illness&Template=/ContentManagement/ContentDisplay.cfm&ContentID=23049

Nielsen, R. E., Uggerby, A. S., Jensen, S. O. W., & McGrath, J. J. (2013). Increasing mortality gap for patients diagnosed with schizophrenia over the last three decades—A Danish nationwide study from 1980 to 2010. *Schizophrenia Research, 146*(1–3), 22–27. doi:10.1016/j.schres.2013.02.025

Osby, U., Brandt, L., Correia, N., Ekbom, A., & Sparen, P. (2001). Excess mortality in bipolar and unipolar disorder in Sweden. *Archives of General Psychiatry, 58*(9), 844.

Palazidou, E. (2012). The neurobiology of depression. *British Medical Bulletin, 101*, 127–145.

Panayiotopoulos, C., Pavlakis, A., & Apostolou, M. (2013). Family burden of schizophrenic patients and the welfare system; the case of Cyprus. *International Journal of Mental Health Systems, 7*, 13. doi:10.1186/1752-4458-7-13

Pharoah, F., Mari, J., Rathbone, J., & Wong, W. (2010). Family intervention for schizophrenia. *Cochrane Database of Systematic Reviews, 12*, Art. CD000088. doi:10.1002/14651858.CD000088.pub3

Phelan, J., Bromet, E. J., & Link, B. J. (1998). Psychiatric illness and family stigma. *Schizophrenia Bulletin, 24*, 115–126.

Pickett-Schenk, S. A., Lippincott, R. C., Bennett, C., & Steigman, P. J. (2008). Improving knowledge about mental illness through family led education: The journey of hope. *Psychiatric Services, 59*, 49–56.

Pratt, C. W., Gill, K. J., Varrett, N. M., & Roberts, M. M. (2007). *Psychiatric rehabilitation*. Burlington, MA: Elsevier Academic Press.

Rapp, C. A., & Goscha, R. J. (2006). *The strengths model: Case management with people with psychiatric disabilities*. New York, NY: Oxford University Press.

Rice, M. J. (2011). Assertive community treatment: Evidence based hope for the seriously mentally ill. *Journal of the American Psychiatric Nurses Association, 17*, 13–15.

Rimes, K. A., & Watkins, E. (2005). The effects of self-focused rumination on global negative self-judgements in depression. *Behaviour Research and Therapy, 43*(12), 1673–1681.

Robson, D., & Gray, R. (2007). Serious mental illness and physical health problems: A discussion paper. *International Journal of Nursing Studies, 44*(3), 457–466. doi:10.1016/j.ijnurstu.2006.07.013

Schulze, B., & Rossler, W. (2005). Caregiver burden in mental illness: Review of measurement, findings and interventions in 2004–2005. *Current Opinion in Psychiatry, 18*, 684–691.

Segrin, C. (2000). Social skills deficits associated with depression. *Clinical Psychology Review, 20*(3), 379–403.

Spaniol, L., & Nelson, A. (2013). *Family recovery: Stages of change*. Unpublished manuscript, Centre for Psychiatric Rehabilitation, Boston.

Stanley, S. H., & Laugharne, J. D. (2011). Clinical guidelines for the physical care of mental health consumers: A comprehensive assessment and monitoring package for mental health and primary care clinicians. *Australian and New Zealand Journal of Psychiatry, 45*(10), 82–829. doi:http://dx.doi.org/10.3109/00048674.2011.614591

Stein, C. H., Aguirre, R., & Hunt, M. G. (2013). Social networks and personal loss among young adults with mental illness and their parents: A family perspective. *Psychiatric Rehabilitation Journal, 36*(1), 15–21. doi:10.1037/h0094742

Swartz, M. S., Perkins, D. O., Stroup, T. S., Davis, S. M., Capuano, G., Rosenheck, R. A., . . . Lieberman, J. A. (2007). Effects of antipsychotic medications on psychosocial functioning in patients with chronic schizophrenia: Findings from the NIMH CATIE study. *American Journal of Psychiatry, 164*, 428–436.

Topor, A., Borg, M., Mezzina, R., Sells, D., Marin, I., & Davidson, L. (2006). Others: The role of family, friends, and professionals in the recovery process. *American Journal of Psychiatric Rehabilitation, 9*(1), 17–37.

Tsang, H. W. H., Leung, A. Y., Chung, R. C. K., Bell, M., & Cheung, W.-M. (2010). Review of vocational predictors: A systematic review of predictors of vocaional outcomes among individuals with schizophrenia: An update since 1998. *Australian and New Zealand Journal of Psychiatry, 44*, 495–504.

Tschopp, M. K., Berven, N. L., & Chan, F. (2011). Consumer perceptions of Assertive Community Treatment interventions. *Community Mental Health Journal, 47*, 408–414.

Waghorn, G., Lloyd, C., Abraham, B., Silvester, D., & Chant, D. (2008). Comorbid physical health conditions hinder employment among people with psychiaric disabilities. *Psychiatric Rehabilitation Journal, 31*, 243–246.

Watson, A. C., & Eack, S. M. (2011). Oppression and stigma and their effects. In N. R. Heller & A. Gitterman (Eds.), *Mental health and social problems: A social work perspective* (pp. 40–62). New York, NY: Routledge.

Whitley, R., Gingerich, S., Lutz, W. J., & Mueser, K. T. (2009). Implementing the illness management and recovery program in community mental health settings: Facilitators and barriers. *Psychiatric Services, 60*, 202–209.

Wijngaarden, B. V., Koeter, M., Knapp, M., Tansella, M., Thornicroft, G., Vázquez-Barquero, J.-L., & Schene, A. (2009). Caring for people with depression or with schizophrenia: Are the consequences different? *Psychiatry Research, 169*, 62–69.

Willner, P., Scheel-Krüger, J., & Belzung, C. (2013). The neurobiology of depression and antidepressant action. *Neuroscience & Biobehavioral Reviews, 37*, 2331–2371.

World Health Organisation. (2001). *International classification of functioning, disability and health: ICF*. Geneva, Switzerland: Author.

World Health Organisation. (2008). *The global burden of disease: 2004 Update*. Geneva, Switzerland: Department of Health Statistics and Informatics in the Information, Evidence and Research Cluster of WHO.

CHAPTER 8

Brain Injury and the Family: A Guide for Rehabilitation Counselors

CHARLES EDMUND DEGENEFFE AND GLORIA K. LEE

At least 1.7 million traumatic brain injuries (TBIs; Faul, Xu, Wald, & Coronado, 2010) and 795,000 nontraumatic injuries (e.g. strokes) occur every year (Roger et al., 2012). Prevalence rates are rising in Asia, Latin America, South America, the Caribbean, and Europe (see Julio César, Torres Norma, Lozano, & Zúñiga Carrasco, 2008; Puvanachandra & Hyder, 2008; Tagliaferri, Compagnone, Korsic, Servadei, & Kraus, 2006). The United States leads this trend with an average incidence rate of 58% of the population—five times the prevalence in India (Puvanachandra & Hyder, 2008) and at least double most other regions. Despite the growing burden on individuals, families, and communities (Baker, Tandy, & Dixon, 2002; Degeneffe & Olney, 2008), brain injury remains a "silent epidemic" (De Silva et al., 2008) that receives comparatively less public attention and funding than other disabilities and chronic illnesses.

Families of persons with brain injuries are thrown into the complicated and costly world of medical rehabilitation unprepared for the profound changes and challenges that face them (Bishop, Degeneffe, & Mast, 2006). The experience often forces families to redefine their roles and the nature of their supporting relationships. Spouses become permanent sources of instrumental and affective care (Degeneffe, 2001). The supervisory parental role extends past the time of childhood transition into adult independence (Sachs, 1991) and falters in an indeterminate future.

Rehabilitation counselors are often underresourced and underprepared to help the family with these complex TBI rehabilitation issues. Long-term community support services are difficult to find for the client and even harder for the family (Degeneffe et al., 2008). Formal training on supporting families following brain injury is not common in rehabilitation counseling education programs as it is not a recognized topic in the graduate-level canon (see Council on Rehabilitation Education, 2012). This paucity of knowledge coupled with rehabilitation counseling's traditional focus on the individual makes the family as foreign to the profession

as the profession is to the family. This is an unfortunate and hopefully transitory failing of practice, especially given the intensity of family involvement in rehabilitation
efforts, its essential presence in long-term support, and the wealth of intimate client
knowledge it possess.

This chapter provides a broad-based foundation for a rehabilitation counseling
understanding of the family experience of brain injury through a biopsychosocial
lens (see WHO, 2001). Two case studies will be used to illustrate the key points of
discussion. Highlights include professional supports, planning for future caregiving,
and an insider's perspective on family interactions with professionals. We review
the psychosocial impact of brain injury on the family, its challenges with change,
and postinjury family needs. The chapter concludes with a discussion of best-
practice professional approaches toward supporting families that feature environmental resources, innovations, empowerment, and effective professional–family
collaborations.

CASE STUDIES

Two case studies are presented to illustrate the key points of the chapter. Both case
studies are a combination of fictionalized accounts and actual data from research
studies. The case of Susan and Jim explores the challenges faced by an adult sibling
of a person with TBI. The story material was drawn from a database used in a series
of qualitative and quantitative studies investigating sibling depression (Degeneffe &
Lynch, 2006), caregiving participation (Degeneffe & Burcham, 2008), future concerns (Degeneffe & Olney, 2008), rehabilitation needs (Degeneffe, 2009), life changes
(Degeneffe & Olney, 2010), family systems changes (Degeneffe, Gagne, & Tucker,
2013), perceptions of family members' postinjury quality of life (Degeneffe & Lee,
2010), and adequacy of professional services (Degeneffe & Bursnall, in press). The
conclusions of this research suggest that siblings (a) often encounter negative psychosocial outcomes; (b) are actively involved in the lives of their family members
with TBI; (c) often revise priorities, values, and relationships; (d) have needs similar
to other family members; and (e) convey important information insights about the
well-being of their brothers and sisters with TBI and other family members.

The case of George, Grace, and Henry focuses on family care strategies and the
interactions of parents and adult siblings in planning for future care of a loved one
who incurred a stroke. This case illustrates the fact that many families do not discuss
and are not prepared to meet the future care needs of the injured family member.
Case material was drawn from a study (Degeneffe, 2012) of parent–adult sibling
dyads and their caregiving experiences with family members with brain injury.
In this study, parents identified the adult siblings as having the most involvement
with the family member with brain injury. Participants also reflected on the subjective burden of providing care and the extent to which families actively planned
for future care arrangements. As the case reveals, many families are conflicted and

ambivalent about the future: expecting increasing responsibilities over time but dreading the prospect and avoiding its preparations. Families' reported stress, depression, and anxiety underscore the deep emotional toll of care in later life.

Susan and Jim

Susan is a 33-year-old, single, college-educated woman. She is the youngest of four siblings. She works in the human resource department in a corporate office with an annual income of $95,000. Susan is active in her church and close to her parents, emotionally and geographically. She is also close to her younger brother Jim (30 years old) who sustained a TBI as a result of a motor vehicle accident 2 years ago. Jim experiences problems with making decisions and has significant short-term memory deficits that make learning new routines very difficult. His frustration often leads to anger and verbal outbursts, and he is prone to frequent mood shifts. Susan acts as his primary caregiver. Lately, she has been spending a considerable amount of time helping him through a sustained period of depression.

Susan considered Jim's hospital care good to excellent. Since his early release (by a non–health care professional) her appraisal of service quality has plummeted to grossly inadequate. The social worker provided no coordination. The family was forced to navigate a complex medical system without experience, skill, or technical support. Jim needs more independent living support than he is getting. Jim cannot navigate his neighborhood shops and tend to his affairs without supervision. Consequently, he is dependent on family, mostly Susan, to help him through his routines. Susan has become concerned about Jim's antisocial behaviors (e.g., threatening gestures, low frustration tolerance, sudden explosive anger expressed in outbursts of inappropriate language, emotional lability, poor impulse control), but she could not secure services to evaluate or address them. Incompetent vocational resources left Jim unemployed, disheartened, and isolated. All of this angered and frustrated Susan. It left her with the distinct impression that the health care team was more concerned with billing than client welfare. She searched for answers and people to talk to. The local library had some generic materials. She had better luck online with the Brain Injury Association of America. There was no chapter in the state and no support group nearby, but reading the personal stories helped her feel more connected. She recently signed up for the mailing list. It was lonely work at times, but she refused to accept that her brother would be treated this way. Her dissatisfaction with the system gave her strength and motivation to press on.

Lack of services and support placed a great deal of stress on the family. When Jim moved back in with his parents, they were immediately overwhelmed by his needs. The family business was neglected, foundered, and quickly collapsed under the strain. Susan's older brother stepped in to handle the bankruptcy proceedings. He argued with their father and chided Susan for not forewarning him about the business problems. Mother and father curtailed their travel plans at first and then stopped traveling completely. Susan stepped in to halt the apparent downward slide. Susan became the primary care provider for Jim and something of a counselor to her parents. Her older brother pitched in as well, providing occasional and welcome respite for Susan.

Even with the redistribution of support, care issues remained. Susan's social life was languishing. Budgets were impossibly tight. Most of all, she worried about her aging parents. The risk of injury in the course of Jim's care was increasing with their physical decline. They were aware of this, of course, and made it clear that the responsibility would be an inevitable shift to Susan. She resented being the one chosen to shoulder this burden. She also felt guilty for feeling so resentful toward her siblings. Susan loved her sister dearly; they were quite close . . . but opposite in character. The sister was a free spirit who was not fond of commitment. The eldest brother was distant in all ways. His interest was limited to running the financial aspects of care. Susan often bristled at his attitude and self-appointed authority. He seemed to be more interested in the estate than family. He certainly had no idea how much this care actually cost. Susan felt boxed in by everyone else's plans. Her future was not her own.

George, Grace, and Henry

Henry incurred a stroke about a year ago at the age of 50. He has moderate left-side hemiparesis that precludes sustained standing or walking. He fatigues easily, uses a frame for walking more than 20 feet and a wheelchair for public outings. His speech is slurred and somewhat labored. He chokes on food especially when he is distracted. Reading is very difficult; he has trouble tracking. His spatial perception has been affected as well. He requires assistance in dressing, self-care, and feeding. His cognitive deficits are minimal though he has trouble concentrating. He doesn't have the head for numbers he used to and has trouble keeping his medication schedule straight. Before the stroke, Henry had a career as an attorney. At 51, he is not receiving support from the vocational rehabilitation to return to work in such a capacity. This disappoints him greatly. He is moderately depressed over his situation.

Although he is married and lives with his spouse, his primary caregiver is his 76-year-old father, George. George jokes that while all of his friends are off enjoying their retirement, he has taken on a new career in health care. Henry's mother is too frail to help with physical aspects of care, but she assists with light housekeeping and meal preparation. Henry's sister Grace is conflicted in her helping role with Henry. Grace is 40 years old and married with children. She has little time to offer presently, but George expects that Grace will be Henry's primary caregiver when he and wife are no longer able to perform this role.

George feels that Grace would perform well as a primary caregiver. No plans are in place to prepare her, but George feels Grace would pick up on it easily. However, George has not asked Grace to step up and has no plans to do so in the future. "It'd be a burden now, what with the grandkids," George offers, "but she will come around in a couple of years when they are older." To date, Grace has only expressed resistance to the covert efforts made to engage her in some small way. Grace does not wish to be Henry's future primary caregiver. She does not believe families are responsible on a long-term basis for other family members. Her family comes first: "I have two babies to consider. They need all of my attention and the money's tight. I am going to have to go back to work eventually. Besides, Henry does alright without me and taking care of him gives the folks something to do. I have to keep my boundaries with them or pretty soon I would get caught up in constantly feeling that I'm not doing enough. When I was pregnant, I actually dreaded having a child, because we were all so overwhelmed, over taxed, and just did not have enough energy to deal with Henry's crisis on top of everything else. I'm feeling a bit more at peace now—seeing how much joy the babies bring to our family. When Henry's wife gives up her career to care for him, then I'll reconsider my role. She's working two jobs at the moment, which is why Dad is over there all the time. I don't see how she can keep it up. But she seems happy enough. I don't know, I watch and see what needs to be done and figure out what to do as it comes. Everything changes daily it seems."

DEFINING BRAIN INJURY

Brain injury is any insult to the structures of the brain caused by trauma, or nontraumatic events (e.g., apoxia, infection, or intracranial hemorrhage), that results in more or less permanent disruption of biological and psychological functions. A TBI occurs as a result of external forces acting on the skull and brain (Cunningham, Chan, Jones, Kamnetz, & Stoll, 2005), whereas nontraumatic forms of brain injury do not.

Brain injuries present a varying array of cognitive, physical, and psychosocial impairments that limit activities and participation in daily living, work, relationships, and other social pursuits. Post–brain injury physical challenges include seizures, hemiparesis, and bowel and bladder dysfunction (Lynch, 1986). Cognitive issues include challenges with information processing, memory, and abstract reasoning (National Institutes of Health, 1999).

To address postinjury cognitive impairments, cognitive rehabilitation (Cunningham et al., 2005; Rosenthal & Ricker, 2000) offers effective interventions including retraining (i.e., relearning the impaired skill), substitution (i.e., using a different cognitive skill to complete the task), and compensation (i.e., using devices such as planners and audio recorders to supplement the lost cognitive skill). Psychosocially, persons with brain injuries can experience changes with their preinjury personality and difficulty with behavior that is emotionally uncontrolled and agitated (Cunningham et al., 2005). How one experiences these possible impairments is largely dependent on the specific region of the brain damaged (Lynch, 1986) and the presence of possible mechanisms secondary to the brain injury, such as infections (Cunningham et al., 1995).

Activities and Participation

In the first case example, activities and participation in major life activities are compromised for Jim, which also creates a higher level of care responsibility for his family members. Before his car accident, Jim was independent in meeting his financial, self-care, and emotional needs. He is now dependent on his parents and siblings to meet these needs. This new reality requires that Jim, his parents, and Susan redefine their roles and sense of family as a collective system. The lack of quality brain injury supports in the local area has made this difficult. Only now has Susan found a support network that she accesses on the Internet. For Susan, this transition seemed to be defining her in a smaller circle with fewer outside relationships. Jim's parents have seen their retirement dream deferred and drastically changed.

It needs to be acknowledged that although the caregiving experience is sometime burdensome and stressful, it can also be an experience that illuminates a new understanding of the self. With Susan, she was able to grow from the experience in ways perhaps unexpected. Susan conveyed that she has grown as a person with regard to gaining a deeper understanding about what is important in life, she has learned new skills, she is more sensitive toward persons with disabilities, and she feels closer to her family.

With Henry, he is not able to return to employment as an attorney given that his residual cognitive functioning following his stroke does not match the requirements of his preinjury career. Henry is in a transitional stage of life where he needs to redefine his sense of vocational identity and develop a means to live more independently. Henry is now unable to meet his needs for self-sufficiency and thus relies on his wife as well as his father George and sister Grace to meet his care needs. Possibly due to the current challenges that George and Grace face in meeting Henry's support needs, neither would prefer that Grace assume greater future caregiving responsibility. However, George is able to look at this situation from a pragmatic point of view and realize that Grace will likely take on this role when he and wife are no longer able to serve in this capacity.

As reflected in the case examples of Jim and Henry, employment is often problematic for persons with brain injury. Persons with brain injury do not often return to preinjury levels of pay or hours worked (Ownsworth, Fleming, Desbois, Grant, & Strong, 2006), and chronic unemployment is a reality for many (Kreutzer et al., 2003; Wehman, Targett, West, & Kregel, 2005). Reduced earning capacity is an additional financial burden often passed on to the family that is already the primary resource for instrumental care.

The structural insult on the brain often causes functional challenges that exacerbate challenges to social integration. Inappropriate sexual behavior (Kreutzer & Zasler, 1989), substance abuse (Rosenthal & Ricker, 2000), and depression (Franulic, Carbonnel, Pinto, & Sepulveda, 2004) are common barriers to social relationships and productive and enjoyable activities. The family can become an increasingly isolated source for the person's social and emotional needs. For example, Degeneffe and Burcham (2008) reported that siblings often provide more affective care than instrumental care. The researchers specifically reported that general support and encouragement, companionship, and occasional check-in on their siblings with TBI are the most common types of affective support. In terms of instrumental support, siblings reported that they do provide assistance in transportation, direct caregiving assistance such as medical care, running errands, and dealing with service providers and agencies.

Studies have also shown that stigma and discrimination also affect the caregiver's mental health. Phelan et al. (2011) examined outcomes among 70 family caregivers of veterans with TBI in the United States. They found that caregiver mental health was adversely affected by stigma and discrimination directed at both veterans and their family caregivers. Other studies have demonstrated the negative effect of society's and professionals' negative attitudes toward the person with TBI. In a study of attitudes of experienced nurses versus trainee nurses toward patients with brain injury in the United Kingdom, experienced nurses (compared with trainees) were found to be less willing to socially engage, less oriented to help, and more likely to hold prejudicial attitudes when they believed (through a hypothetical example) that the patient was responsible for his or her brain injury through drug use (Linden & Redpath, 2011). Whiteneck, Gerhart, and Cusick (2004) found that participants with TBI were often worried that they would not be supported (emotionally and physically) by their coworkers.

FAMILY CAREGIVING AND ADJUSTMENT FOLLOWING BRAIN INJURY

Rehabilitation counselors should understand that families of persons with brain injuries encounter a range of challenges, psychosocial outcomes, and coping responses in coming to terms with their postinjury lives. In the early stages following brain injury, families are presented with new terminology, medical interventions, and decisions they are unprepared to make given the random nature of brain injury. In the acute phase, families are assisted by state-of-the-art interventions and medical care (Greenwald, 2010), a system of support that continues to evolve due in part to advances in battlefield responses to improvised explosive devices in the Iraq and Afghanistan military conflicts (United States Department of Veterans Affairs, 2009). Cullen, Vimalesan, and Taggart (2013), for example, demonstrated the efficacy of a functionally based neurorehabilitation program. This program resulted in greater levels of functional independence and reduction of functional limitations for persons with brain injuries. One of the implications of this study is that this program would therefore decrease caregiver burden and stress for family caregivers.

Families of persons with brain injuries frequently assume ongoing and at times extensive caregiving responsibilities (Degeneffe, 2001). Family caregiving involves both affective (i.e., emotionally based) as well as instrumental (e.g., managing services, monitoring medication use, assistance with activities of daily living, etc.) forms of assistance (Degeneffe & Burcham, 2008). Brain injury presents a unique array of functional limitations from person to person; the types and amount of caregiving likewise differ among families. Griffin et al. (2012) determined 22% of the injured family members had a high intensity of need (i.e., those needing assistance with one or more activities of daily living), whereas others required a less intensive form of support.

Families provide care from a sense of family obligation (DeJong, Batavia, & Williams, 1990), but more likely in response to the lack of available community-based services to meet the long-term needs of persons with brain injuries and their families. The United States (Degeneffe et al., 2008) and other parts of world (Arango-Lasprilla et al., 2010) lack coordinated, well-funded, and effective systems of supports to meet the needs of families and their members with brain injuries.

Family Adaptation Models

When faced with a chronic stressor, family adjustment and adaptation functions through the interplay of three areas: (a) family demands (i.e., chronic stressor demands, normative family demands, and consequences of poor family coping following the acute injury stage); (b) family strengths, resources, and capabilities; and (c) family situational appraisal (Kosciulek, McCubbin, & McCubbin, 1993; Pearlin et al., 1990). In the case of Jim and Susan, there are few supports for family members for the aging parents to provide intensive care to Jim as well as helping the parents to cope with the stressors (e.g., counseling). With the accumulative normative and chronic stressor demands, complicated by the lack of resources (professional) and capabilities (aging parents), the parents and sibling worry tremendously about the future of Jim. From the perspective of a family adaptation model, Jim's family has struggled with successful adaptation as it struggled to engage effective social supports, positive coping behaviors, and recognition of how it can successfully manage the multiple demands of caregiving. It eventually found alternative support through a virtual community online (e.g., Brain Injury Association of America) and progress began to be made as the family studied coping strategies, read stories of recovery, and began to correspond with other families and groups. From the point of view of an adaptation model, one of the most potent interventions is introductions like these.

In the case of George, Grace, and Henry, they too face challenges in successfully adapting to providing care to a person with brain injury since they primarily focus on the chronic stressors they face and significant worries about the future. Like the case of Susan and Jim, this is a reflection of the poor state of long-term community supports for families of persons with brain injuries. From the point of view of a family adaptation model, they would benefit from professional intervention to help develop more effective means of coping, link the families to available resources in their local community, and create a means to more positively appraise the ability of their families to successfully adapt to the demands of caregiving. For example, Grace, Henry, and George have access to a vibrant local brain injury family support organization that offers support groups, information, and referral services, all free of charge. Also, they likely underestimate the positive ways the family has rallied to meet Henry's support needs and how it has strengthened their family as a unit. Recognition of resources and family strengths are the consistent factors that led to successful adjustment as suggested by family adaptation models.

Family Outcome Research

High levels of chronic stress, anxiety, and depression (Stevens et al., 2012) are the central and consistent findings of family research. These findings reflect the multiple sources of stress presented by long-term caregiving for a person with a brain injury and of the lack of improvement in long-term, community-based family systems. Family response to brain injury can also be positive. Families can grow more resilient, develop closer family bonds, and refine their personal sense of morality and attitudes (e.g., Degeneffe & Olney, 2010; Gill & Wells, 2000). This research has received less attention than negative indicators of postinjury family adjustment. Understanding how positive outcomes can emerge from great challenge is central to understanding the true nature of disability in the family.

Negative Outcomes

Research into the negative impact of brain injury on family function is hampered by a lack of an explicit conceptual framework to guide the design and interpretation of findings (Thompson, 2009), an overreliance on convenience samples, and the use of psychometrically insufficient instruments. Despite these problems, a rather substantive body of research suggests some consistently reliable themes (Degeneffe, 2001; Stevens et al., 2012). Both characteristics of the person with a severe TBI and characteristics of the family caregiver are predictive of caregiver outcomes. Persons with TBI who are socially isolated have diminished physical function, require more intensive supervision, express poor life satisfaction, and excessively use alcohol. Family caregivers are more likely to experience higher burden and depression when they lack social support, express unmet rehabilitation needs, experience physical health problems, utilize escape-avoidance coping strategies, and lack effective problem-solving techniques. A higher caregiver burden is likely to occur as caregivers rate their family member with TBI negatively with regard to physical changes, behavioral problems, and level of social contact.

Positive Outcomes

Gill and Wells (2000) conducted an interview-based, qualitative study on eight siblings (between the ages of 14 and 30) of persons with TBI. At the time of the study, the noninjured siblings were living with their brothers and sisters with TBI and their parents. Among the four themes of responses identified, participants experienced changes in their self-concept and priorities. These perceptions changed largely as a result of added caregiving responsibilities and increased self-awareness. Being placed into a position of providing care and support to their injured brothers and sisters, the participants in the Gill and Wells study were forced to step back and rethink the assumptions they had made about their abilities, interests, and what is most important in life. Reaching the level of insight and perspective appears attributable to the disability experience they shared in caring for, and growing up with, their injured brothers and sisters. Similar findings in Degeneffe and Olney (2010) demonstrated the deeply textured impact that caring has on the children and families. While participants reported a number of negative outcomes following the TBI, they also reported that their families benefited from increased communication and closeness, the development of new career goals, a deeper appreciation for family, and a new understanding of what is most important in life: "I do not care very much for the person I was before all of this. I was much less sensitive or understanding. . . . Since I have been so close to him, it seems that much of the recovery process applies to me as well as to him" (Degeneffe & Olney, 2010, p. 1423).

SUPPORT FOR PERSONS WITH BRAIN INJURIES AND THEIR FAMILIES

Families are at the center of effective rehabilitation following brain injury during both acute and long-term care. Families serve many roles in the brain injury rehabilitation process such as advocate, gatekeeper, and information provider to the rehabilitation team on the best ways to understand, motivate, communicate, and support the person with a brain injury. When professionals facilitate these roles in the rehabilitation process, they also enable family resilience, which in turn improves rehabilitation outcomes for the family member with a brain injury. Given this, rehabilitation counselors should understand that families require their attention and support, as well as recognition that families can be an integral part of the rehabilitation team supporting the person with brain injury. Families are intimately aware of the lifestyles, choices, challenges, and strengths of their family members with brain injury, both before and after the injury, and are likely knowledgeable about the day-to-day functioning of their family members with brain injury due to the extensive care they often provide. An orientation on attending to the needs of family is a departure from traditional rehabilitation counseling practice where the focus of professional attention is only on the person with the disability. Instead of being viewed as partners, families might instead be considered to be barriers to effective rehabilitation.

Family Needs Following Brain Injury

Research into postinjury family needs has consistently found high levels of stress, burden, and depression among family members. To professionally respond to these negative indicators of adjustment, this area of research identifies the specific types of support families say they need following brain injury. In this early phase of these studies, researchers found that families wanted emotional support. They wanted to be treated with respect and kindness, especially in their interactions with professionals. Within the context of this relationship, they wanted information that would help them cope, including financial counseling, information on community resources, and disability-specific prognoses and appraisals of current functioning (Mauss-Clum & Ryan, 1981).

In research on postinjury family needs, there are consistent findings (Bishop et al., 2006) that families want accurate information from professionals, want to be actively involved with professionals in the rehabilitation process, and require ongoing professional support. The Family Needs Questionnaire (FNQ; Kreutzer & Marwitz, 1989) has been employed in many studies examining post–brain injury family needs and has been used across studies and populations (Thompson, 2009) to address family needs in regard to (a) health information, (b) professional support, (c) instrumental support, (d) emotional support, (d) involvement with care, and (e) community support network. Research with the FNQ reveals differences in family needs based on such variables as the type of relationship to the person, perceptions of injury severity, and time since the injury. These differences underscore the importance of rehabilitation counselors assessing family members' needs at various points in time and acknowledging the needs of each family are unique.

In a study (Serio, Kreutzer, & Gervasio, 1995) on parent versus spouse needs, parents reported more needs as being met the more they perceived physical problems for the injured sons and daughters. Spouses indicated less health information, and professional support needs were met the more they perceived physical problems for their injured husbands and wives. This difference could be due to the different role demands and support available for parents versus spouses. Spouses may be less comfortable meeting the physical care needs of their wives and husbands. Compared with two-parent households, they alone were required to meet the physical care needs of their spouse with brain injury. Parents sometimes encourage physical dependence as a means of attaining greater control over their children with brain injury.

In regard to the differences of family needs over time, a group of family caregivers 2 years postinjury were compared (Stebbins & Leung, 1998) with a group more than 2 years postinjury. It was found that the group at more than 2 years postinjury had significantly more unmet needs and rated more needs as important. In the early period (i.e., less than 2 years postinjury), the primary needs families endorsed were for health information and professional support. Family needs expanded over time to include financial assistance and community, caregiver, and family support to respond to the cumulative demands of extended caregiving.

In a study (Degeneffe, 2009) of adult sibling needs following TBI, the most cited need was for health information, which was also the need most often met. Needs for emotional support was the second highest rated area and was the least met need. Emotional support specifically includes providing general support and encouragement, companionship, and occasional checking-in. In addition, participants also reported the needs for instrumental support, including transportation, direct caregiving assistance, running errands, and dealing with service providers and agencies. A total of 55.2% of the participants indicated they wished to be involved with the care of their brothers and sisters with TBI, a need that was met 40.7% of the time. These findings serve as an important reminder that all members of the family system are likely to be affected and wish to assist in their family member's rehabilitation regardless of the amount of daily assistance they might provide.

Shortcomings in Meeting Postinjury Needs

The lack of comprehensive and integrated support services past acute care appears to be a root cause of much unnecessary psychosocial strain. Rehabilitation has refined medical interventions that make it possible for people to physically survive brain injury, but has not fully addressed how this translates to their social welfare. In a survey of brain injury rehabilitation service gaps perceived by those in leadership positions in 28 Brain Injury Association of America State Affiliates, residential care, respite, sexuality training, supported employment, and neuropsychology were not consistently offered across regions. Where services were ostensibly offered, they were often inadequate to consumers and their families (Degeneffe & Tucker, in press). Participants reported that residential care, state/federal vocational rehabilitation services, supported employment, and Veterans Affairs services were each available but inadequate in 85.7% of the states surveyed. Sexuality training was not available in any form at all in 70.4% of the states surveyed.

Family participation in support services is challenged by content, availability, accessibility, quality, and coordination. Compared with services for persons with intellectual disabilities or mental illness, brain injury service lacks public commitment to meet the long-term care needs of persons and their families. Service options and strategies vary widely across the United States and are moderated in their reach by funding at municipal, state, and federal levels. For example, not all states offer Medicaid Home and Community Services Waiver funding for persons with brain injuries (Spearman et al., 2001), which dramatically affects delivery and coordination of core community living supports (e.g., respite care, residential habilitation, transitional living, and vocational rehabilitation). Service options vary considerably among states offering this program. Families of veterans with brain injury in the United States are eligible to receive monetary stipends through the Caregiver and Veterans Omnibus Health Services Act of 2010 (Griffin et al., 2012). The civilian population faces a fragmented and inconsistent system of monetary support from state to state. In Ireland, family carers leaving the workforce are eligible for cash payments in recognition of the family role and the social contract with government (Citizens Information, 2013). There is no comparable program in the United States.

Even when services are available, families may not effectively access them. Degeneffe, Green, and Jones (2013) found that family caregivers' use of outpatient services such as vision care, home health care, and neuropsychological assessment was not based solely on need, but was influenced by the lack of insurance or lack of awareness of the resource. Families challenged by their own lack of mastery in the rehabilitation system are doubly confounded by interactions with professionals who conversely lack adequate mastery of brain injury rehabilitation and long-term support. This professional deficit appears across practitioner roles including psychologists, case managers, social workers, attorneys, physicians, and other medical professionals (Degeneffe & Bursnall, in press; Degeneffe & Tucker, in press; Walker, Boling, & Cobb, 1999).

Family Empowerment in the Rehabilitation Process

Moving forward as a family through the early crises of brain injury, developing a sustainable new identity in the face of unremitting demands of support, and negotiating an effective relationship with a rehabilitation system that is both spotty and undertrained require a family that is empowered within and without to take control of its own destiny. Man (1998) identified four factors at work in empowerment of family caregivers in Hong Kong, using the Family Empowerment Questionnaire (FEQ): (a) efficacy (i.e., having strategies and skills to respond to caregiving-related problems, (b) support (i.e., internal and external sources), (c) knowledge (i.e., use of information in caregiving), and (d) aspiration (i.e., how the caregiver will prepare for long-term burdens). Man found that efficacy comprised 33.7% of the 48.8% explained variance for the FEQ. Also, Degeneffe, Chan, Dunlap, Man, and Sung (2011) explored the strong influence of efficacy evinced in Man's study (33.7% of explained variance) in the development of the Caregiver Empowerment Scale (CES) with a sample of family caregivers of persons with TBI in Wisconsin. This study articulated the construct of efficacy in socially relevant factors: (a) advocacy self-efficacy, (b) community self-efficacy, (c) caregiver self-efficacy, and (d) personal self-efficacy. Authors suggest that efficacy is a complex phenomenon with psychological and social facets that interact in daily life to effect physical, social, and financial well-being.

An example of a service approach that incorporates the ideals of family empowerment is the Brain Injury Family Intervention (BIFI; Kreutzer et al., 2009). The BIFI is given over five 90- to 120-minute sessions and is designed to produce psychological well-being, life satisfaction, access to services, and enhanced family functioning for injured persons and their families. The five sessions are entitled (a) Effects of Brain Injury on the Survivor and Family; (b) Understanding Recovery; (c) Solving Problems and Setting Goals; (d) Managing Stress and Intense Emotions; and (e) Strategies for Optimal Recovery. The BIFI involves principles of family systems theory and a variety of family therapy techniques (e.g., building empathic reflections, validation, reframing, etc.). The BIFI also utilizes a technique called collaborative self-examination. Kreutzer et al. (2009) described this as, "Using collaborative self-examination, each family member shares their perspectives about events, one another's behavior and their interactions with one another, encouraging perspective taking, self-monitoring and enhanced awareness" (p. 538). Caregivers were found to have more met needs (as measured on the FNQ) and fewer obstacles to receiving services (as measured on the Services Obstacles Scale) at the conclusion of the intervention and at a 3-month follow-up.

The WECARE website (Rotondi, Sinkule, & Spring, 2005) was developed for persons with brain injury and their family caregivers as an alternative to face-to-face support. Website links entitled (a) Support Groups, (b) Ask an Expert, (c) Questions and Answers Library, (d) Reference Library, (e) Calendar of Community Events, (f) Community Resources Library, and (g) Technical Support provided a wide array of supports, information, and community resources. Rotondi and associates examined the use of WECARE among 17 female caregivers who reported that the site facilitated self-disclosure, was easy to use, and helped to create feelings of acceptance, understanding, and support. The support group tool was the most (68%) utilized feature of WECARE.

Finally, caregivers and their family members with brain injury can benefit from collaboration and teamwork with professionals (Degeneffe, 2001). As Degeneffe (2001) stated, "Professionals benefit from the intimate knowledge families have of their family members with brain injury. Families benefit from the years of specialized skill and training that professionals possess. Often in these partnerships, professionals provide caregivers with training and consultation regarding how to perform various rehabilitative roles" (p. 264). McKinlay and Hickox (1988) provided an example of professional partnerships in demonstrating the value of training caregivers to proactively respond to memory and anger control problems experienced by their family members with TBI.

CONCLUSION

In this chapter, we provided an overview of the functional consequences of brain injury and how families work to meet the needs of their family members with brain injury. Furthermore, the chapter highlighted the many ways families are affected by brain injury and the current shortcomings of professional supports in meeting the long-term needs of families. In addition, we provided an overview of how families can be empowered in the rehabilitation process and work in partnership with professionals to advance well-being for themselves and their injured family members.

It is our hope this chapter will motivate rehabilitation counselors to advocate for better funding and programs to meet the needs of persons with brain injuries. As noted, the bulk of rehabilitation support occurs during the acute phase of rehabilitation and much less is available on a long-term basis. Also, we advance the idea that rehabilitation counselors should approach their work with consumers with brain injury by (a) acknowledging the important role that families play in effective rehabilitation and (b) seeking their input and assistance. Furthermore, it also stresses the need for rehabilitation counselors to evaluate and attend to the needs of the families of the consumers with brain injuries to whom they provide service regardless of whether their services take place in veteran support services, state or federal vocational rehabilitation services, college/university student support services, or nonprofit community rehabilitation provider agencies.

REFERENCES

Arango-Lasprilla, J. C., Quijano, M. C., Aponte, M., Cuervo, M. T., Nicholls, E., Rogers, H. L., & Kreutzer, J. (2010). Family needs in caregivers of individuals with traumatic brain injury from Colombia, South America. *Brain Injury, 24*, 1017–1026.

Baker, K. A., Tandy, C. C., & Dixon, D. R. (2002). Traumatic brain injury: A social worker primer with implications for practice [Electronic version]. *Journal of Social Work in Disability & Rehabilitation, 1*(4), 25–42.

Bishop, M., Degeneffe, C. E., & Mast, M. (2006). Family needs after traumatic brain injury: Implications for rehabilitation counseling. *Australian Journal of Rehabilitation Counseling, 12*, 73–87.

Citizens Information. (2013). *Carer's benefit.* Retrieved from http://www.citizensinformation .ie/en/social_welfare/social_welfare_payments/carers/carers_benefit.html

Council on Rehabilitation Education. (2012). *Accreditation manual for rehabilitation counselor education programs.* Schaumburg, IL: Author.

Cullen, N., Vimalesan, K., & Taggart, C. (2013). Efficacy of a functionally-based neurorehabilitation programme: A retrospective case-matched study of rehabilitation outcomes following traumatic brain injury. *Brain Injury, 27*, 799–806.

Cunningham, J. M., Chan, F., Jones, J., Kamnetz, B., & Stoll, J. A. (2005). Traumatic brain injury rehabilitation. In F. Chan, M. J. Leahy, & J. L. Saunders (Eds.), *Case management for rehabilitation health professionals* (2nd ed., pp. 91–131). Osage Beach, MO: Aspen Professional Services.

Degeneffe, C. E. (2001). Family caregiving and traumatic brain injury. *Health and Social Work, 26*, 257–268.

Degeneffe, C. E. (2009). The rehabilitation needs of adult siblings of persons with traumatic brain injury: A quantitative investigation. *Australian Journal of Rehabilitation Counselling, 15*(1), 12–27.

Degeneffe, C. E. (2012, August). *Parent and adult sibling future care planning for persons with brain injury: A qualitative study.* Poster presentation for the 2012 meeting of the American Psychological Association, Orlando, FL.

Degeneffe, C. E., Boot, D., Kuehne, J., Kuraishi, A., Maristela, F., Noyes, J., . . . Will, H. (2008). Community-based interventions for persons with traumatic brain injury: A primer for rehabilitation counselors. *Journal of Applied Rehabilitation Counseling, 39*, 42–52.

Degeneffe, C. E., & Burcham, C. (2008). Adult sibling caregiving for persons with traumatic brain injury: Predictors of affective and instrumental support. *Journal of Rehabilitation, 74*(3), 10–20.

Degeneffe, C. E., & Bursnall, S. (in press). Quality of professional services following traumatic brain injury: Adult sibling perspectives. *Social Work.*

Degeneffe, C. E., Chan, F., Dunlap, L., Man, D., & Sung, C. (2011). Development and validation of the Caregiver Empowerment Scale: A resource for working with family caregivers of persons with traumatic brain injury. *Rehabilitation Psychology, 56*, 243–250.

Degeneffe, C. E., Gagne, L. M., & Tucker, M. (2013). Family systems changes following traumatic brain injury: Adult sibling perspectives. *Journal of Applied Rehabilitation Counseling, 44*, 32–41.

Degeneffe, C. E., Green, R., & Jones, C. (2013, August). *Outpatient brain injury services: Service use patterns among family caregivers.* Poster presentation for the 2013 meeting of the American Psychological Association, Honolulu, HI.

Degeneffe, C. E., & Lee, G. (2010). Quality of life after traumatic brain injury: Perspectives of adult siblings. *Journal of Rehabilitation, 76*(4), 27–36.

Degeneffe, C. E., & Lynch, R. T. (2006). Correlates of depression in adult siblings of persons with traumatic brain injuries. *Rehabilitation Counseling Bulletin, 49*(3), 130–142.

Degeneffe, C. E., & Olney, M. (2008). Future concerns of adult siblings of persons with traumatic brain injury. *Rehabilitation Counseling Bulletin, 51*(4), 240–250.

Degeneffe, C. E., & Olney, M. (2010). "We are the forgotten victims": Perspectives of siblings of persons with traumatic brain injury. *Brain Injury, 24*(12), 1416–1427.

Degeneffe, C. E., & Tucker, M. (2014). Community-based support and unmet needs among families of persons with brain injuries: A mixed methods study with the Brain Injury Association of America state affiliates. In S. M. Wadsworth and D. S. Riggs (Eds.), *Military deployment and its consequences for families* (pp. 293–313). New York, NY: Springer Publishing.

DeJong, G., Batavia, A. I., & Williams, J. M. (1990). Who is responsible for the lifelong well-being of a person with a head injury? *Journal of Head Trauma Rehabilitation, 5*, 9–22.

De Silva, M. J., Roberts, I., Perel, P., Edwards, P., Kenward, M. G., Fernandes, J., . . . Patel, V. (2008). Patient outcome after traumatic brain injury on high, middle, and low-income countries: Analysis of data on 8926 patients in 46 countries. *International Journal of Epidemiology, 38*, 1–7.

Faul, M., Xu, L., Wald, M. M., & Coronado, V. G. (2010). *Traumatic brain injury in the United States: Emergency department visits, hospitalizations, and deaths*. Atlanta, GA: Centers for Disease Control and Prevention, National Center for Injury Prevention and Control.

Franulic, A., Carbonell, C. G., Pinto, P., & Sepulveda, I. (2004). Psychological adjustment and employment outcome 2, 5 and 10 years after TBI. *Brain Injury, 18*(2), 119–129.

Gill, D. J., & Wells, D. L. (2000). Forever different: Experiences of living with a sibling who has a traumatic brain injury. *Rehabilitation Nursing, 25*, 48–53.

Greenwald, B. D. (2010). *Traumatic brain injury and acute impatient rehabilitation*. Retrieved from http://www.uab.edu/tbi

Griffin, J. M., Friedemann-Sanchez, G., Jensen, A. C., Taylor, B. C., Gravely, A., Clothier, B., . . . van Ryn, M. (2012). The invisible side of war: Families caring for US service members with traumatic brain injuries and polytrauma. *Journal of Head Trauma Rehabilitation, 27*(1), 3–13. doi:10.1097/HTR.0b013e3182274260

Julio César, C. M. C., Torres Norma, C. G., Lozano, J. C., & Zúñiga Carrasco, I. R. (2008). Aspectos clínicos y epidemiológicos del trauma cráneo encefálico en México. *Vigilancia Epidemiologia, 26*, 1–4.

Kosciulek, J. F., McCubbin, M. A., & McCubbin, H. I. (1993). A theoretical framework for family adaptation to head injury. *Journal of Rehabilitation, 59*, 40–45.

Kreutzer, J., & Marwitz, J. (1989). *The family needs questionnaire*. Richmond, VA: The National Resource Center for Traumatic Brain Injury.

Kreutzer, J. S., Marwitz, J. H., Walker, W., Sander, A., Sherer, M., Bogner, J., . . . Bushnik, T. (2003). Moderating factors in return to work and job stability after traumatic brain injury. *Journal of Head Trauma Rehabilitation, 18*(2), 128–138.

Kreutzer, J. S., Stejskal, T. M., Ketchum, J. M., Marwitz, J. H., Taylor, L. A., & Menzel, J. C. (2009). A preliminary investigation of the brain injury family intervention: Impact on family members. *Brain Injury, 23*, 535–547.

Kreutzer, S., & Zasler, N. D. (1989). Psychosexual consequences of traumatic brain injury: Methodology and preliminary findings. *Brain Injury, 3*, 177–186.

Linden, M. A., & Redpath, S. J. (2011). A comparative study of nursing attitudes towards young male survivors of brain injury: A questionnaire survey. *International Journal of Nursing Studies, 48,* 62–69.

Lynch, R. T. (1986). Traumatic brain injury: Implications for rehabilitation counseling. In T. F. Riggar, D. R. Maki, & A. W. Wolf (Eds.), *Applied rehabilitation counseling* (pp. 262–270). New York, NY: Springer.

Man, D. W. K. (1998). The empowering of Hong Kong Chinese families with a brain damaged member: Its investigation and measurement. *Brian Injury, 12,* 245–254.

Mauss-Clum, N., & Ryan, M. (1981). Brain injury and the family. *Journal of Neurosurgical Nursing, 13,* 165–169.

McKinlay, W. W., & Hickox, A. (1988). How can families help in the rehabilitation of the head injured? *Journal of Neurological Nursing, 16,* 36–44.

National Institutes of Health. (1999). *Report of the NIH consensus development conference on the rehabilitation of persons with traumatic brain injury.* Bethesda, MD: U.S. Department of Health and Human Services.

Ownsworth, T. J., Fleming, J., Desbois, J., Grant, E., & Strong, J. (2006). The associations among self-awareness, emotional well-being, and employment outcome following acquired brain injury: A 12-month longitudinal study. *Rehabilitation Psychology, 51,* 50–59.

Pearlin, L. I., Mullan, J. T., Semple, S. J., & Skaff, M. M. (1990). Caregiving and the stress process: An overview of concepts and their measures. *The Gerontologist, 30*(5), 583–594.

Phelan, S. M., Griffin, J. M., Hellerstedt, W. L., Sayer, N. A., Jensen, A. C., Burgess, D. J., & Van Ryn, M. (2011). Perceived stigma, strain, and mental health among caregivers of veterans with traumatic brain injury. *Disability and Health Journal, 4,* 177–184.

Puvanachandra, P., & Hyder, A. A. (2008). Traumatic brain injury in Latin America and the Caribbean: A call for research. *Salud Pública de México, 50*(Suppl. 1). doi:http://dx.doi.org/10.1590/S0036-36342008000700002

Roger, V. L., Go, A. S., Lloyd-Jones, D. M., Benjamin, E. J., Berry, J. D., Borden, W. B., . . . & Stroke, S. S. (2012). Executive summary: Heart disease and stroke statistics—2012 update: A report from the American Heart Association. *Circulation, 125*(1), 188.

Rosenthal, M., & Ricker, J. (2000). Traumatic brain injury. In: R. G. Frank & T. R. Elliott (Eds.), *Handbook of rehabilitation psychology* (pp. 49–74). Washington, DC: American Psychological Association.

Rotondi, A. J., Sinkule, J., & Spring, M. (2005). An interactive web-based intervention persons with TBI and their families. *Journal of Head Trauma Rehabilitation, 20*(2), 173–185.

Sachs, P. R. (1991). *Treating families of brain-injury survivors.* New York, NY: Springer.

Serio, C., Kreutzer, J., & Gervasio, A. (1995). Predicting family needs after traumatic brain injury: Implications for intervention. *Journal of Head Trauma Rehabilitation, 10,* 32–45.

Spearman, R. C., Stamm, B. H., Rosen, B. H., Kayala, D. E., Zillinger, M., Breese, P., & Wargo, L. M. (2001). The use of Medicaid waivers and their impact on services. *Journal of Head Trauma Rehabilitation, 16*(1), 47–60.

Stebbins, P., & Leung, P. (1998). Changing family needs after brain injury. *Journal of Rehabilitation, 64,* 15–22.

Stevens, L. F., Arango-Lasprilla, J. C., Deng, X., Schaaf, K. W., De Los Reyes Aragon, C. J., Quijano, M. C., & Kreutzer, J. (2012). Factors associated with depression and burden in Spanish speaking caregivers of individuals with traumatic brain injury. *NeuroRehabilitation, 31,* 443–452.

Tagliaferri, F., Compagnone, C., Korsic, M., Servadei, F., & Kraus, J. (2006). A systematic review of brain injury epidemiology in Europe. *Acta Neurochir, 148*(3), 255–268.

Thompson, H. J. (2009). A critical analysis of measures of caregiver and family functioning following traumatic brain injury. *Journal of Neuroscience Nursing, 41*, 148–158.

United States Department of Veterans Affairs. (2009). *Federal benefits for veterans, dependents and survivors: Chapter 2 service connected disabilities.* Retrieved from http://www1.va.gov/opa/publications/benefits_book/benefits_chap02.asp

Walker, N. W., Boling, M. S., & Cobb, H. (1999). Training of school psychologists in neuropsychology and brain injury: Results of a national survey of training programs. *Child Neuropsychology, 5*, 137–142.

Wehman, P., Targett, P., West, M., & Kregel, J. (2005). Productive work and employment for persons with traumatic brain injury. *Journal of Head Trauma Rehabilitation, 20*(2), 115–127.

Whiteneck, G. G., Gerhart, K. A., & Cusick, C. P. (2004). Identifying environmental factors that influence the outcomes of people with traumatic brain injury. *Journal of Head Trauma Rehabilitation, 19*(3), 191–204.

World Health Organization. (2001). *International classification of functioning, disability and health: ICF.* Geneva, Switzerland: Author. Retrieved from http://www.who.int/classification/icf

CHAPTER 9

The Family Role in Progressive Illness

Michael Frain, Malachy Bishop, Judy Frain,
Julianne Frain, Tim Tansey, and Molly K. Tschopp

In the 1920s, chronic health conditions overtook infectious diseases as the most significant U.S. health care problem (Sydenstricker, 1933). The associated public health problems have increased since then. More than 50 million Americans with a chronic disability account for nearly half of all medical expenditures (Trupin, Rice, & Max, 1985). The prevalence of chronic illness will increase with the aging population. Given that 20% of the population will be 65 and older by 2030 (U.S. Bureau of the Census, 2000), chronic illness will be a major public health issue for the foreseeable future.

Chronic illness is a persistent recurring health condition that is prolonged in duration, does not resolve spontaneously, and is rarely cured completely. Progressive chronic illness is a subset of this domain, characterized by decreased function, increased symptoms, and declining health and ability over the course of the illness. The psychosocial impact of progressive chronic illness is highly variable and affected by the interactive features of the illness and the environment including the degree of functional limitation, the impact on social roles and relationships, the illness prognosis, medical treatment and rehabilitation interventions, and the impact on family and friends (Livneh & Antonak, 2005).

Progressive chronic illness can also exert complex and profound effects on the family system. Adapting to the impact of disability has been identified as one of the most difficult tasks that a family can confront. The experience can even be more distressing for the family than it is for the individual with chronic illness or disability (CID). The challenge to family adjustment is underscored by health care trends that are shifting from hospital-based to community-based care without an adequate pool of trained paraprofessionals to provide this integrated service (McCann & Wadsworth, 1992). Medical advances that extend the lives of persons with the most severe CID also increase the time and intensity of family care responsibilities (Wolitski, Valdiserri, Denning, & Levine, 2001). Today, one in three Americans provide care for a family member with a CID. This number will rise with the growing needs of a growing population. Families will be challenged by constantly evolving demands over a lifetime. They will be seeking support from a system in flux and exacting a very deep, personal, and often positive, meaning from the experience (Ylven, Bjorck-Akesson, & Granlund, 2006).

Rehabilitation counselors work with individuals with CID and the profession is responding to the growing need for family support. There has been a call for family inclusion in research agendas and training programs (Muzzio, 2004). In this chapter, we describe the impact of progressive chronic illness on the family, explore its meaning in the context of rehabilitation counseling, and identify the role of the rehabilitation counselor in serving the family. To put this discussion in context, we specifically describe research concerning the impact on families and rehabilitation counseling of HIV and multiple sclerosis (MS) as examples of chronic illness.

PSYCHOSOCIAL ADAPTATION TO CHRONIC ILLNESS

The majority of rehabilitation literature framing psychosocial adaptation to CID has focused on antecedents, process, and outcomes (Livneh, 2005). The family is involved in all aspects of psychosocial adaptation. Its involvement is usually conceptualized and evaluated in the research as an environmental condition during the antecedent period and a direct influence on functional abilities during the process and outcome periods (Livneh, 2005). Ideally, the family facilitates the adaptation to the disability, assisting the individual to become independent and overcome environmental obstacles.

The role of the family in psychosocial adaptation changes over time. The pre-diagnosis characteristics and dynamics of the family affect and are affected by the individual's response to and experience of the chronic illness. Diagnosis of the illness is often a time when the family is emotionally confronted by its lack of knowledge and shocked by the sudden and profound change. Early challenges involve trying to understand what the disease means and deal with the turmoil of uncertainty concerning the disease trajectory (Mishel, 1999). As diagnosis leads to treatment, families often become de facto health providers. A family's primary role may be to help increase self-management to the medical regimen in order to maintain the most functioning for the longest amount of time. During the first onset of symptoms, the family's role may shift to helping the individual adjust to a life with changes in functioning and uncertainty concerning the course of the progressive illness. The course of progressive disease fluctuates between exacerbation and stability of symptoms (Moss-Morris et al., 2013). Between cycles, the family copes with current care needs and hopes for remission, but progression and aging trend toward diminishing function and increasing needs. As the disease progresses, critical family decisions surrounding self-care, family employment situations, and mobility issues become transitional moments that redefine the family care dynamics (Moss-Morris et al., 2013). There are opportunities for gain and threats of loss, added burden, and potential for growth. One thing is certain: Family experiences in navigating crisis and long-term coping will change the trajectory of their roles and relationships with each other (Shewchuk & Elliott, 2000).

Each person's response to the onset and diagnosis of progressive chronic illness is unique and dependent on a complex interaction of person, illness, and environmental factors (Livneh & Antonak, 2005). Characteristics of the individual that influence the response include personality traits, goals, values, religious and spiritual beliefs, cultural influences and identities, gender, age, educational background, and prior experiences with chronic illness. Characteristics of the chronic condition that affect the individual's experience include visibility, severity, course, prognosis, and the associated functional implications. The individual's social and physical environments influence the experience of disability through personal relationships with family, loved ones, and friends; the broader social attitudinal environment of the community and society in which the individual lives; and the physical accessibility of the environment and the availability of modifications and resources for enhancing access (Bishop, 2008).

For families, the response to the onset of progressive chronic illness can be seen in similar interactional terms. The family's response may be affected by such factors as (a) characteristics of, and prior experiences with, the disease process; (b) the affected individual's immediate and ongoing response to and experience of living with the condition; and (c) the existing and historical characteristics of the family, including broad demographic and sociocultural variables and the physical and broader social environment in which the family lives, and the specific nature and patterns of relationships and communication between family members.

The response of each family to the onset of chronic illness is unique. There are, however, commonly experienced reactions that rehabilitation counselors should be familiar with in order to provide appropriate and effective assessment and support. For the purpose of the present chapter, we will review frequently described responses and experiences from the perspective of families with MS and HIV/AIDS as relatively representative experiences of CID.

MULTIPLE SCLEROSIS

Mark was 28 when he first noticed something was a little different. For a while he thought it might be lingering aches from his weekly pickup basketball game or maybe from helping his friend move, but the feeling didn't get better. He thought he should go see a doctor, but he wasn't sure who his primary care physician was and he was pretty busy with work and social obligations. When he couldn't walk the whole way to his car without resting that Tuesday, he realized he had let a little too much time slip by. He called a doctor the next morning and then began some blood work testing and referrals to a number of other doctors. Mark was scared, never having been sick with anything worse than the flu and having only been in the hospital for his ACL surgery; Mark feared for his life, his career, and his family.

After a few weeks of various doctors and testing, Mark was told he had a relapsing-remitting form of MS. The news was devastating to Mark and his wife, although they weren't really sure what MS was. They were too shocked to ask their doctor many questions, and examining the Internet made them sad and confused. Mark's boss was understanding and sympathetic but suggested Mark might be better off retiring at age 28 to take care of this disease. Confused and worn out from the testing and news, Mark did quit his job 3 weeks after diagnosis. While this allowed Mark some time to make sense of the disease and get more information from his doctors, it created an immense financial burden for the family, even with Julie going back to work.

He learned that there would be good times and bad times for his body. Some months he may have to rest in the middle of the day or even twice a day, and in other months it was if he didn't have MS at all. But they still had bills. In talking to others with relapsing-remitting MS, and through support groups and information he received from the National Multiple Sclerosis Society (NMSS) and his neurologist, Mark was encouraged to find a new job as an engineer. He found a position that allowed him to work from home when necessary, although the position offered less money and responsibility. In time, he told his coworkers and supervisors about his condition and why his work could seem uneven at times. In general, they were supportive and found ways to make his schedule work. Mark worked a bit more than he thought he should at times when he was healthy, but appreciated the overall support of his workplace, so he did so with complaints only to his spouse at home.

His role as a father had changed. Mark had been an active parent with his son (5 years) and daughter (6 months). But the diagnosis had frightened him. Initially, he was afraid he would give it to his children, as crazy as he knew that sounded. He felt guilty for making his wife and kids go through his disease and the financial changes that were still occurring due to his MS. His wife tried to help, learning about the condition and its treatment, and supporting him by helping him with his medication regimes and medical appointments, but sometimes there was more arguing than problem solving.

If you asked Mark now, at age 35, he would tell you that the effect of MS on his body is not that big of a deal and he copes with the ups and downs. He is still married, and the children are growing up. Sometimes he wishes that they were in a bigger house or taking a better vacation, and he worries that his children will have problems in their life that he won't be able to take care of the way he should. He worries that he embarrasses his family during difficult months with the way he walks or because sometimes he is a no-show at social events. Other times, he thinks that his children are better and more resilient people for having a parent with a chronic illness, and he could not be prouder of them. He knows that his marriage is stronger for the experience, and he loves his wife more than ever. He knows his life is good and that his MS has provided him with a lot of experiences that he treasures and that he wouldn't trade. He knows that there are new and better treatments coming out all the time. Still, he worries about the future. He still feels guilty sometimes, and he still gets angry at his MS and at himself sometimes and thinks about how things might have been different.

MS is a chronic immune-mediated disease of the central nervous system that affects more than 400,000 people in the United States, or approximately 1 in 750

Americans at any one time (NMSS, 2012). Generally diagnosed during early to mid-adulthood, MS is a chronic and typically progressive condition associated with a wide array of physical and cognitive symptoms and an unpredictable course and prognosis (Bishop, Frain, & Tschopp, 2008). It is one of the most commonly diagnosed neurological conditions and the leading nontraumatic cause of nervous system disabilities in young adults (Myhr, 2008).

The MS disease process is associated with damage to the myelin and underlying nerve fibers in the central nervous system. Myelin is a fatty substance that insulates and supports nerve fibers and facilitates the conduction of electrical impulses along the neural axons. The destruction of the myelin, and the subsequent development of scleroses, or scar tissue, results in the disruption or distortion of nerve impulses between the brain and spinal cord and the rest of the body, potentially affecting physical, sensory, mental, or emotional activity.

The clinical course of MS is characterized by episodes of neurological symptoms, frequently followed by fixed neurological deficits resulting in increasing disability, mobility limitation, and physical decline (Buchanan, Wang, Martin, & Ju, 2006). Within 10 to 15 years of onset, approximately 80% of persons with MS develop gait problems due to muscle weakness, spasticity, fatigue, and balance impairments; approximately 50% use an assistive walking device within 15 years of diagnosis and 83% within 30 years (Munschauer & Weinstock-Guttman, 2005). Most people with MS have a normal or near-normal life span.

Because the experience of symptoms depends on the location and extent of the MS lesions, the symptoms of MS vary widely across individuals. The most commonly reported symptoms of MS include fatigue, numbness, difficulty walking, balance and coordination problems, bladder and bowel dysfunction, vision problems, dizziness and vertigo, sexual dysfunction, pain, cognitive dysfunction, emotional changes, depression, and spasticity. In addition to the physiological accompaniments, MS often has a negative impact on one's cognitive abilities, affective responses, and coping skills. As many as 60% to 65% of people diagnosed with MS experience some degree of cognitive impairment that affects their attention, conceptual reasoning, executive functioning, social judgment, and memory, depending on the location of lesions in the brain (Polman, Thompson, Murray, Bowling, & Noseworthy, 2006). Psychiatric morbidity is also increased in MS with more than 50% of patients experiencing symptoms at some stage in their illness (Polman et al., 2006). Depression is the most frequently experienced affective disorder among people with MS. Research has consistently shown that approximately half of all people with MS experience at least one major depressive episode during the course of the illness (McReynolds & Koch, 2001). Bipolar disorder is diagnosed in approximately 15% of people with MS (LaRocca, 2004), and euphoria, a persistent feeling of well-being and optimism in spite of negative circumstances, is often exhibited by people with MS in isolation of other symptoms (McReynolds & Koch, 2001). Anxiety disorders are also common, although they are often treated effectively with antianxiety medication (Fitzgerald, Rumrill, & Bishop, 2013).

People with MS typically experience at least one of four types, or clinical courses, of MS: (a) relapsing-remitting, (b) primary progressive, (c) secondary progressive, and (d) progressive relapsing. Most people with MS are initially diagnosed with relapsing-remitting MS, which is characterized by clearly defined flare-ups (also called relapses, exacerbations, or attacks) that may last from days to weeks, with or without asymptomatic periods, and are followed by partial or complete recovery periods, or remissions, during which no disease progression occurs. Secondary-progressive MS is characterized by a steady progressive course, with or without flare-ups, remissions, or plateaus (NMSS, 2012). Primary-progressive MS is characterized by a slow decline in neurologic function from initial onset, with a variable rate of progression and no distinct relapses or remissions but occasional periods of stability and temporary minor improvements. Progressive-relapsing MS is characterized by steadily worsening function from onset, as well as clear attacks of worsening neurologic function. People with progressive-relapsing MS may or may not experience periods of some recovery following the relapses, but the underlying disease course continues to progress without remissions in either case.

Psychosocial Experience With Onset and Diagnosis

As a result of the uncertainty associated with the course, symptoms, and prognosis of MS, people with MS frequently report a reduced sense of control and experience increased rates of anxiety, fear, and depression (Hwang, Cvitanovich, Doroski, & Vajarakitipongse, 2011). At the period of diagnosis, frequently reported psychological responses include anxiety, denial, depression, and anger (Livneh & Antonak, 2005). However, the diagnosis of MS can be a lengthy process, involving a series of tests and procedures, and often comes after a previous diagnosis with a different condition or after years of experiencing symptoms. In a recent national analysis of more than 5,000 adults with MS, there was an average of approximately 6 years between the time participants first experienced symptoms and the time they were diagnosed with MS (Bishop et al., 2013). The eventual diagnosis can be a relief for some and a cause for optimism as uncertainty is replaced by a plan for treatment and a sense of what they may expect in the future.

Effective coping and adjustment, social and family support, and an accessible physical environment have been found to promote psychosocial adaptation and long-term well-being among people with MS (Hwang et al., 2011). However, the return of symptoms (i.e., experience of a relapse, recurrence, seizure, or attack, depending on the condition) after a period of stability can cause a temporary increase in feelings of uncertainty, anxiety, and depression. Psychosocial adaptation may begin as a psychological adjustment to the diagnosis of an incurable disease and the prospects for loss (Sullivan, Mikail, & Weinshenker, 1997) but becomes in time a continual process of adjustment to actual loss (McNulty, 2007).

The Family and MS

The onset and experience of living with MS can have a significant and enduring impact on family members, for whom the prediagnosis and early stages of MS can be marked by uncertainty about the future, feelings of helplessness and loss of control, and social isolation (Bowen, MacLehose, & Beaumont, 2011). In the period following diagnosis, family members often have many unanswered questions about MS, its treatment, prognosis, and immediate and long-term impact. The amount of information that people have can vary significantly, even within the same family (Bowen et al., 2011). Bowen et al. noted that the children of parents with MS often have the least information, especially if there is a "family culture" of not talking about illness. Parents often try to protect their young children by not discussing the MS or related concerns, particularly if there are few current symptoms. Hiding concerns can lead to childhood feelings of isolation, unspoken anxiety, and a reticence to discuss their own concerns either at home or elsewhere (Mutch, 2005).

Incomplete or inconsistent information from health care professionals and limited communication between family members can lead to family members not being emotionally prepared for relapse or deterioration when it occurs, or to holding extreme or unfounded fears (e.g., that the family member may die at any moment). This can lead to a state of continual preparation, wariness, or misplaced concern about the illness outcome (Bowen et al., 2011). The implications of this common dynamic for health care professionals are that while providing information is critical to the family's immediate and long-term coping and adjustment, simply providing information to the person with the chronic condition or to family members is not sufficient, as information does not necessarily translate into comprehension and understanding. It is important, therefore, to check that information has been received and understood. Rehabilitation counselors can serve as an informed advocate for the family in this respect, helping to check understanding, providing accurate information where possible, promoting effective communication between the family and health care providers, and continuing to assess and support the family (Bishop et al., 2008).

Relationships within the family may undergo substantial changes with the onset of MS. As the individual with MS responds to the diagnosis and living with the condition, adaptive changes in his or her beliefs, values, activities, and outlook, level of dependence or independence, and previously established relationships and modes of relating with family members may be significantly affected (Bowen et al., 2011). These changes often bring families closer together, but also may cause conflict and frequently strain relationships. As the MS progresses, family members have been found to be at high risk for stress as roles change, and this is particularly true for spouses and partners who may take on the added role of caregiver (Bowen et al., 2011).

Several characteristics of MS influence its unique impact on the family. These include that the typical age at MS onset in young adulthood often means that an individual with MS and his or her partner, spouse, or caregiver's education, marriage, career development, and family life will be affected (Kouzoupis, Paparrigopoulos,

Soldatos, & Papadimitriou, 2010). Also, due to the unpredictability of the MS illness course, caregivers are often unable to predict their family member's symptomatology, relapses, disease progression, or functional capacity on a daily basis (McKeown, Porter-Armstrong, & Baxter, 2004).

The Role of the Family in Caregiving

The many challenges associated with family caregiving for a loved one with a CID can have deleterious effects on the caregiver's physical, social, and mental wellness. An individual's need for personal and homecare assistance is likely to increase over the course of the disease. These tasks are typically provided by a spouse, partner, or parent (Bishop et al., 2013) and often require significant and unwelcome changes in personal, vocational, and family roles and functions (Elliott, Shewchuk, & Richards, 1999). Financial strain, physical burden, and diminished opportunities for socializing (Khan, Pallant, & Brand, 2006) can add to the negative perception of caregivers about their new roles.

Family caregivers for people with MS may face challenges and stressors unique to the condition. Unlike disabilities and chronic illnesses with stable courses, the unpredictable nature of MS and other progressive and episodic or relapsing-remitting conditions is such that caregivers may not be able to predict a relapse, the progression of the illness over time, or the patient's functionality over the course of a day (McKeown et al., 2004).

Family member and caregiver distress and quality of life have been found to be strongly affected by the neuropsychiatric symptomatology of the disease. Caregivers may have to cope with changes in the psychological and cognitive aspects of MS, including emotional liability, depression, anxiety, and changes in cognitive capacity, such as memory and attention problems. Due to the progressive nature of MS, with successive relapses, caregivers are continually affected by the need to change roles, responsibilities, and expectations. Increasing physical disability may be an additional source of stress requiring continual adaptation and adjustment.

Family in Employment and Housing

Prediagnosis employment rates for people with MS mirror the general public (Rumrill, Hennessey, & Nissen, 2008). Employment rates for working-age U.S. citizens postdiagnosis falls to 40% to 45% (Bishop et al., 2013). Increasing functional limitations account for some (Roessler, Neath, McMahon, & Rumrill, 2007), but not all, of this "wholesale disengagement from work" (Rumrill et al., 2008, p. 84). Most left their jobs voluntarily, often before their symptoms made them incapable of working (Rumrill et al., 2008). Many of the unemployed are capable and motivated to return to work (Gordon, Feldman, Shipley, & Weiss, 1997). Vocational demonstration projects have been limited. The two randomized control studies that addressed VR practice found no evidence that present service models were effective for the population (Khan, Ng, & Turner-Stokes, 2011).

The impact of the employment situation on families of people with MS is complex and understudied. Beyond the psychological issues of identity and the economic threat of lost income, loss of insurance coverage becomes a pressing and systemic problem. Employment and insurance (health, life, and disability) subsidize the housing modifications required to facilitate independent living through aids to daily living and home-based care. As these tend to be linked resources in the United States, unemployment is potentially catastrophic for families dealing with CID. The Patient Protection and Affordable Care Act is a step in the right direction, but access to health, disability, and life insurance through employers has historically been options limited for persons with MS (Roessler et al., 2007). Private insurers have rejected or imposed restrictions on applicants with MS, often leaving them dependent on public programs with strict eligibility requirements for health insurance (e.g., Medicare and Medicaid) and for income support (e.g., Social Security Disability Insurance and Supplemental Security Income; Iezzoni & Ngo, 2007). Although most adults with MS in the United States have some form of health insurance, many are dependent on employment benefits of a significant other and chronically at risk of being shifted to public assistance (Bishop et al., 2013). Although this aspect of the psychosocial impact of MS has received relatively little attention, the implications for additional stress on the family are clear.

Another significant psychosocial concern for many living with MS and their family members is accessible housing and care in the home. Maintaining one's housing has been identified as a major concern among both working-age and older adults with MS (Finlayson, 2004). Over one in four Americans with MS reports being "worried a lot" about not having sufficient money for food, housing, and utilities (Iezzoni & Ngo, 2007). In a study of the concerns of older adults with MS, Finlayson (2004) found that their three primary concerns were loss of mobility and independence, becoming a burden to others, and the fear of having to go into a nursing home. For younger adults, independence and autonomy at home and in the community are important components of accessing employment, establishing and maintaining social and family relationships, and participating in community activities. Being restricted in one's home, or entering nursing care, can represent a significant erosion in quality of life.

Key housing-related issues for Americans with MS include the limited availability of specialized or accessible housing, housing discrimination, and limited access to residential modifications (Sheppard-Jones et al., 2013). The vast majority of American homes have been constructed without consideration for people with disabilities or attention to the broader principles of universal design. According to Smith, Rayer, and Smith (2008), more than 90% of the housing units in the United States are inaccessible to people with disabilities, with limited access to persons using mobility devices such as wheelchairs, scooters, or walkers.

The lack of affordable accessible housing and adapted transportation particularly affects families in the low-to-moderate income bracket, which is the economic reality for many families with MS (Smith et al., 2008). For those families with a member with MS who wants to maintain his or her current housing in the face of experienced or expected functional limitations, modification of the existing home may be an option. Unfortunately, many families are unaware of these options, fail to recognize the need for or benefit of housing modifications, or lack the economic resources necessary to pay for these modifications (Bishop & Sheppard-Jones, 2013). According to the National Center for Health Statistics, 75% of home modifications are paid for by the consumer alone (Tabbarah, Silverstein, & Seeman, 2000). Home modifications may be expensive, and persons with lower incomes, which statistically includes most people with disabilities, are less likely to live in dwellings with modifications or adaptive features (Struyk, 1987). Many people with disabilities live in older homes with an architectural design or structural integrity that will not support modification or justify the high expenditure associated with the process (Sheppard-Jones et al., 2013).

HIV/AIDS

Robert was 26 years old when he was diagnosed with HIV. His partner had died of AIDS only 3 months ago. He knew others too. It was a nightmare that lived in his neighborhood. His circle of friends seemed to get closer the smaller it got. They had become his family, a real family, and he sought them out directly. They grieved some, and then they carried on. Robert did not share his secret beyond them. Instead, he distanced himself from everyone who might threaten his livelihood or privacy.

His antiretroviral therapy was a disaster. He went from asymptomatic to bouts of nausea, vomiting, and diarrhea so bad that it interfered with work. He was a salesman and being weak and pale and listless was not only wearing, but it was difficult to come up with a cover story. He started to lose money. His coworkers, other salespeople in a competitive market, were circling like sharks. He felt vulnerable and depressed. He stopped taking his medication. Within a year, Robert contracted pneumonia and was hospitalized for several days. More of Robert's friends had died from AIDS and those who were left were too sick to offer support or overwhelmed with their own emotional trauma. Desperate and running out of options, Robert decided to confide in his birth family. It was a very emotional, even cathartic event. His family members had not been very supportive when he told them he was gay, but they had not rejected him either. Still, they had become rather distant and some time had passed since he felt at home in their presence. His mother had intuited from his behavior that something was wrong and she had been beside herself with grief that he would not come to her in his moment of need. Robert's father still struggled to understand, but family was family after all. They talked all night, and then Robert came home.

Robert sought out an HIV/AIDS support group where he learned how to deal with the side effects of the medications, improve his diet, reduce stress, and so on. Eventually the medication became tolerable, and slowly his health improved. His mother joined PFLAG, an advocacy group of family and friends, which shocked and amused Robert. His father was more reserved in his participation, but he did attend the occasional awareness-raising event.

Robert has now been living with HIV for more than 20 years. He has a partner who is also HIV positive, and they own property near the park. Robert is no longer as physically strong as he once was, and his gait is affected by the peripheral neuropathy he acquired as a side effect of some early, experimental medication. He uses a cane to steady himself and calls on his brother to help with yard work when he needs it. Robert found a less stressful career working as a tax accountant and now works out of his home. He does the family taxes and maintains their estate. Now that his father has passed away, he spends more time with his mother.

Though not quite 50, Robert would tell you he feels older than his years. Precious few of his "other" family survived. He remembers every face, but the funerals all run together in his mind. He has a new circle of close friends now. They all have their own stories, and sometimes they share. They all went down to see the AIDS memorial quilt when it came to town.

HIV/AIDS is, in the first part, a viral infection (HIV) that causes, in the second part, an acquired immunodeficiency syndrome (AIDS) or disease of the human immune system. It is contracted through unprotected sex, contaminated blood transfusions, the sharing of contaminated hypodermic needles, from mother to child in utero or upon delivery, and potentially through breast feeding. The disease gradually breaks down the body's immune systems, leaving the individual increasingly vulnerable to opportunistic infection and tumors. Although the disease itself is not particularly lethal, the illnesses acquired as a result of a compromised immune system are (e.g., cervical cancer, cryptococcal meningitis, lymphoma, pneumocystis pneumonia, tuberculosis).

HIV-associated neurocognitive disorders (HAND) have been identified and described in terms of neurocognitive impairment. Symptoms include slower physical movement and information processing; deficits in visual perception, memory, attention, and executive functions; and possibly impairments in speech and language (Woods, Moore, Weber, & Grant, 2009). Diagnosis is further articulated by the degree of declining function in day-to-day tasks. Severity runs from asymptomatic to a severe impairment or dementia. Severe cases are rare given current treatment regimens, but milder forms are common (Heaton et al., 2010). The course is potentially progressive, but varies greatly, even within the individual.

HIV-associated distal sensory polyneuropathy (Schifitto et al., 2002) is another common neurological complication affecting up to 35% of persons with AIDS. It is described by painful sensations, numbness, weakness, and burning sensations in the feet. It can become severe enough to impede walking and activities of daily living. It is more prevalent and pronounced in more severe cases of AIDS.

HIV/AIDS entered our social consciousness as an epidemic in the gay community. The U.S. government's indifference to the suffering was obvious (Shilts, 1987) and change in attitudes wouldn't gain momentum until celebrities stepped forward, the gay community began organizing, and the populations affected spread to people with hemophilia and other recognized minority groups. The initial public health response was highly medicalized, and great progress was made in the development of antiretroviral therapies. In the intervening decades, a diagnoses of HIV/AIDS became a chronic illness to be managed, rather than a death sentence. At present, more than 1 million people in the United States are living with HIV; each year 50,000 new cases are diagnosed and 15,000 deaths can still be attributed to HIV (Centers for Disease Control and Prevention [CDC], 2013). The crisis may have abated, but a low-grade epidemic remains.

Family Issues in HIV

Family has an interesting political perspective regarding care for persons with HIV/AIDS. The literature began to consider the psychosocial aspect of families and family care when minority women were identified as an at-risk group (Pequegnat et al., 2001). Prior to this point, gay men were basically biological entities studied in isolation—not considered in the context of the traditional family. This seems apropos to the history of the lesbian, gay, bisexual, and transgender (LGBT) community, which coalesced in the face of oppression to form its own support network, one that has been effective in providing increased resilience and wellness for persons with HIV/AIDS (Kubicek, McNeeley, Holloway, Weiss, & Kipke, 2013). Even as families were identified, they were not the traditional nuclear families that medical care tends to assume. Families coping with HIV have been diverse, fluid, and hard to define. They build on a variety of blood, social, romantic, and instrumental values (Pequegnat et al., 2001) united only by the strength of their social-emotional bonds, what researchers have called "networks of mutual commitment" (NIMH in Pequegnat & Bray, 1997). It is against this most liberal backdrop of family that we project the challenges they face.

Functional Issues in Care

The physical ramifications of HIV/AIDS varies over time, and outside of opportunistic infections there is nothing intrinsic to the disease that prevents the individual from managing his or her own care. However, the opportunistic infections can present formidable health challenges. Health crises, hospitalizations, and extended recuperation depend heavily on family support.

The neurologic impairments create a second level of care need that increases with time and severity. HAND cognitive symptoms can increasingly interfere with independent function, but dementia is the exception rather than the rule; for the most part the impact on cognition is more of interference than barrier. Physical symptoms can be more limiting. Physically, persons with HIV/AIDS become fatigued more easily (Waldrop-Valverde, Jones, Gould, Kumar & Ownby, 2010). Over time, they lose muscle mass, weight, and energy with decreasing physical activity. This encroaching frailty results in higher hospitalization rates and increasing dependence on family resources (Onen et al., 2009). Peripheral neuropathy is one of the physical symptoms that are beginning to wane with advances in medical treatment (Schifitto et al., 2002). As an acquired damage to the neurological system that does not tend to remediate, it remains a problem for long-term survivors (Lichtenstein et al., 2005). Mobility can be an issue, and the family home must adapt. The pain and disability associated with peripheral neuropathy results in high treatment costs, decreased productivity, decreased quality of life, and a decrease in the ability to perform activities of daily living, which increase the caregiver burden (Berg et al., 2009).

General Psychosocial Issues

Pequegnat and Bray (1997) suggest a range of general psychosocial challenges for the family. And it is the number and variety of challenges that distinguish the HIV/ AIDS experience and ensures that each family is unique in its constellations of issues. The shock of the diagnosis remains a powerful stress. Its effect is multiplied when one is forced to reveal his or her sexual orientation at the same time, or be forced to admit to other reasons that explain the predicament, that is, sexual indiscretion or intravenous drug use. Family guilt and conflict erupt as a result of having infected a loved one with a deadly disease or from exposing him or her to the possibility. The course and complexity of the illness is often varied and unknown to the family creating a bewildering present and an uncertain future. Fears within the family include concern over the loss of physical health and financial security, the loss of the opinions of others, and the social isolation that follows. These fears can become reality along with the inevitable disruption of normal routines. Forced attention to the details of medical regimes, appointments, therapies, and tests replace one's previous life. Navigating service systems is frustrating and often demeaning. Care in crises is exhausting, and respite does not come. Discrimination in housing, employment, and services is a realistic concern. Families can become overwhelmed with depression, anxiety, and hopelessness; behind it all the stigma of HIV/AIDS remains.

Stigma

Stigma is the social exercise of power in which the stigmatized are assigned a discredited identity that justifies the oppression and the oppressor (Mahajan et al., 2008). It has been powerfully linked to HIV/AIDS from its social inception. It was convenient to blame the victim when HIV/AIDS was the "gay plague" (Kinsella, 1989), homophobia was acceptable practice, and gay bashing was a common occurrence. The discrimination and disenfranchisement of HIV/AIDS is but one source of oppression. Minority communities disproportionately affected by HIV find the burden added to existing struggles to resist castification by race, gender, ethnicity, or other devalued labels (Szymanski & Trueba, 1994).

Fear of stigma delays and diminishes care seeking resulting in unnecessary health complications (Sayles, Wong, Kinsler, Martins, & Cunningham, 2009). The perception of devaluation in the course of medical care creates further deterrence, while health care practitioners acting on their prejudice actively undermine the quality of care (Sayles et al., 2009). Such systemic stigmatization results in diminished social networks, poor service outcomes, and decreased physical and mental health (Emlet, 2007).

Fear of stigma has similar impact on care within the family. Family members caring for persons living with HIV have reported more reliance on support within the family and less on outside social support than families dealing with other chronic diseases (Martin et al., 2012). Family caretakers report experiencing social stigma and isolation, which contribute to high levels of depressive symptoms, negatively affecting their caretaking ability (Mitchell & Knowlton, 2009).

Role-Related Issues

Mothers with HIV/AIDS were the first full reckoning of the complex role of families in research. Minority women were identified as an at-risk population. They often received insufficient treatment as they were responsible for the care of dependent children, and often infected partners as well (Demi, Bakeman, Moneyham, Sowell, & Seals, 1997), leading to emotional and economic problems for the mother and complicating the lives of the children. Children of mothers living with HIV experience increased stress, exhibit more disruptive behaviors, and are more challenged in achieving developmental milestones (Murphy, Marelich, & Hoffman, 2002). Where HIV is transmitted to the child, further complications arise in another level of care.

Being the first generation to survive into old age, current seniors with HIV/AIDS struggle with their "fit" in the service paradigm (Emlet & Poindexter, 2004). Older adults with HIV can feel unwelcome at AIDS service organizations (ASOs) that they perceive to geared to younger adults. They also feel just as uncomfortable in the aging care network, where staff is often unfamiliar and sometimes uncomfortable with the needs of older adults with HIV. Aging is part of the family's life cycle and the issues of adjustment for its aging members with HIV/AIDS mirror and are amplified in the need for marshaling support in the face of dwindling social networks and isolation (Bhavan, Kampalath, & Overton, 2008), forming new roles as old ones become untenable, and adapting the environment to accommodate diminished function (Kahana & Kahana, 2001)

Disclosure

Fear of rejection and HIV stigma can prevent people from disclosing their illness to friends and family (Shippy & Karpiak, 2005). When persons with HIV do disclose their status to their family, the stigma associated with it becomes their burden as well

(Williams, Jones, Shen, Robinson, & Kroenke, 2004). Children are accordingly the center of these concerns. Parents often agonize over what, when, and how to tell children. They balance concern for unnecessarily complicating their lives and explaining changes in family life. Studies suggest that the parental relationship, not disclosure, is the most important aspect of child coping (Armistead, Klein, Forehand, & Weirson, 1997).

Family in the Psychosocial Approach

As mortality rates for HIV/AIDS dropped, the focus on treatment has shifted to long-term management in the community. The challenge is in integrating a very medical regime into a psychosocial model. There will always be a core of medical consultation surrounding medication, but the scope of care is expanding toward paraprofessionals, family wellness interventions, prevention, and a participatory role for the social support of family and friends (Armistead et al., 1997).

Knowledge

Psychoeducational training content has proven successful in the past when preparing for death and bereavement were key issues. Current practice now focuses on providing family information on living with the challenges of chronic illness. Implementation has been shown to be effective, but not consistently, suggesting a complex relationship among demographic characteristics, content, and delivery (Rotheram-Borus et al., 2012).

Support

Social support has been demonstrated to be an important factor in increasing immune function (e.g., Lutgendorf et al., 2009), and family is the primary source. Supporting the family in turn is an effective strategy in organizing long-term care. Family resilience is fortified by facilitating access to resources and helping it cope with stressors as it adapt to new life regimes and episodic problems (Demi et al., 1997). Integrating medical care into destigmatized, family-friendly community settings (Rotheram-Borus et al., 2012) increases family utilization of and satisfaction with resources. Family support groups of parents who share HIV status are effective at improving child/adolescent behavior in the family unit (Rotheram-Borus, Stein, & Lester, 2006).

Self-Management

Minimizing family burden of care is most immediately addressed through learning and practicing the skills necessary to carry on an active and emotionally satisfying life in the face of a chronic condition or disability (Lorig, 1993). This psychosocial self-management increases perceived control over both illness- and nonillness-related aspects of life among people with chronic conditions (Bishop & Frain, 2011) and empowers consumers in long-term ownership of their quality of life (Frain, Bishop, Tschopp, Ferrin, & Frain, 2009). Families support acquisition of these skills as active agents in the training process and as instrumental resources; for example, providing child care and transportation for the member with HIV (Frain et al., 2009).

REHABILITATION IMPLICATIONS

Rehabilitation professionals should recognize the roles family members will take such as caregivers, de facto health providers, partners, and key social supports for the member with a CID (Shewchuk & Elliott, 2000). Research indicates that family members can benefit from training on caregiving and problem solving in a number of ways. Rehabilitation professionals should design programs to work with family members to provide support and appropriate training (Shewchuk & Elliott, 2000). This training should focus on four problem-solving skills: defining a problem, generating alternative solutions, deciding on a solution, and implementing and evaluating the solution (Berry, Elliott, Grant, Edwards, & Fine, 2012).

Rehabilitation professionals should help families understand the adjustment to disability process and design interventions and training to fit the stage. When a disability has been acquired (e.g., through myocardial infarction, a spinal cord injury), counseling should focus on support and insight, perhaps using Rogerian-type interventions (Livneh & Antonak, 2005). During this time, the counselor may have family sessions where each member can talk about his or her feelings, grief, and mourning associated with the CID. The counselor should be supportive and allow members to discuss their feelings while also giving insight into the expected course of the illness in an attempt to decrease the uncertainty that surrounds the new condition (Mishel, 1999). Early interventions can also develop skills that will be helpful throughout the rehabilitation process such as self-assertiveness and independence (Livneh & Antonak, 2005). Professionals work with the family to maximize function and participation at this point of the process, perhaps integrating a planned behavior approach to encourage clients and families to increase their sense of behavior control and successfully increase functional behaviors (Quinn et al., 2012).

In the later stages of adjustment to the disability, the needs of the family change. The rehabilitation professional should work with the family in a more goal-directed, active manner perhaps using cognitive-behavioral techniques in conjunction with person-centered approaches. At this point, the focus of interventions could turn to family development of long- and short-term goals, as well as action plans for reaching these goals. Counseling may focus on improving family relationships. Although families may come together at the time of crisis, they may need help staying together for the long term. Counseling can focus on acceptance of family members and understanding of things that may have happened in the past which caused resentment. At this later stage of adjustment, the family has had time to understand the impact of the CID, work with residual functioning, and prepare for the future. Ultimately, the counselor's role is transitory and must focus on imparting value that a resilient family can use beyond the counselor's tenure, in times of continuing change.

REFERENCES

Armistead, L., Klein, K., Forehand, R., & Wierson, M. (1997). Disclosure of parental HIV infection to children in the families of men with hemophilia: Description, outcomes, and the role of family processes. *Journal of Family Psychology, 11*(1), 49–61.

Berg, A. T., Mathern, G. W., Bronen, R. A., Fulbright, R. K., DiMario, F., Testa, F. M., & Levy, S. R. (2009). Frequency, prognosis, and surgical treatment of MRI structural abnormalities in childhood epilepsy. *Brain, 132*, 2785–2797.

Berry, J., Elliott, T., Grant, J., Edwards, G., & Fine, P. (2012). Does problem-solving training for family caregivers benefit their care recipients with severe disabilities? A latent growth model of the project CLUES randomized clinical trial. *Rehabilitation Psychology, 57*, 98–112.

Bhavan, K. P., Kampalath, V. N., & Overton, E. T. (2008). The aging of the HIV epidemic. *Current HIV/AIDS Reports, 5*, 150–158.

Bishop, M. (2008). Counseling persons with disabilities. In D. Capuzzi & D. Gross (Eds.), *Introduction to the counseling profession* (5th ed., pp. 553–558). Boston, MA: Allyn & Bacon.

Bishop, M., & Frain, M. (2011). The Multiple Sclerosis Self-Management Scale: Revision and psychometric analysis. *Rehabilitation Counseling Bulletin, 36*, 150–159.

Bishop, M., Frain, M., & Tschopp, M. K. (2008). Self-management, perceived control, and subjective quality of life in multiple sclerosis: An exploratory study. *Rehabilitation Counseling Bulletin, 51*(1), 45–56.

Bishop, M., & Sheppard-Jones, K. A. (2013). *Specialized housing needs in multiple sclerosis: A comprehensive analysis and national agenda. Final Report* (Report to the National Multiple Sclerosis Society). Lexington: University of Kentucky.

Bishop, M., Sheppard-Jones, K., Roessler, R. T., Rumrill, P. D., Waletich, B., & Umeasiegbu, V. (2013). Specialized housing needs of Americans with multiple sclerosis: Descriptive results of a national analysis. *Journal of Vocational Rehabilitation, 39*, 111–125.

Bowen, C., MacLehose, A., & Beaumont, J. G. (2011). Advanced multiple sclerosis and the psychosocial impact on families. *Psychology and Health, 26*(1), 113–127.

Buchanan, R. J., Wang S., Martin, R. A., & Ju, H. (2006). Utilization of rehabilitation therapies by nursing home residents with MS at admission. *NeuroRehabilitation, 21*, 223–232.

Centers for Disease Control and Prevention. (2013). *HIV surveillance report.* Retrieved from http://www.cdc.gov/hiv/topics/surveillance/resources/reports

Demi, A., Bakeman, R., Moneyham, L., Sowell, R., & Seals, B. (1997). Effects of resources and stressors on burden and depression of family members who provide care to an HIV-infected woman. *Journal of Family Psychology, 11*(1), 35–48.

Elliott, T. R., Shewchuk, R. M., & Richards, J. S. (1999). Caregiver social problem-solving abilities and family member adjustment to recent-onset physical disability. *Rehabilitation Psychology, 44*, 104–123.

Emlet, C. A. (2007). Experiences of stigma in older adults living with HIV/AIDS: A mixed-methods analysis. *AIDS Patient Care and STDs, 21*, 740–752.

Emlet, C. A., & Poindexter, C. C. (2004). Unserved, unseen, and unheard: Integrating programs for HIV-infected and HIV-affected older adults. *Health & Social Work, 29*(2), 86–96.

Finlayson, M. (2004). Concerns about the future among older adults with multiple sclerosis. *American Journal of Occupational Therapy, 58*, 54–63.

Fitzgerald, S., Rumrill, P., & Bishop, M. (2013). Demographic characteristics, disease-related and functional factors, and residential circumstance as predictors of the specialized housing needs of Americans with multiple sclerosis. *Journal of Rehabilitation, 79*, 23–32.

Frain, M., Bishop, M., Tschopp, M., Ferrin, M., & Frain, J. (2009). Increasing adherence to medical treatment advice: Rehabilitation counselor's role in adherence among their clients with chronic illness and long-term disability. *Rehabilitation Counseling Bulletin, 52*, 237–250.

Gordon, P., Feldman, D., Shipley, B., & Weiss, L. (1997). Employment issues and knowledge regarding ADA of persons with multiple sclerosis, *Journal of Rehabilitation, 63*(4), 52–58.

Heaton, R. K., Clifford, D. B., Franklin, D. R., Woods, S. P., Ake, C., . . . CHARTER Group. (2010). HIV-associated neurocognitive disorders persist in the era of potent antiretroviral therapy. *Neurology, 75*, 2087–2096. doi:10.1212/WNL.0b013e318200d727

Hwang, J. E., Cvitanovich, D. C., Doroski, E. K., & Vajarakitipongse, J. G. (2011). Correlations between quality of life and adaptation factors among people with multiple sclerosis. *American Journal of Occupational Therapy, 65*, 661–669.

Iezzoni, L., & Ngo, L. (2007). Health, disability, and life insurance experiences of working-age persons with multiple sclerosis. *Multiple Sclerosis, 13*, 534–546.

Kahana, E., & Kahana, B. (2001). Successful aging among people with HIV/AIDS. *Journal of Clinical Epidemiology, 54*, 54–56.

Khan, F., Ng, L., & Turner-Stokes, L. (2011). Effectiveness of vocational rehabilitation intervention on the return to work and employment of persons with multiple sclerosis. *Cochrane Database of Systematic Reviews*, (1), CD007256.

Khan, F., Pallant, J., & Brand, C. (2006). Caregiver strain and factors associated with caregiver self-efficacy and quality of life in a community cohort with multiple sclerosis. *Disability and Rehabilitation, 29*, 1241–1250.

Kinsella, J. (1989). *Covering the plague: AIDS and the American media*. New Brunswick, NJ: Rutgers University Press.

Kouzoupis, A. B., Paparrigopoulos, T., Soldatos, M., & Papadimitriou, G. N. (2010). The family of the multiple sclerosis patient: A psychosocial perspective. *International Review of Psychiatry, 22*(1), 83–89.

Kubicek, K., McNeeley, M., Holloway, I. W., Weiss, G., & Kipke, M. (2013). "It's like our own little world": Resilience as a factor in participating in the ballroom community subculture. *AIDS and Behavior, 17*, 1524–1539. doi:10.1007/s10461-012-0205-2

LaRocca, N. (2004). Stress and emotional issues. In R. Kalb (Ed.), *Multiple sclerosis: The questions you have the answers you need* (pp. 273–296). New York, NY: Demos.

Lichtenstein, K. A., Armon, C., Baron, A., Moorman, A. C., Wood, K. C., & Holmberg, S. D. (2005). Modification of the incidence of drug associated symmetrical peripheral neuropathy by host and disease factors in the HIV outpatient study cohort. *Clinical Infectious Diseases, 40*, 148–157.

Livneh, H., & Antonak, R. F. (2005). Psychosocial adaptation to chronic illness and disability: A primer for counselors. *Journal of Counseling & Development, 83*(1), 12–20.

Lorig, K. (1993). Self-management in chronic illness: A model for the future (self-care and older adults). *Generations, 17,* 11–14.

Lutgendorf, S., DeGeest, K., Sung, C., Areualu, J., Penedo, F., Lucci, J., Goodheart, M., . . . Cole, S. (2009). Depression, social support, and beta-adrenergic transcription control in human ovarian cancer. *Brain, Behavior and Immunity, 23,* 176-183.

Mahajan, A. P., Sayles, J. N., Patel, V. A., Remeien, R., Ortiz, D., Szekeres, G., & Coates, T. J. (2008). Stigma, in the HIV/AIDS epidemic: A review of the literature and recommendations for the way forward. *AIDS, 22*(2), 67–79.

Martin, S., Calabrese, S. K., Wolters, P. L., Walker, K. A., Warren, K., & Hazra, R. (2012). Family functioning and coping styles in families of children with cancer and HIV disease. *Clinical Pediatrics, 51,* 58–64.

McCann, K., & Wadsworth, E. (1992). The role of informal caregivers in supporting gay men who have HIV-related illness. *AIDS Care, 4,* 25–34.

McKeown, L. P., Porter-Armstrong, A. P., & Baxter, G. D. (2004). Caregivers of people with multiple sclerosis: Experiences of support. *Multiple Sclerosis, 10,* 219–230.

McNulty, K. (2007). Coping with multiple sclerosis: Considerations and interventions. In E. Martz & H. Livneh (Eds.), *Coping with a chronic illness and disability.* New York, NY: Springer.

McReynolds, C., & Koch, L. (2001). Psychological issues. In P. Rumrill & M. Hennessey (Eds.), *Multiple sclerosis: A guide for rehabilitation and health care professionals* (pp. 44–78). Springfield, IL: Charles C. Thomas.

Mishel, M. H. (1999). Uncertainty in chronic illness. *Annual Review of Nursing Research, 17,* 269–294.

Mitchell, M. M., & Knowlton, A. (2009). Stigma, disclosure, and depressive symptoms among informal caregivers of people living with HIV/AIDS. *AIDS Patient Care and STDs, 23*(8), 611–617.

Moss-Morris, R., Dennison, L., Landau, S., Yardley, L., Silber, E., & Chalder, T. (2013). A randomized controlled trial of cognitive behavioral therapy for adjusting to multiple sclerosis (the saMS trial): Does CBT work and for whom does it work. *Journal of Consulting and Clinical Psychology, 81,* 251–262.

Munschauer, F. E., & Weinstock-Guttman, B. (2005). Importance of adherence to and persistence with prescribed treatments in patients with multiple sclerosis. *US Neurology Review,* 61–63.

Murphy, D. A., Marelich, W. D., & Hoffman, D. (2002). A longitudinal study of the impact on young children of maternal HIV serostatus disclosure. *Journal of Clinical Child & Adolescent Psychology, 7,* 55–70.

Mutch, K. (2005). Information for young people when multiple sclerosis enters the family. *British Journal of Nursing, 14*(14), 758–760.

Muzzio, T. (2004). *RSA training update.* Paper presented at the National Training Conference on Rehabilitation Education, Washington, DC.

Myhr, K. M. (2008). Diagnosis and treatment of multiple sclerosis. *Acta Neurologica Scandinavica, 117*(s188), 12–21.

National Multiple Sclerosis Society. (2012). *Multiple sclerosis information sourcebook.* Retrieved from http://www.nationalmssociety.org

Onen, N., Aqbebi, A., Shacham, E., Stamm, K., Onen, A., & Overton, E. (2009). Frailty among HIV-infected persons in an urban outpatient care setting. *Journal of Infection, 59,* 346–352.

Pequegnat, W., Bauman, L. J., Bray, J. H., DiClemente, R., DiIorio, C., Hoppe, S. K., Jemmott, L. S., . . . Szapocznik, J. (2001). Measurement of the role of families in prevention and adaptation to HIV/AIDS. *AIDS and Behavior, 5*(1), 1–19.

Pequegnat, W., & Bray, J. H. (1997). Families and HIV/AIDS: Introduction to the special series. *Journal of Family Psychology, 11*, 3–10.

Polman, C., Thompson, A., Murray, T., Bowling, A., & Noseworthy, J. (2006). *Multiple sclerosis: The guide to treatment and management.* New York, NY: Demos.

Quinn, F., Johnstone, M., Dixon, D., Johnstone, D. W., Pollard, B., & Rowley, D. I. (2012). Testing the integration of ICF and behavioral models of disability in orthopedic patients: Replication and extension. *Rehabilitation Psychology, 57*, 167–177.

Roessler, R. T., Neath, J., McMahon, B. T., & Rumrill, P. D. (2007). Workplace discrimination outcomes and their predictive factors for adults with multiple sclerosis. *Rehabilitation Counseling Bulletin, 50*(3), 139–152.

Rotheram-Borus, M. J., Rice, E., Comulada, W. S., Best, K., Elia, C., Peters, K., . . . Valladares, E. (2012). Intervention outcomes among HIV-affected families over 18 months. *AIDS and Behavior, 16*, 1265–1275. doi:10.1007/s10461-011-0075-z

Rotheram-Borus, M. J., Stein, J. A., & Lester, P. (2006). Adolescent adjustment over six years in HIV affected families. *Journal of Adolescent Health, 39*, 174–182.

Rumrill, P., Hennessey, M., & Nissen, S. (2008). *Employment issues and multiple sclerosis* (2nd ed.). New York, NY: Demos Medical.

Sayles, J. N., Wong, M. D., Martins, D., & Cunningham, W. E. (2009). The association of stigma with self-reported access to medical care and antiretroviral therapy adherence in persons living with HIV/AIDS. *Journal of General Internal Medicine, 24*, 1101–1108.

Schifitto, G., McDermott, M. P., McArthur, J. C., Marder, K., Sacktor, N., Epstein, L., & Kieburtz, K. (2002). Incidence of and risk factors for HIV-associated distal sensory polyneuropathy. *Neurology, 58*, 1764–1768. doi:10.1212/WNL.58.12.1764

Sheppard-Jones, K., Bishop, M., Kinyanjui, B., Roessler, R. T., Rumrill, P. D., Waletich, B., & Umeasiegbu, V. (2013). Specialized housing policies, resources, and services for Americans with multiple sclerosis: Priorities for a national agenda. *Journal of Rehabilitation, 79*(4), 15–22.

Shewchuk, R., & Elliott, T. (2000). Family caregiving in chronic disease and disability: Implications for rehabilitation psychology. In R. G. Frank & T. Elliott (Eds.), *Handbook of rehabilitation psychology* (pp. 553–563). Washington, DC: American Psychological Association Press.

Shilts, R. (1987). *And the band played on: Politics, people, and the AIDS epidemic.* New York, NY: St. Martin's.

Shippy, R. A., & Karpiak, S. E. (2005). The aging HIV/AIDS population: Fragile social networks. *Aging & Mental Health, 9*(3), 246–254.

Smith S., Rayer, S., & Smith, E. (2008). Aging and disability implications for the housing industry and housing policy in the United States. *Journal of the American Planning Association, 74*, 289–306.

Struyk, R. (1987). Housing adaptations: Needs and practices. In V. Regnier & J. Pynoos (Eds.), Housing the aged, design, directives and policy considerations (pp. 259–275). Washington, DC: Elsevier.

Sullivan, M., Mikail, S., & Weinshenker, B. (1997). Coping with a diagnosis of multiple sclerosis. *Canadian Journal of Behavioural Science, 29*, 249–257.

Sydenstricker, E. (1933). *The vitality of the American people: Recent trends in the United States.* New York, NY: McGraw-Hill.

Szymanski, E. M., & Trueba, H. T. (1994). Castification of people with disabilities: Potential disempowering aspects of classification in disability services. *Journal of Rehabilitation, 60*(3), 12–20.

Tabbarah, M., Silverstein, M., & Seeman, T. (2000). A health and demographic profile of noninstitutionalized older Americans residing in environments with home modifications. *Journal of Aging and Health, 12*(2), 204–228.

Trupin, L., Rice, D., & Max, W. (1985). *Medical expenditures for people with disabilities in the United States.* Washington, DC: US Department of Education, National Institute on Disability and Rehabilitation Research.

U.S. Bureau of the Census. (2000). *Statistical abstract for the United States* (120th ed.). Washington, DC: Author.

Waldrop-Valverde, D., Jones, D. L., Gould, F., Kumar, M., & Ownby, R. L. (2010). Neurocognition, health-related reading literacy, and numeracy in medication management for HIV infection. *AIDS Patient Care and STDs, 24*(8), 477–484.

Williams, L., Jones, J., Shen, R., Robinson, R., & Kroenke, K. (2004). Outcomes of newly referred neurology outpatients with depression and pain. *Neurology, 63*, 674–677.

Wolitski, R., Valdiserri, P., Denning, P., & Levine, W. (2001). Are we headed for a resurgence of the HIV epidemic among men who have sex with men? *American Journal of Public Health, 91*(6), 883–888.

Woods, S. P., Moore, D. J., Weber, E., & Grant, I. (2009). Cognitive neuropsychology of HIV-associated neurocognitive disorders. *Neuropsychology Review, 19*, 152–168.

Ylven, R., Bjorck-Akesson, E., & Granlund, M. (2006). Literature review of a positive functioning in families with children with a disability. *Journal of Policy and Practice in Intellectual Disabilities, 3*, 253–270.

CHAPTER 10

Family and Spinal Cord Injury

IRMO MARINI AND ALICIA D. BROWN

The initial life-changing chaos that accompanies the traumatic event of spinal cord injury (SCI) profoundly disrupts family rhythm, routine, and identity. Challenges erupt from all facets of life. Familiar roles are shaken. Relationships are irrevocably changed. Emotions reel in shock, loss, and grief. Precarious financial upheaval threatens the budget. Plans and calendars are appropriated by medical care (McCubbin, Thompson, & McCubbin, 1996). The higher the lesion, the greater the challenge to the family: In higher lesion injuries, medical treatment is more pervasive and care is more extensive. Government programs in the United States do not provide for 24/7 attendant care for high-lesion SCI, and coverage by ancillary services is limited in all respects. In the long term, the family absorbs the cost of care—or risks a loved one's life relegated to nursing home care (National Alliance of Care-giving & The American Association of Retired Persons, 2004).

Successful negotiation of crisis and acute care, months of rehabilitation, and transition to community living depend on a well-coordinated interdisciplinary team approach by medical professionals, the person, and the family. If the family is purposefully supported, then adaptation can proceed with few complications. With appropriate discharge planning, family education, and coordination with community resources (e.g., home health care, vocational rehabilitation, Center for Independent Living), many families are able to adapt to the new rhythm and routine that incorporates their injured loved one. They learn to be a new version of themselves, with more experience and new skills (Elliott & Berry, 2009). The family left to its own devices in this highly medicalized world risks a disordered and problematic transition to community life, secondary physical health complications, and emotional maladjustments that can threaten the quality of life and well-being for all.

CASE STUDIES

The family experience in SCI is illustrated in this chapter through two case studies contrasting care issues with loved ones with tetraplegia and paraplegia. Specific profiles of function for each individual are addressed, providing succinct details pertaining to family involvement in the home, in the community, and interfacing with service systems and community resources. The stories provide contrasting perspectives on the relationship between the nature of care and residual physical function. They share a common theme in the challenge of adapting to the inevitable physical decline of aging. Rehabilitation counselors must be cognizant and anticipate potential long-term problems for the individual and his or her family. Prevention preparedness of secondary complications and access barriers must be at the forefront of long-term planning.

Case Study I: Tommy Ramsey's Family

Tommy Ramsey is a 35-year-old man who sustained an American Spinal Injury Association category B (ASIA-B) SCI involving a T6 paraplegia after falling from a tree house while playing with his 3-year-old son Landon 3 months ago. After experiencing some initial setbacks in the hospital with a bladder infection and a sacral decubitus ulcer, Tommy returned home a month ago. His wife Yanin had prepared for his homecoming by negotiating with the rehabilitation hospital's occupational therapist and the vocational rehabilitation counselor to ramp the entrances, widen doorways, and install a wheel-in shower and wheel-under sink in the master bathroom.

Accessibility to his former life has thus far stopped at the front door. The vehicle modifications for a power-elevated swivel driver's seat for his half-ton truck are still not complete. The steep terrain of his neighborhood limits his local outings, and the suburban location offers no mass transit options to the marketplace. He is feeling a little trapped without his truck.

Tommy's work leave expires in 3 weeks. He is a marketing representative for a nationally recognized corporation where he was recently promoted to oversee project implementation in the western region. The Ramseys moved to the area 6 months ago and have yet to develop any strong friendships. Yanin's sister lives in the nearby city where she attends college. Tommy independently performs all of his activities of daily living. His wife reports that Tommy is fiercely independent and becomes angry with her when she tries to help. He struggles to do the laundry since the room is small and could not be modified. He plans to buy a riding lawnmower and rig-up hand controls to cut the grass. He is determined to reclaim his preinjury household chores. Yanin observes that Tommy obsesses about returning to work but won't talk directly to her about his concerns. Despite being irritable about the subject, he insists that everything is fine. She feels as though Tommy is pretending as if everything is the same as before the accident. She wants to be there for him but he won't let her physically help him, and he is emotionally closed off. Their level of sexual intimacy has dropped significantly since he returned home from the hospital. He is offended at the thought of taking Cialis to be able to perform longer and believes it's for old men.

Tommy admits that he's angry about the injury. He doesn't like Yanin doing things for him. He dwells on life before the accident and how proud he was to help her cook and clean the house. He tears up when talking about how he won't be able to teach Landon to play sports, and that he can't fully provide for his family like he did before. He does not think he will be able to return to work. He has many work-related concerns, including finding accessible parking downtown, finding wheelchair access at work, his reluctance to ask for accommodations, and maintaining his bimonthly travel schedule to the other state offices. He asks, "How am I going to get on the plane? What if I have to go to the bathroom on the plane? How do I rent a car when I get to my destination? Are there accessible taxis in different cities? How easy is it to get an accessible hotel room in these different cities?" But his biggest concern is "How is everyone going to react or treat me now that I'm in a wheelchair?" He knows Yanin loves him and is there for him, but he doesn't want to be pitied, and he can't help but worry that she will get bored and look for somebody who's not disabled. Overall, although Tommy appears somewhat together on the outside, he is emotionally distraught and anxious about the future and his family's continuing welfare.

Case Study II: Emmanuelle Preston's Family

Emmanuelle Preston is a 24-year-old African American man who sustained a C4–C5 tetraplegia ASIA-A as the result of a motor vehicle accident 9 months ago. He was living with his girlfriend in an inaccessible apartment and had to move back to his mother's home following rehabilitation. Emmanuelle has a high school education and was a FedEx truck driver. His mother is an LPN at a local hospital and has become his primary caregiver along with his 17-year-old sister Tasha. Emmanuelle's grandmother helps out during the day when Mrs. Preston works until Tasha comes home from school. Mrs. Preston, Tasha, and Emmanuelle describe the last 9 months since the injury:

Mrs. Preston: "When Emmanuelle came home, we struggled to meet his needs. It was a test of faith, but we are closer as a family now. I help Emmanuelle dress and get into his wheelchair in the morning before work. He needs help with his indwelling catheter that drains into a bag that any of us can empty as needed. We make his meals. I sponge-bathe him since the bathroom is inaccessible. We are on a waiting list for government home health care, so God-willing, we will get help soon. I worry about his future. He's bored at home watching TV every day, but we can't afford an accessible van, so he stays home most of the time. His friends do not come around much anymore, and his girlfriend stopped talking to him months ago. We pray that Emmanuelle will get stronger and we will get the support we need so he can go back to school. I worry that if something happens to me or Tasha, he will end up in a nursing home."

Tasha: "It is hard to see my brother like this. Before his accident he was playing basketball in high school and running around delivering packages for FedEx. I wish I could do more to help my mother. Emmanuelle seems to relate to me better. Mom sometimes treats him like a child. He gets upset when my mom treats him that way. I had to quit my after-school job at MacDonald's to relieve my grandmother so she could go home and take care of my grandfather who had a stroke last year. My mom feels guilty that she can't help take care of her dad like she was before Emmanuelle's car accident. I wanted to go to college after I graduate so I can help people like my brother, but I may have to put off school until we can get more help."

   Emmanuelle: "I feel useless and I don't know what I'm going to do or what is out there for me. I was saving for college but now there is nothing I can do. My doctor told me I had to watch out for bladder infections, and pressure sores all the time. I don't think I'll ever get married or be able to have kid. I don't like my mom, sister, and grandma having to take care of me like a child when I should be taking care of them. My friends and girlfriend don't know what to say to me and have pretty much stopped coming around. I'm stuck here at home every day bored and wondering what I can do. I don't want to live on a disability check the rest of my life because that doesn't pay for anything."

PHYSIOLOGY AND FUNCTION OF SCI

The neurological level and extent of lesion is important in diagnosing the significance of functional limitation. The continuum of SCI impairments are grossly categorized into tetraplegia (formerly quadriplegia), which results from lesions located higher on the spinal cord and involves motor/sensory input to all four limbs; and paraplegia, which results from lesions located lower on the spinal cord and involves the lower extremities only (Blackwell, Krause, Winkler, & Steins, 2001). Lesions can be described as either "complete" or "incomplete" injuries. Complete injuries typically result in total lack of functional motor or sensory ability below the lesion level. With an incomplete injury, the individual has some motor/sensory function below the lesion. ASIA classifies SCI into five anatomical categories (ASIA-A to -E) that describe degree of residual motor/sensory function (see Blackwell et al., 2001).

Tetraplegia

Specific structural and functional loss is directly associated with damage at specific cervical segments of the spine. From high to low lesion location, they are (C3) respiration; (C4) neck, shoulder, and deltoid muscles; (C5) biceps; (C6) wrist extensors; (C7) triceps; and (C8–T1) forearm musculature, gross and fine finger dexterity, and grasp (see Consortium for Spinal Cord Medicine, 1999). Ambulation for individuals with a C5 lesion or higher is typically performed with a power wheelchair, while those with C6–C8 will generally use a manual wheelchair.

   Family caregiving concentrates on instrumental physical needs such as dressing, grooming, toileting, and cleaning. Caregiver appropriation of individual activities of daily living (ADL) varies from minimal to complete. The need for some level of support across ADL is relatively constant, however. Functionality will require standby (C7–C8) or full assistance (C1–C6) for transferring to/from wheelchair to bed, commode, car, and so on. A manual or powered lifting device is routinely recommended for full-assistance transfers. Emmanuelle will be able to bring food to his mouth with an eating splint; however, he will have no ability to cut his food. Persons with lesions above C4 will require someone to feed them since they typically have no arm or hand movement. Individuals with C3 lesions are typically ventilator dependent and require more intensive personal care with the ventilator, tracheotomy attachments, gastronomy tube feeding, and equipment operation and maintenance (Blackwell et al., 2001).

Persons with neck injuries often have a little to no control over urine and fecal elimination. Personal assistance will usually be required to catheterize intermittently (4–6 times per day). Alternatively, men will wear a drainage condom that is connected to a tube and empties into a urinary bag that requires periodic emptying. Emmanuelle can obtain a reflex erection from direct stimulation, but will likely require prescription medication for longer sexual intercourse activities. Bowel care and grooming for individuals with tetraplegia require minimal to complete assistance regarding suppository insertion and occasional digital stimulation by caregiver.

Individuals with C5–C6 injuries and lower are often able to drive a modified van with hand controls from their wheelchair or require assistance transferring into an automobile seat. People with higher level injuries will be physically unable to drive and will depend on others for transportation. Persons with C7–C8 injuries will have some gross finger movement to hold utensils, a pen/pencil, and possibly type on a regular keyboard. Emmanuelle will require assistive devices such as an eating splint or larger adaptive keyboard for typing, or voice recognition software for direct word processing on computer.

Maintaining healthy skin is a priority for persons with tetraplegia. Persons with C7–C8 injuries can routinely perform pressure releases by using their triceps to periodically lift themselves up off their wheelchair cushion. The higher level injuries require periodic physical assistance with such positioning needs through the day and night, including bed turning side to side nightly every 2 to 3 hours depending on the type of bed used. They will also require someone to check their skin for pressure ulcers and assist in bathing and nail care. Emmanuelle can only reduce buttock pressure by either leaning side to side or using a power wheelchair that has a tilt/recline function. Most physiatrists recommend that persons with SCI perform pressure releases every 15 to 30 minutes.

Paraplegia

Persons with paraplegia have full use of their upper extremities, with varying levels of lower extremity paralysis and sensory loss depending on lesion level and severity. Lesion location corresponds with affected motor and sensory functions, descending from the chest and abdomen region down through the hips, thighs, calves, and foot muscles and sensations (Consortium for Spinal Cord Medicine, 1999). Thoracic levels T1–T9 are essentially independent with all their activities of daily living (e.g., hygiene, dressing, transfers, light housekeeping), but need approximately 3 hours of homemaking assistance services per day (e.g., laundry, cooking, cleaning). Individuals with an L2–S5 lesion can usually grossly ambulate with leg braces, knee-ankle-foot orthosis, and/or cane or forearm crutches. All other lesion injuries ambulate mainly by manual wheelchair. Although many of these levels are able to ambulate with these aids, most use a manual wheelchair for longer distances due to the excessive stamina exertion required.

Tommy has the capacity to complete the majority of his instrumental ADLs, but requires some level of daily assistance (depending on the severity of the lesion) for certain housekeeping tasks. The extent and length of time for ADL assistance is also based on accessibility of the home or work setting. Tommy's T6 injury level gives him normal motor and sensation functions above injury level from his abdomen, but below this level, he lacks any motor or sensation function. He must catheterize himself 4 to 6 times per day and maintains a bowel routine requiring a suppository for emptying every second day. He is able to independently perform all his grooming and hygiene needs.

Tommy is able to transfer himself independently, but must be careful not to drag his buttocks for fear of skin shearing and subsequent decubitus ulcers. He must be diligent in checking his skin for decubiti or other abrasions at night before bed using a mirror for hard-to-see areas. Because his upper extremities are fully functioning and he can perform all transfers, Tommy is able to drive independently and engage in community activities without relying on others for assistance. He is also able to push his lightweight manual wheelchair on any level surface inside and throughout the surrounding community, provided there is adequate physical access.

Common secondary complications of persons with SCI include septicemia, decubitus ulcers, urinary tract infections, cardiovascular disease, repetitive motion shoulder injury and chronic pain, deep vein thrombosis, respiratory dysfunction, osteoporosis, heterotrophic ossification, autonomic dysreflexia, and spasticity (Krause, 1998; Rodgers & Marini, 1994). Some complications gradually occur over a number of years. Others such as decubiti, urinary tract infections, autonomic dysreflexia (for those with T6 injuries and above), and deep vein thrombosis can develop in a day. Those with SCI and their family or caregiver(s) must be diligent in monitoring and practicing prevention strategies of secondary complications. Neglect or negligence in doing so can result in long and costly hospitalizations and sometimes even death.

Psychological Functioning

The psychosocial response of individual and family to SCI is framed by adjustment and adaptation to traumatic injury. Adjustment in the acute phase is a systems confrontation with the chaos of social disruption and immediate physical crisis that precipitates cognitive, behavioral, and emotional upheaval and immediate attempts to regain equilibrium. Persons who sustain a traumatic SCI often grieve the loss of lifestyle and function for weeks or months following their injury (Livneh & Antonak, 2012). They wrestle with issues of self-esteem as a person with a disability (Marini, Rogers, Slate, & Vines, 1995) who has yet to have any experience with the role. Significant numbers become clinically depressed following injury (Craig, Hancock, &

Dickson, 1994). Suicide rates spike in the first year of postinjury adjustment (DeVivo, Black, Richards, & Stover, 1991).

Adaptation refers to the ongoing, complex ecological interactions that signify the evolving reestablishment of individual and family identity as they face the challenges of SCI (see Marini, 2012a) in daily life. Personal adaptation to SCI takes place within the family as it deals with role and lifestyle changes; job loss and financial pressures; access to affordable transportation, housing, health, and community services; loss of social status and supports; reduced community mobility; social isolation; and negative societal attitudes (Dijkers, Abela, Gans, & Gordon, 1995; Graf, Marini, & Blankenship, 2009; Li & Moore, 1998; Marini, Bhakta, & Graf, 2009).

Emmanuelle has numerous instrumental daily physical needs, but also is presently in need of effective support to deal with his uncertain future in terms of work, school, fatherhood, and social relationships (Blackwell et al., 2001). Tommy's present issues are primarily emotional ones of job uncertainty, self-esteem related to expected societal roles for men, and the need for information and counseling related to adjusting to his new SCI identity. With his biggest worries related to continuing with his job, he will be relieved to know that mandated laws should grant him access and accommodation. However, it remains to be seen as to how others will react to him using the wheelchair. Family involvement for a member with paraplegia will generally be less focused on physically assisting with personal care and ADLs, but can involve more physical assistance for higher level paraplegia, poor wheelchair access (Tommy's laundry room), and those with premorbid conditions such as obesity.

Family Participation

How well people with SCI adapt to their circumstances is a function of their relationship with a social support network (Degeneffe & Lynch, 2006; Li & Moore, 1998; Power & Dell Orto, 2004), with the family at the core. Psychologically, families support development of community independence, self-esteem and confidence, better quality of life, and positive affect. Physiologically, supportive families reduce the number of rehospitalizations and secondary complications (e.g., pressure sores and urinary tract infections) and improved the person with SCI's self-appraisal of health (Blackwell et al., 2001). Regardless of role within the family before or after the injury, family participation is perhaps the most influential aspect of care and arbiter of good outcomes.

Family Psychosocial Response

The experience of SCI resonates through all family members as they move from injury to recovery as a group Lyons, Leon, Roecker-Phelps, & Dunleavy, 2010; Power & Dell Orto, 2004; Shewchuk & Elliott, 2000). Initial feelings of being overwhelmed with fear and anxiety, shock and denial, emotional numbness, guilt, helplessness, deep sorrow, and even clinical depression (Power & Dell Orto, 2004) set an emotional benchmark against which progress in adjustment and adaptation are gauged (Marini, 2012a, 2012b). Families struggle with the reality of abrupt and violent change in the order of their lives too, not as patients in acute care, but as the next of kin in the waiting room. They must deal with the chaos of emotions simultaneously with the pressured need to make important crisis decisions early on. They continue to confront their emotional issues as recovery progresses through a series of decisions that affect roles, housing, funding, employment, and other definitive aspects of their former lives. They are equally challenged in adaptation by the emerging new identity and the assorted stressors that require new coping strategies (Boschen, Tonack, & Gargaro, 2005; Elliott & Berry, 2009; Marini, 2012b). As a result of this unrelenting stress, family caregivers often experience diminished physical (Shewchuk, Richards, & Elliott, 1998) and mental health (Blanes, Carmagnani, & Ferreira, 2007; Boschen et al., 2005; Cleveland, 1980) and fluctuations in social support and isolation.

Family adjustment to SCI disability is established through the development of care and care-support routines (Janoff-Bulman, 2004). The stress and strain of caregiving are ameliorated by competent assistance in the caregiving tasks, intermittent respite from the role (Knestrict & Kuchey, 2009), and moderation in the number of hours on task (Byrne, Hurley, Daly, & Cunningham, 2010). Resilience comes from finding meaning and intrinsic motivation in the task of care (Reid, Moss, & Hyman, 2005), developing strong intrafamily support and communication, and the acquisition of new group problem-solving skills (Elliott & Berry, 2009). Resilience is a precursor of adaptation.

Family Role Through the Lifecycle

Whether the injured loved one is a child or parent, the family must adapt over time as all members begin to age. Persons with paraplegia usually remain functionally independent into their late 50s, unless obesity, substance abuse, or other secondary complications hasten the need for assistance (Blackwell et al., 2001; Graf, 2012a; Krause, 1998). For persons with higher level tetraplegia like Emmanuelle, the number of hours needed for daily assistance will start to increase from ages 50 to 55 (Blackwell et al., 2001) onward. How direct care is provided changes with the age of the caregiver as well. Younger caregivers may directly lift and transfer, but older family caregivers will require medical equipment such as a Hoyer lift, commode chair, or shower chair to minimize the risk of injury to themselves and the person with SCI. If finances are not available for personal care assistance or needed medical equipment for these aging caregivers, physical and mental health problems have an increased likelihood of occurring (Blackwell et al., 2001; Shewchuk et al., 1998).

Family Within the Community

The interdependency among family members, their functionality as a unit, and their overall affect is also intimately interconnected with their experiences within the community (Li & Moore, 1998; Vissers et al., 2008). Alfano, Neilson, and Fink (1994) found that family members of loved ones with SCI reported greater distress and depression when their injured family member was depressed. In terms of family experiences within the community, several researchers have found injured members and their families continue to experience physical access barriers, discriminatory attitudes, and disjointed social and medical services (Kroll et al., 2006; National Organization on Disability, 2000). The resulting impact of such encounters for all family members includes stress, frustration, anger, fear, anxiety, and social isolation periodically when negative attitudes and/or physical access barriers are encountered (Alfano et al., 1994; Blackwell et al., 2002; Graf et al., 2009; Marini et al., 2009). Problematic access to the public spaces (buildings, parks, public transportation) that provide the context for community interaction has repeatedly been identified as the most common complaint and frustration for individuals and their families (Graf et al., 2009; Marini et al., 2009; Vissers et al., 2008). Families' participation with their loved one with SCI is largely dependent on access to the community and community resources. With approximately 80% of all caregiving in the United States being provided by unpaid family members and no pending legislation in the foreseeable future to remedy this situation, a greater emphasis is now being focused on environmental influences and community-based rehabilitation (National Alliance of Care-giving & The American Association of Retired Persons, 2004).

Environmental Resources

Universal design, easier service system navigation, and positive societal attitudes would address the majority of complaints expressed by people with SCI and their families. The National Institute on Disability and Rehabilitation Research and Healthy People 2010 proceedings focused community attention on the importance of evaluating and eliminating environmental barriers for people with disabilities (National Center for Health Statistics, 2012).

Adaptive Technology

Assistive or adaptive technology (AT) refers to products, equipment, or devices that are used to improve, maintain, or increase the functional independence for individuals with disabilities (Brodwin, Siu, & Cardoso, 2012). Whether they are commercial products for mass distribution or customized products designed for a specific individual, or whether they are high tech or low, adaptive technologies enhance independence and thereby generate deeper and more meaningful community inclusion.

Devices and aids that assist individuals and/or their family in accomplishing home ADLs could, and do, fill a catalog. From lever door handles to voice-activated switches to voice recognition software, to smart homes fitted with high-end environmental control units (ECU)—these devices allow persons with SCI to become more functionally independent (Davis, English, Ambrose, & Petty, 2001; Marini & Harper,

2005; Scherer, 2007). The 1993 National Council on Disability (see Brodwin et al., 2012) reported that AT helped 62% of adults to be less reliant on family members for ADL assistance and 58% were able to reduce the cost of paid assistance. In addition, approximately 40% of senior citizens indicated they were able to avoid institutionalization with the assistance of AT, and 67% of working-age individuals indicated AT helped them obtain employment. SCI is quite amenable to AT across a range of needs. ATs are as varied as the needs they fill, and so it is common to find that the more severe impairments are met with an increasingly sophisticated panoply of technical solutions. Technology needs change from environment to environment. Steins (1998) suggests that technology can be conceptualized for planning purposes in terms of its applications in immediate (in direct contact with the person), intermediate, and community environments (personal space at home or at work), and (c) community environment (space adjusted for public utilization). This perspective illustrates the importance of integration across these nested levels, that is, awareness of universal design principles. For example, both Tommy and Emmanuel should be able to access public transportation, such as a bus. The "kneeling" bus, the ramp, and the seating arrangements must all accommodate the different technologies they employ (evidenced by their wheelchairs), while simultaneously serving the public.

Mobility. Ambulation by wheelchair is the primary means of mobility for most individuals with SCI. Because physical access is the most common and greatest barrier to participation in the community (Chaves et al., 2004; Marini et al., 2009) for people with SCI, wheelchairs have long been at the epicenter of rehabilitation engineering design and innovation. The prototypical wheelchair of the 1950s and 1960s was the heavy hospital model that was designed to push a passive patient around the halls. It was not designed to navigate the outside world without a caretaker in charge. With the advocacy movement and the creation of lightweight and durable composite materials, the wheelchair of today reflects the user's choice instead of the hospital program. There is not one design but many, and each model can be customized for individual function and style. Manual and power wheelchairs have become an extension of the person in his or her desire to participate in competitive sports, traverse outdoor terrains, move quickly between the car and the office; or in his or her pursuit of better health via exercise wheelchairs and those that will stand, tilt, and recline for pressure relief, circulation, and weight-bearing (see http://www.sportaid.com for examples).

Transportation. The wheelchair serves the most proximal environment and mobility within it, but travel in wider circles is essential for full community inclusion (Chaves et al., 2004). Persons with SCI who are capable of driving and possess their own modified vehicle are also capable of independent and spontaneous travel for the price of a gallon of gasoline. Modifications such as simple hand controls, van ramps, lowered floors, push button dashboards, and modified steering (Scherer, 2007) offer access to a power that is often taken for granted in cities designed around the automobile, commuter culture, and highways designed for long-distance travel. In a world where access is defined by distance, access to transportation is fundamental to inclusion. Persons with SCI who cannot drive, or cannot afford the cost of driving, find their worlds constricted to the routes and timetables of public transportation or dependent on the schedules and largesse of helpful others. Inevitably, limited access to transportation leads to limited access to everything else and an impoverished quality of life (Brodwin et al., 2012; Chaves et al., 2004).

Societal Attitudes

Physical appearance is idealized by Western culture (Marini, Wang, Etzback, & Del Castillo, 2013). At the societal level, negative attitudes can become social patterns of segregation and discrimination and can have a negative impact on the psychosocial and vocational experiences for persons with disabilities (Graf et al., 2009; Li & Moore, 1998; Marini, 2012c; Marini et al., 2009). The media often portrays persons with disabilities as being victims, jobless, objects of pity or admiration, asexual, and often unattractive (Marini, 2012c; Marini et al., 2013). With a visible disability such as SCI, the wheelchair often becomes the most salient characteristic of the individual for those without disabilities who are unaccustomed to being around disability (Crewe & Krause, 2002). Wright (1983) describes the widespread phenomenon whereby those without disabilities infer that a wheelchair user likely has a cognitive disability as well. Family support has often been shown by researchers as one of the primary factors in enhancing its disabled loved one's self-concept (Graf, 2012b; Li & Moore, 1998; Rosenthal, Kosciulek, Lee, Frain, & Ditchman, 2009).

Service Systems and Policies

Rehabilitation professionals generally come into contact with individuals with SCI in clinical settings to deal with isolated clinical issues. Formal medical care affords little time to build relationships in inpatient rehabilitation. The professional–patient relationship lacks a holistic appreciation of the social context of disability, almost by design. Rehabilitation professionals do not usually understand the complexities of life after discharge from acute rehabilitation (Kroll, Groah, Gilmore, & Neri, 2008). Postdischarge, the value of rehabilitation professionals to families is their utility in resolving the pragmatic problems of daily life. In at least one way, they may be more of a hindrance than help. Managed care has traded cost savings, measured in days of hospitalization, for any psychosocial good a more benign transition might have offered the family. With length of inpatient rehabilitation limited to no more than 2 to 3 months postinjury, families are often left scrambling to prepare their home and lives for the lifetime of support and care that will attend the returning family member. Thus, efficient case management is as important as therapy in adjustment and adaptation outcomes. Integrating postdischarge planning in managed care extends to strategic considerations of the physical environment and acclimating the family therein. An important part of this transition process is planning for the skills and tools the family will need to continue with care at home. Training in transferring, adaptive aids, neurogenic bowel and bladder care, and monitoring for secondary complications (Power & Dell Orto, 2004) is capacity building in the environment and resilience building in the family.

Accessing Service. To maximize independence for persons with SCI, the individual and his or her family must be included as part of the interdisciplinary team, particularly in discharge planning (Power & Dell Orto, 2004). Obtaining information and referral for community integration is essential. Applying the ICF framework to program planning, rehabilitation professionals explore the connection between the individual's physical impairments, limitations of activities, and participation restrictions, while identifying environmental factors that act as barriers or facilitators to functioning (Jackson, Dijkers, DeVivo, & Poczatek, 2004). On a practical level, this includes making sure the home is accessible, home health care and transportation is arranged (if feasible), and referral to vocational rehabilitation and independent living services is facilitated (Power & Dell Orto, 2004).

Other than attendant care for those who require it, coordinating medical care is important due to the potential for secondary complications. This historically has often been one of the most frustrating experiences reported by persons with SCI and their families (Blanes et al., 2007; Graf et al., 2009; Kroll et al., 2006; National Organization on Disability, 2004). Smedley, Stith, and Nelson (2003) identified access to care as one of the main barriers to health care and outcomes. The problems in the system are deeply engrained, complex, and not easily solved. Inaccessible examination rooms attended by physicians and medical staff inadequately trained in holistic SCI care, providing inadequate service within a fragmented system, is exhausting to contemplate, much less navigate. Yet this can be the stage on which care is negotiated, especially for the economically disadvantaged and minority groups (Marini, Bhakta, & Graf, 2009). Research on racial and ethnic minority patients with SCI indicates that persons of minority were found to have shorter hospital lengths of stay (LOS), higher rehospitalization rates, higher levels of depression, more days of poorer health, greater degrees of unemployment, more difficulties with mobility, and lower self-reported subjective well-being and quality of life (Gary, Nicholls, Shamburger, Stevens, & Arango-Lasprilla, 2011).

Policies and Legislation. Other than the 1990 Americans with Disabilities Act (ADA; particularly Title II regarding access to Public Services such as public buses and recreation and state parks, and Title III Public Accommodation access to restaurants, all public entertainment venues, and retail outlets), there are several other laws pertaining to persons with physical disabilities (United States Access Board, 2004). Another law establishing access and nondiscrimination to individuals with physical disabilities is access to rental, sales, or financing of housing included under Title

VIII (Fair Housing Act) of the 1968 Civil Rights Act (United States Department of Justice, 2005). The 1968 Architectural Barriers Act mandates all newly constructed or altered buildings that are federally funded or owned after 1969 must be accessible (Architectural Barriers Act, 1968; United States Access Board, 2004). Despite what seemingly appears to be very old protective legislation on discrimination, there continues to be hundreds of such lawsuits filed annually with the Office of Civil Rights regarding noncompliance issues (Blackwell et al., 2002).

Community access itself is sometimes viewed as the glass being half empty for some and half full for others (Marini, 2012c). Although the United States has made great gains in civil and human rights for persons with disabilities since the 1990 ADA, there unfortunately remain pockets of poor physical access in various urban and rural areas that remain out of compliance with the ADA (Blackwell et al., 2002). Thousands of ADA complaints continue to be filed annually regarding employment discrimination and noncompliance with the public access components of the law, sometimes leaving persons with SCI and family feeling frustrated and angry or apathetic. Despite these periodic clashes with an inaccessible environment and/or negative attitudes, many persons with disabilities report their subjective quality of life to otherwise be very good (Blackwell et al., 2002; Graf et al., 2009; Graf, 2012b; Marini, 2012c).

Support and Family Constellation Network

The home and community environment in which a family lives incorporates many factors such as service provider's attitudes, service systems, extended family members, and available support systems (e.g., respite care). Family members who become caregivers for loved ones with an SCI sometimes report difficulties with back pain, depression, and feelings of isolation and stress if they have little or no assistance (Marini, 2012b). The family's and individual's overall adaptation is often reciprocal on one another as well as their interaction with the environment (Alfano et al., 1994; Kroll et al., 2006; Shewchuk et al., 1998). Factors such as family composition and interdependence, level of acculturation, socioeconomic status, and fear of stigma impact minority group member's experiences of caregiving. Key cultural differences have been addressed among African Americans, Asian Americans, Hispanic/Latino Americans, Native Americans, and European Americans (Graf, 2012b; Millington, 2012).

Chronister (2009) summarizes research suggesting that the relationship between real or perceived social support and chronic disability is positive for the injured loved one's adjustment, subjective well-being, employment, and survival rates. Chronister notes, however, that researchers must better distinguish among the different kinds of support (e.g., structural or functional, emotional, tangible or informational) and acknowledges that not all social support is necessarily beneficial for some persons with disabilities.

REHABILITATION COUNSELING CONSIDERATIONS
IN COMMUNITY-BASED REHABILITATION

Insured length of stay for hospitalization and SCI rehabilitation were significantly reduced with the 1973 Health Management Organization Act. From 1990 to 1997, the average length of stay dropped from 74 to 60 days (Eastwood, Hagglund, Ragnarsson, Gordon, & Marino, 1999). This savings on the front end was offset by a subsequent increase in rehospitalization for secondary complications (see Eastwood et al., 1999). From the family perspective, the net result of this push for cost savings has increased pressures on them to provide more care with less and less time to prepare, both physically and emotionally for the task ahead. Less time to make their home wheelchair accessible, to obtain needed medical equipment, and to absorb all of the new knowledge about SCI shifts the burden from the formal care providers, but does not remove the problem from the system. Tommy and Emmanuelle, for example, found that their informational and emotional needs were given scant attention in the formal care schema. At a most crucial transition to life at home, Emmanuelle's entrance and bathroom were inaccessible. As Tommy was contemplating his return to work, his truck was unavailable and on someone else's time table. Both were isolated within their own lives from day one. What was communicated by formal care in overlooking this aspect of the transition was more about the agenda of the funding source than the needs of the client.

The family challenges profiled in these stories illustrate the need for a more community-responsive approach to rehabilitation and the early inclusion of the family in the process. Discharge planning ideally begins on admission to the rehabilitation hospital if not sooner and generally involves an interdisciplinary team approach typically composed of the physiatrist, occupational and physical therapists, social worker, rehabilitation nurse, and psychologist if needed (Power & Dell Orto, 2004). Although in decades past the patient and his or her family had decisions *made for them* by professionals, in contemporary model system SCI hospitals, the patient and family are involved, educated, and empowered to participate in discharge planning. As such, a family's involvement and education before discharge are critical to the emotional and medical well-being of its loved one with SCI (Elliott & Berry, 2009; Li & Moore, 1998).

Rehabilitation counselors involved in this process at the acute or posthospitalization phase should be intricately aware of both the physical and emotional needs of their client and his or her family. This may involve assessing physical access for independence in the home, school, or work setting as well as ensuring the critical lifeline of transportation options. Emotionally, injured individuals as well as family members often experience initial duress from the abrupt lifestyle changes and potential caregiving demands (Marini, 2012a, 2012b). Rehabilitation counselors must be prepared to assist with both the physical and emotional needs of the family for successful community reentry (Elliott & Berry, 2009; Power & Dell Orto, 2004).

Rehabilitation for individuals with SCI cannot be fulfilled by only one type of service or one division. Educational, health, independent living, and vocational services comprise the multidimensional support that community-based rehabilitation (CBR) provides by involving the family and community. When rehabilitation counselors begin to develop a rehabilitation plan with a client, exploration of daily routines among the family is essential. Physical, social, and psychological consequences of acquiring an SCI are evident in both the acute and chronic phases of the condition and have the potential to influence reintegration into the community (Rauch, Bickenbach, Reinhardt, Geyh, & Stucki , 2010; World Health Organization [WHO], 2002). CBR counseling should entail information and referral to local centers for independent living (CIL) for peer and other support, home health care agencies if needed, medical and AT equipment suppliers, and relevant social services (Lightfoot, 2004). For Tommy and Emmanuelle, they could benefit from peer-support services provided by most CILs as well as perhaps generalized counseling for adjustment and couples therapy for Tommy. Both individuals would benefit from public vocational rehabilitation that could integrate support needs for physical access with a family networked strategy for seeking employment. Tommy has a job. There is no aspect of his current employment that cannot be accommodated. What he needs is confidence and a plan that moves quickly toward his strengths using technology, training, and social support. Emmanuelle's employment is more problematic. His vocational future will depend on education and training (see Blackwell et al., 2001), and the integration of adaptive technology into all facets of the process including transportation, classroom, and the eventual search and placement in a job. He requires a long view on employment and a very supportive and stable emotional environment to see him through it. In both cases, family provides the foundation for vocational strategy.

For persons with SCI and their family, ensuring accessible and affordable housing, transportation, home personal care services, and relevant AT become the cornerstones for the CBR counselor to ensure success for his or her consumers in vocational or any other rehabilitation goal. Since most persons with SCI remain medically stable postdischarge, monitoring and maintaining physical and mental health are important, as are information and referral to CBR resources. Because complications are to be expected, physical health will decline, and support needs will increase with age, the CBR partnership with the family may be intermittent, but it is ongoing. Both formal and family care are best served when the person moves in and out of care as needed and the family is provided resources on the basis of a responsive life care plan . . . not a capitation schedule. This is a challenge for counselors: to make optimal use of the full resources of a networked community across agencies and to place the person and his or her family at the center and helm of this plan.

REFERENCES

Alfano, D. P., Neilson, P. M., & Fink, M. P. (1994). Sources of stress in family members following head or spinal cord injury. *Applied Neuropsychology, 1*, 57–62.

American with Disability Act of 1990, 42 U.S.C. 12101 *et seq.* (West 1993).

Architectural Barriers Act of 1968, 42 U.S.C. (As Amended through 1984), 4151–4157.

Blackwell, T. L., Krause, J. S., Winkler, T., & Steins, S. A. (2001). *Spinal cord injury desk reference.* New York, NY: Demos Medical.

Blackwell, T. M., Marini, I., & Chacon, M. (2002). The impact of the Americans with Disabilities Act on independent living. *Rehabilitation Education, 15*(4), 395–408.

Blanes, L., Carmagnani, M. I., & Ferreira, L. M. (2007). Health-related quality of life of primary caregivers of persons with paraplegia. *Spinal Cord, 45*, 399–403.

Boschen, K., Tonack, M., & Gargaro, J. (2005). The impact of being a support provider to a person living in the community with a spinal cord injury. *Rehabilitation Psychology, 50*, 397–407.

Brodwin, M. G., Siu, F. W., & Cardoso, E. (2012). Users of assistive technology: The human component. In I. Marini & M. Stebnicki (Eds.), *The psychological and social impact of illness and disability* (6th ed., pp. 331–339). New York, NY: Springer.

Byrne, M. B., Hurley, D. A., Daly, L., & Cunningham, C. G. (2010). Health status of care-givers of children with cerebral palsy. *Child: Care, Health & Development, 36*(5), 696–702.

Chaves, E. S., Boninger, M. L., Cooper, R., Fitzgerald, S. G., Gray, D., & Cooper, R. A. (2004). Assessing the influence of wheelchair technology on perceptions of participation in spinal cord injury. *Archives of Physical Medicine and Rehabilitation, 85*, 1854–1858.

Chronister, J. A. (2009). Social support and rehabilitation theory, research, and measurement. In F. Chan, E. Cardoso, & J. A. Chronister (Eds.), *Understanding psychosocial adjustment to chronic illness and disability: A handbook for evidence-based practitioners in rehabilitation* (pp. 149–183). New York, NY: Springer.

Cleveland, M. (1980). Family adaptation to traumatic spinal cord injury: Response to crisis. *Family Relations, 29*, 558–565.

Consortium for Spinal Cord Medicine. (1999). *Outcomes following traumatic spinal cord injury: Clinical practice guidelines for health-care professionals.* Washington, DC: Paralyzed Veterans of America.

Craig, A. R., Hancock, K. M., & Dickson, H. G. (1994). A longitudinal investigation into anxiety and depression in the first two years following spinal cord injury. *Paraplegia, 32*, 675–679.

Crewe, N., & Krause, J. (2002). Spinal cord injuries. In M. Brodwin, F. Tellez, & S. Brodwin (Eds.), *Medical, psychosocial and vocational aspects of disability* (pp. 279–291). Athens, GA: Elliott & Fitzpatrick.

Davis, L. L., English, B. A., Ambrose, S. M., & Petty, F. (2001). Pharmacotherapy for post-traumatic stress disorder: A comprehensive review. *Pharmacotherapy, 2*(10), 1583–1595.

Degeneffe, C. E., & Lynch, R. T. (2006). Correlates of depression in adult siblings of persons with traumatic brain injury. *Rehabilitation Counseling Bulletin, 49*, 130–142.

DeVivo, M. J., Black, K. L., Richards, S., & Stover, S. L. (1991). Suicide following spinal cord injury. *Paraplegia, 29*, 620–627.

Dijkers, M., Abela, M. B., Gans, B. M., & Gordon, W. A. (1995). The aftermath of spinal cord injury. In S. L. Stover, J. A. DeLisa, & G. G. Whiteneck (Eds.), *Spinal cord injury: Clinical outcomes from the model systems* (pp. 185–212). Gaithersburg, MD: Aspen.

Eastwood, E. A., Hagglund, K. J., Ragnarsson, K. T., Gordon, W. A., & Marino, R. J. (1999). Medical rehabilitation lengths of stay and outcomes for persons with traumatic spinal cord injury—1990–1997. *Archives of Physical Medical Rehabilitation, 80*(11), 1457–1463.

Elliott, T., & Berry, J. W. (2009). Brief problem-solving training for family caregivers of persons with recent onset spinal cord injuries: A randomized controlled study. *Journal of Clinical Psychology, 65*(4), 406–422.

Gary, K. W., Nicholls, E., Shamburger, A., Stevens, L. F., & Arango-Lasprilla, J. C. (2011). Do racial and ethnic minority patients fare worse after SCI? A critical review of the literature. *Neuro-Rehabilitation, 29,* 275–293.

Graf, N. M. (2012a). Disability and quality of life over the lifespan. In I. Marini, N. Glover-Graf, & M. J. Millington (Eds.), *Psychosocial aspects of disability: Insider perspectives and counseling strategies* (pp. 259–286). New York, NY: Springer.

Graf, N. M. (2012b). Family adaptation across cultures toward a loved one who is disabled. In I. Marini, N. Glover-Graf, & M. J. Millington (Eds.), *Psychosocial aspects of disability: Insider perspectives and counseling strategies* (pp. 169–194). New York, NY: Springer.

Graf, N. M., Marini, I., & Blankenship, C. (2009). 100 Words about disability. *Journal of Rehabilitation, 75*(2), 25–34.

Jackson, A. B., Dijkers, M., Devivo, M. J., & Poczatek, R. B. (2004). A demographic profile of new traumatic spinal cord injuries: Change and stability over 30 years. *Archives of Physical Medical Rehabilitation, 85*(11), 1740–1748.

Janoff-Bulman, R. (2004). Posttraumatic growth: Three explanatory models. *Psychological Inquiry, 15*(1), 30–34.

Knestrict, T., & Kuchey, D. (2009). Welcome to Holland: Characteristics of resilient families raising children with severe disabilities. *Journal of Family Studies, 15,* 227–244.

Krause, J. S. (1998). Aging and life adjustment after spinal cord injury. *Spinal Cord, 36,* 320–328.

Kroll, T., Groah, S., Gilmore, B., & Neri, M. (2008). Consumer-directed teaching of health care professionals involved in the care of people with spinal cord injury: The consumer-professional partnership program. *Journal of Continuing Education in Nursing, 39*(5), 228–234.

Kroll, T., Jones, G. C., Kehn, M. E., & Neri, M. T. (2006). Barriers and strategies affecting the utilization of primary preventative services for people with physical disabilities: A qualitative inquiry. *Health and Social Care within the Community, 14*(4), 284–293.

Li, L., & Moore, D. (1998). Acceptance of disability and its correlates. *Journal of Social Psychology, 138*(1), 13–25.

Lightfoot, E. (2004). Community-based rehabilitation: A rapidly growing method for supporting people with disabilities. *International Journal of Social Work, 47,* 455–468.

Livneh, H., & Antonak, R. F. (2012). Psychological adaptation to chronic illness and disability: A primer for counselors. In I. Marini & M. Stebnicki (Eds.), *The psychological and social impact of illness and disability* (6th ed., pp. 95–107). New York, NY: Springer.

Lyons, A., Leon, S., Roecker-Phelps, C., & Dunleavy, A. (2010). The impact of child symptom severity on stress among parents of children with ASD: The moderating role of coping styles. *Journal of Child & Family Studies, 10,* 516–524.

Marini, I. (2012a). Theories of adjustment and adaptation to disability. In I. Marini, N. Glover-Graf, & M. J. Millington (Eds.), *Psychosocial aspects of disability: Insider perspectives and counseling strategies* (pp. 133–166). New York, NY: Springer.

Marini, I. (2012b). Implications of social support and caregiving for loved ones with the disability. In I. Marini, N. Glover-Graf, & M. J. Millington (Eds.), *Psychosocial aspects of disability: Insider perspectives and counseling strategies* (pp. 287–310). New York, NY: Springer.

Marini, I. (2012c). The history of treatment towards persons with disabilities. In I. Marini, N. Glover-Graf, & M. J. Millington (Eds.), *Psychosocial aspects of disability: Insider perspectives and counseling strategies* (pp. 3–27). New York, NY: Springer.

Marini, I., Bhakta, M. V., & Graf, N. (2009). A content analysis of common concerns of persons with physical disabilities. *Journal of Applied Rehabilitation Counseling, 40*(1), 44–49.

Marini, I., & Harper, D. (2005). Empirical validation of medical equipment replacement values in life care plans. *Journal of Life Care Planning, 4*(4), 173–182.

Marini, I., Rogers, L., Slate, J., & Vines, C. (1995). Self-esteem differences among persons with spinal cord injury. *Rehabilitation Counseling Bulletin, 38*(3), 198–206.

Marini, I., Wang, X., Etzback, C., & Del Castillo, A. (2013). Ethnic, gender, and contact differences in intimacy attitudes towards wheelchair users. *Rehabilitation Counseling Bulletin, 56*(3), 135–145.

McCubbin, H. I., Thompson, A. I., & McCubbin, M. (1996). *Family assessment: resiliency, coping, and adaptation.* Madison: University of Wisconsin.

Millington, M. J. (2012). Culturally different issues and attitudes toward disability. In I. Marini, N. Glover-Graf, & M. J. Millington (Eds.), *Psychosocial aspects of disability: Insider perspectives and counseling strategies* (pp. 61–95). New York, NY: Springer.

National Alliance of Care-giving & The American Association of Retired Persons. (2004). *Caregiving in the U.S.* Washington, DC: Authors.

National Center for Health Statistics. (2012). *Healthy people 2010 final review* (DHHS Publication No. 2012–1038). Retrieved from http://www.cdc.gov/nchs/data/hpdata2010/hp2010_final_review.pdf

National Organization on Disability. (2004, June 24). *Landmark survey finds pervasive disadvantages* (Press release) Washington, DC: Author.

National Organization on Disability/Harris Community Participation Study. (2000). *2000 Survey of community participation.* Washington, DC: Author.

Pederson, S., & Revenson, T. A. (2012). Parental illness, family functioning, and adolescent well-being: A family ecology framework to guide research. In I. Marini & M. A. Stebnicki (Eds.), The professional counselor's desk reference (pp. 249–272). New York, NY: Springer.

Power, P. W., & Dell Orto, A. E. (2004). An approach to family assessment. In P. W. Power & A. E. Dell Orto (Eds.), *Families living with chronic illness and disability: Interventions, challenges, and opportunities* (pp. 101–121). New York, NY: Springer.

Rauch, A., Bickenbach, J., Reinhardt, J. D., Geyh, S., & Stucki, G. (2010). The utility of the ICF to identify and evaluate problems and needs in participation in spinal cord injury rehabilitation. *Topics in Spinal Cord Injury Rehabilitation, 15*(4), 72–85.

Reid, C. E., Moss, S., & Hyman, G. (2005). Care-givers reciprocity: The effects of reciprocity, carer self-esteem and motivation on the experience of care-giver burden. *Australian Journal of Psychology, 57*(3), 186–196.

Rodgers, S., & Marini, I. (1994). Physiological and psychological aspects of aging with spinal cord injury. *SCI Psychosocial Process, 7*(3), 98–103.

Rosenthal, D. A., Kosciulek, J., Lee, G. K., Frain, M., & Ditchman, N. (2009). Family adaptation to chronic illness and disability. In F. Chan, E. Cardoso, & J. A. Chronister (Eds.), *Understanding psychosocial adjustment to chronic illness and disability: A handbook for evidence-based practitioners in rehabilitation* (pp. 185–203). New York, NY: Springer.

Scherer, M. J. (2007). *Living in the state of stuck: How technology impacts the lives of people with disabilities* (4th ed.). Cambridge, MA: Brookline Books.

Shewchuk R., & Elliott, T. R. (2000). Family caregiving in chronic disease and disability. In R. G. Frank & T. R. Elliott (Eds.), *Handbook of rehabilitation psychology* (pp. 553–561). Washington, DC: American Psychological Association.

Shewchuk, R., Richards, J. S., & Elliott, T. R. (1998). Dynamic process in health outcomes among caregivers of patients with spinal cord injuries. *Health Psychology, 17*, 125–129.

Smedley, B. D., Stith, A. Y., & Nelson, A. R. (2003). *Unequal treatment: Confronting racial and ethnic disparities in health care.* Retrieved from http://www.precaution.org/lib/iom_on_health_disparities.020601.pdf

Steins, S. A. (1998). Personhood, disablement, and mobility technology: Personal control of development. In D. B. Gray, L. A. Quatrano, M. L. Lieberman (Eds.), *Designing and using assistive technology: The human perspective* (pp. 29–49). Baltimore, MD: Paul H Brookes.

United States Access Board. (2004). *Americans with disabilities act and architectural barriers act accessibility guidelines.* Washington, DC: Author.

United States Department of Justice. (2005). *A guide to disability rights laws.* Washington, DC: Author.

Vissers, M., van den Berg-Emons, R., Sluis, T., Bergen, M., Stam, H., & Bussmann, H. (2008). Barriers to and facilitators of every day physical activity in persons with a spinal cord injury after discharge from the rehabilitation center. *Journal of Rehabilitation Medicine, 40*, 461–467.

World Health Organization. (2002). *International classification of functioning, disability and health: ICF.* Geneva, Switzerland: WHO.

Wright, B. (1983). *Physical disability: A psychosocial approach* (2nd ed.). New York, NY: Harper & Row.

CHAPTER 11

Families of Veterans With Polytrauma Injuries in the United States: A Guide for Rehabilitation Counseling Practice

CHARLES EDMUND DEGENEFFE, MARK TUCKER, AND
JOAN M. GRIFFIN

The United States entered a new period of military conflict on September 11, 2001. Military action in Iraq lasted more than 8 years under Operation Iraqi Freedom (OIF) and its transitional counterpart, Operation New Dawn (OND; Fischer, 2012). The war in Afghanistan (Operation Enduring Freedom [OEF]) is the longest war in the history of the United States commemorating 13 years in October 2014. The human and economic costs have been astounding. The combined operations account for more than 7,200 active-duty military personnel killed and more than 48,000 veterans wounded in battle. The Defense and Veterans Brain Injury Center's most recent estimate of traumatic brain injury (TBI) diagnoses (United States Department of Defense, 2013) within the U.S. Armed forces since 2010 is more than 280,000. The number of TBI diagnoses has increased each year from 2000 to 2013 consistent with the U.S. military presence in Iraq and Afghanistan. Cumulative operations costs in OEF and OIF approach $1.5 trillion (True Cost of War Act, 2013). When the costs associated with care and support of wounded veterans are figured in, estimates go as high $6 trillion.

Today's veterans with disabilities are different from those of the past. They are all volunteers. Many are reservists, not career military personnel. They were often married with children and had civilian careers before deployment (Frain, Bishop, & Bethel, 2010). As of 2011, women comprised 14.5% of all those on active duty (United States Department of Defense, 2012) and performed approximately 80% of military jobs (Mathewson, 2011). The injuries incurred and survived by military personnel are different as well. The signature weapon of the war has been the improvised explosive device (IED), strategically used to kill or maim with its explosive force and shrapnel and causing maximum trauma. Thanks to technical advances in trauma care, battlefield triage and treatment are also different. Veterans are surviving blast injuries that damage internal organs, cause TBIs, burns, loss of hearing and vision, loss of limbs, disfiguring wounds, and posttraumatic stress disorder (PTSD). This is the signature disability of this new military: polytrauma.

Rehabilitation counseling is ill prepared to serve this population in an integrated fashion. The veteran's vocational rehabilitation system traditionally functions independently and in near isolation from public systems of vocational rehabilitation (Jenkins, Patterson, & Szymanski, 1998). There is little crossover in services. The profession has largely ignored the needs of OEF-, OIF-, and OND-injured veterans in research, training, and publications (Frain et al., 2010). Furthermore, the Council on Rehabilitation Education (2013) only mentions the word *veteran* once and does not list the word *military* in its 21 pages of standards. Rehabilitation counselors are neither trained on military culture nor on types of polytrauma injuries associated with combat. Compounding this omission, the families of military personnel and veterans with disabilities are not mentioned at all. Not only are rehabilitation counselors grappling with an unfamiliar population with an unfamiliar disability, they also have no foundation for understanding what makes these families unique, what their challenges are, or how they may be effectively engaged in care.

This chapter aims to provide rehabilitation counselors with an enhanced understanding of what families encounter following a polytrauma injury to a spouse, parent, sibling, or child. Such an explanation requires both an awareness of the contextual landscape and a sensitivity to the circumstances that make these families unique (Griffin, Friedemann-Sánchez, Hall, Phelan, & van Ryn, 2009). Two case studies are used to describe the veteran family experience with polytrauma. They are based on survey and interview data drawn from actual families dealing with polytrauma injuries (see Family and Caregiver Experience Survey [FACES]; Griffin et al., 2012; United States Department of Veterans Affairs [VA], 2010). The case studies provide (a) a description of TBI, PTSD, and other polytrauma-related injuries; (b) a description of the unique stressors families of veterans with polytrauma encounter; and (c) the systems of support in place to meet the needs of veterans with polytrauma and their families. The chapter concludes with a discussion of recommendations for effective rehabilitation counseling practices.

CASE STUDIES

The case studies highlight the immediate polytrauma effects on the veterans, along with descriptions of the long-term effects on their families as they learn to manage family system changes, unexpected role changes, and challenges in accessing needed services and supports. Due to the necessity of maintaining the confidentiality and anonymity of FACES participants, the following case studies present fictionalized accounts on the basis of an aggregate of FACES responses and offer a representative perspective of responses typically endorsed by FACES participants.

CASE STUDY I

Roberto Gomez

Roberto Gomez, a 25-year-old divorced corporal from Arizona, was on his second tour of duty in Iraq with the U.S. Army when his truck was hit by an IED. Gomez's head slammed against the side of the truck and then the force from the deafening blast pushed his body out of the truck and threw him to the side of the road. Nails, rocks, and glass punctured his skin. One fellow soldier was killed in the blast.

Corporal Gomez's mother, Flora, a single mom who worked as an elementary school cafeteria worker in a small rural town, received the call at 1:17 a.m., informing her that her son had been injured in Iraq and was being transferred to Landstuhl, Germany, where he would receive treatment for his injuries. The Army representative on the phone gave her scant details about the injury, saying Gomez was alive, but his injuries were severe and that he was in a coma. Flora immediately called her daughter and the word spread quickly among extended family living nearby. For the next 3 days, Flora received updates from the Army but there wasn't much change. Four days after the blast, the Army called. Her son was coming out of a coma and would be transferred to Walter Reed Army Medical Center in Bethesda, Maryland. Two days later, both Gomez and Flora arrived in Washington, DC. At Walter Reed, Flora was told her son had a severe brain injury, a below-the-knee amputation of his right leg, broken right arm, serious cuts, bruises, third-degree burns on his right side extending from thigh to shoulder, and hearing loss in both ears. He was in severe pain and very confused—but he would survive.

The next 4 months passed in a dark blur for Flora. Her sisters came to comfort her and cooked meals for her. Her brother-in-law helped with home repairs and talked with her about fitting the house with appropriate accommodations. Flora was overjoyed when Roberto was stable enough to transfer to the inpatient polytrauma rehabilitation center at the VA hospital in Richmond, Virginia. The transfer seemed like a big step in his recovery. She talked to him every day on the phone, if only for a few minutes. Flora had a strong faith and prayed for Roberto to be back to his old self soon, fulfilling his dreams of working on a degree in law enforcement, reading detective novels, playing poker on the computer, and hanging out with friends. He made encouraging progress in his recovery at first. His physical injuries healed. He was fitted for a prosthesis and was learning to walk again, and although he had some hearing loss, he was able to decipher most of what people were saying. As the weeks turned to months, his improvement slowed and it was clear that there would be lasting effects from the brain injury. He forgot things easily, he often said and did impulsive or inappropriate things that embarrassed her, and he got angry when he couldn't find the right words when he wanted or needed something.

Five months after the blast, Roberto was discharged. Flora and her family had been working with a case manager to prepare for Roberto's return to her home. He had balance issues that were exacerbated by the prosthesis and residual limitations in range of motion in his right arm due to adhesions and scarring from the burns. Flora's brother-in-law got some specifications from the Internet and the men installed grab bars and a bench seat in the shower, replaced the throw rugs with wall-to-wall Berber carpet, put a rubber runner on the stairs, reinforced the banister, and rehabbed an old riding lawn mower with a carry rack so Roberto could work around the yard. Flora's mother donated an old sleeper sofa. Flora made her bedroom in the kitchen so that Roberto could use her bed. She found memory games that he could play and bought some weights that she thought he could lift to build his strength.

Flora used up her vacation days and her sick leave was running out. Roberto couldn't be left alone for too long or he would wander off and forget where he was, or he would injure himself on the stove. He needed help shaving and sometimes needed help using the toilet. He still had a lot of pain and was often frustrated, and frankly, so was she. She felt trapped. She felt like she wasn't helping him get better. She prayed the rosary and lit a candle for Roberto every night. She met with women from her church who clearly were worried about her. After consulting with the case manager, they figured out a schedule where friends would alternate driving Roberto to the gym, to church, and to a support group. The school worked with her scheduling, but she had to cut back to part-time work. Flora found a second part-time job cleaning offices at night, and her mother would sleep over at the house on those evenings. Flora was making ends meet, but she was not eating or sleeping well. She was, however, grateful for her family—both her relatives and church community. One friend from church, a vet himself, identified a possible job for Roberto at the VFW. It was a supported work initiative. Roberto was not that excited about the work, but he was motivated to spend more time around men with whom he shared a common experience.

CASE STUDY II

Tyler Jones

After graduating from a high school in Tulsa, Oklahoma, Tyler Jones married his 18-year-old sweetheart and enrolled in a course in auto mechanics. After a year in the program and against his wife's wishes, he decided to quit school and, like his dad, join the United States Marines. Just before leaving for boot camp, his wife discovered she was pregnant with their daughter. Already rocky, their relationship became even more strained and deteriorated over Tyler's long absences. Before he left on his first deployment to Iraq, they decided to divorce. Six months later while on leave in San Diego, Tyler met Jessica, a part-time sales clerk at a mall clothing store and a divorced mom with a little boy who was just a few months younger than his daughter. They kept in touch while he was in Iraq, and after his tour, he returned to his base near San Diego. There, they dated for a few months, and when she got pregnant, they decided to get married. Less than a year after their wedding, Tyler was deployed to Afghanistan.

While in Afghanistan, Tyler was exposed to a number of explosions in a short period of time. The first occurred when a car bomb exploded near his truck. He felt lucky that he was protected and wasn't in the direct line of the flying debris, but the power of the blast knocked him to the ground so hard he hit his head. After blacking out for a few seconds, he woke up seeing stars and felt dizzy throughout the next day. A few days later, in a different village, Tyler was part of a team inspecting a housing compound. One of the houses was booby-trapped and a small explosive went off. One of the team was thrown into Tyler by the blast, knocking him hard to the ground. In shielding Tyler from harm, his buddy's leg was shredded by shrapnel and was later amputated. Having to *witness a friend suffer such a horrific and bloody wound and then give first aid was more disturbing than the explosion. He started having difficulty sleeping, but kept up with his demanding routine. Tyler was in the vicinity, but never close to a few other explosions after that. Still, after each one, his head would pound with nauseating pain, sometimes so severe that he could not stand up.*

After his tour in Afghanistan, Tyler completed his military service and moved his family to Tulsa so he could be close to his daughter from his first marriage. He had a couple of jobs, but because of continuing headaches and difficulties concentrating, he had a hard time completing each day's work. He felt employers assumed because he was a veteran he must be "damaged." He finally landed a job doing maintenance work for the municipality. They were flexible and understanding about his pain, so Tyler worked hard to keep the job. Plus, the job was during off-hours and didn't require him to interact with too many people. Since returning, he tended to avoid busy places. Jessica, however, noticed that he wasn't sleeping well and often woke up screaming. He seemed depressed and was bothered when family demands required adjustments to his routine. He had a hard time remembering things, but she wasn't sure if that was due to a lack of sleep or something else. For some reason, her son's rambunctious behavior especially seemed to spark anger in him, leaving her feeling caught in the middle. She tried to minimize loud noises in the house, thinking that might help reduce the conflict and improve sleep. She started to set up reminders on his phone to help him remember small details. She took over paying the bills, and it was then she noticed that he had started to buy things impulsively online—things they didn't need and could not afford. Some of the things he didn't even remember buying. After a couple of heated arguments about his behavior, she convinced him he needed to go to the doctor for some help. When he started at the local VA near their apartment, she wanted to go with him. But he preferred to go alone, saying he didn't want her to have to hear about his difficulties. He did tell her that the doctors diagnosed him with persistent symptoms associated with mild TBI and PTSD and they suggested he go to the VA hospital in Dallas to receive specialized care for these two diagnoses. He felt it was too far away and decided to stick to his local clinic. Jessica offered to put all the appointments and reminders for taking his medication in his phone, but he said he would do it, so now she isn't sure if he goes to his appointments or if he takes his medicine.

Much of Jessica's efforts have been trying to manage Tyler's behavior and moods. She even feels she has to manage his relationship with his ex-wife. Although her family would probably be of little help, they are too far away to know. She hasn't made many friends and those she has met think her husband is unstable and don't want to spend time with him. She is stressed about money, her marriage and kids, and her husband's health. She feels her own health is suffering, too. She is depressed and has gained a significant amount of weight since the move. She hopes that if she can find help for herself, she will be able to do more to help Tyler get better, but she isn't sure where to go for help. It is all so complicated.

A DESCRIPTION OF POLYTRAUMA AMONG OEF, OIF, AND OND VETERANS

Polytrauma is two or more injuries to organ systems or physical regions of the body that result in impairments in cognitive, psychological, psychosocial, or physical areas of functioning. This description is consistent with the World Health Organization's

(WHO, 2011) International Classification of Functioning (ICF). The ICF views disability through two domains. The first domain includes a list of body functions and structures and the second domain includes a list of domains of activity and participation. Rehabilitation counselors, therefore, must consider how veterans change physically and biologically (Domain 1) as well as how these changes affect the veteran's ability to fully participate socially and psychologically in the environments where they work, play, and engage with family and friends (Domain 2).

Because research on combat-related polytrauma is a relatively new field, it draws heavily from the TBI and postconcussive syndrome literature to guide both research and practice. TBI has become the signature injury of the wars in Iraq and Afghanistan and, in many cases, the TBI associated with polytrauma is the biological change with the most persistent effects. Ironically, it is also the change that is often the least visible. Before OEF, OIF, and OND, active-duty military and veterans treated for similar types of injuries incurred TBI at rates comparable to the civilian population due to such causes as falls, motor vehicle accidents, and assaults (Griffin et al., 2009).

IEDs can cause polytrauma due to the destructive and insidious nature of this form of weaponry. Explosions from IEDs cause the formation of shockwaves and near instantaneous expansion of gases (Ramasamy, Hill, Hepper, Bull, & Clasper, 2009). As reviewed by Burke, Degeneffe, and Olney (2009), IED shockwaves can cause polytrauma injuries affecting a variety of areas of function, but because service members are exposed to both physical hazards and psychological trauma, as described in the case studies, it is often difficult to disentangle the cause of the ongoing symptoms. This has caused controversy in the field about the best approaches for treating patients with polytrauma. For example, two of the most common conditions that co-occur after a concussion or mild TBI in the OEF/OIF population are PTSD and pain. As with TBI, these symptoms reduce functioning of the neural systems and impair the ability to respond effectively to anxiety. Burke and associates (2009) describe this combination of comorbid conditions as "a new disability" because the conditions have common sequelae, but together the impairments are, in many ways, distinct from TBI or PTSD in isolation. Burke suggests that both disabilities are connected to common sources, but it is unclear if they coexist or if one precipitates the other. These new forms of disability are complex and pose significant challenges to how families understand the course of rehabilitation and how they care for and support their injured family members. They also pose a related set of challenges to the professionals that support the families.

When a service member sustains polytraumatic injuries, families must contend with their loved one's new functional limitations and shoulder the additional demands of providing care and support. Polytrauma injuries can impair the ability of injured persons to fully participate in valued activities of daily life and successfully reintegrate into civilian life, impairments that are consistent with the second domain of the ICF model of disability, limitations on activity and participation. Roberto Gomez, for example, is not engaged in any type of productive activity, but his family and friends are working to help him integrate back into his community.

For those with and without TBI, struggles with mental health challenges can negatively influence both veteran and family safety and overall quality of life; depression and PTSD are the primary mental health issues. Recent research suggests that certain OEF/OIF groups may be at greater risk for mental health challenges. Women are more likely to experience PTSD than are men. This finding may be due, in part, to incidences of sexual harassment and sexual assault (Mathewson, 2011). An additional mental health issue concerns suicide. The danger of suicide among veterans of recent conflicts should be viewed as a real concern, especially among those with the psychiatric disorders that are so commonly associated with polytrauma-related injuries. Recent research suggests that the use of substances and the presence of associated mental health disorders increase the risk of suicide among these veterans (Ilgen et al., 2012).

Families can be instrumental in helping veterans initiate care for their psychological health, and some interventions in civilian samples, such as Community Reinforcement and Family Training (CRAFT), have shown that engaging families can improve treatment initiation for alcohol abuse treatment (Meis et al., 2013; Meyers, Miller, Smith, & Tonigan, 2002; Miller, Meyers, & Tonigan, 1999). Families can also play a role in helping veterans secure benefits, a task that can be especially taxing when a veteran has mental illness. This is potentially a very important resource, considering veterans' reticence to engage such services (see Bagalman, 2013). Untreated or poorly managed symptoms can lead to harmful behaviors among veterans, such as self-harm, child abuse, domestic violence, and chemical dependency and are sources of stress for families. These behaviors may result in dishonorable discharge from service and render them ineligible for a range of VA compensation and health benefits. Unfortunately, when dishonorable discharge occurs under these circumstances, the veteran may be unable to access many of the services and supports necessary to promote positive family functioning and adaptation.

Employment and engagement in educational activities are critical indicators of full participation in valued activities, although they are not afforded the same level of attention as suicide and other indicators of psychological maladjustment. Veterans with and without polytrauma injuries can find difficulty adjusting back into these activities, especially in civilian environments and having to relate to others without the same type of military experience or those who hold views against U.S. actions in Iraq and Afghanistan. For instance, Tyler Jones continues to struggle with ongoing challenges related to maintaining employment, which in turn creates an additional financial and emotional burden since he is not able to consistently contribute to the family income.

Limited data exist on employment outcomes of veterans with polytrauma injuries. The data that do exist suggest that veterans that have served in Iraq and Afghanistan have higher rates of unemployment than do the general population (United States Department of Labor, Bureau of Labor Statistics, 2013). In particular, unemployment tends to increase when veterans have service-connected disabilities. Although it is possible that a greater proportion of OIF, OND, and OEF veterans with polytrauma injuries are unemployed, given the types of cognitive losses (e.g., problems concentrating, memory losses, diminished problem-solving skills) that commonly occur after a neurological injury like TBI, it is also possible, that like Tyler Jones's experience, employers are likely to see veterans as "unstable" workers. These conclusions cannot yet be confirmed, but are important areas for future research (Degeneffe et al., 2008).

POLYTRAUMA SYSTEMS OF CARE

Families of veterans with polytrauma injuries may engage with multiple levels of resources and care within the active-duty and VA health care systems. Depending on the level of severity and the geographical location, family members often join injured service members soon after they are evacuated to a medical facility abroad, or when they transition to a treatment facility in the United States. Family members are welcome to be fully involved in care decisions and treatment planning during ongoing rehabilitation at the VA, but their presence is often dictated by their financial circumstances, work flexibility, and family circumstances. Both the Department of Defense and the VA aim to have a seamless transition from one system of care to the next, with the VA having 33 liaisons stationed at the hospitals where injured military personnel are medically stabilized. These liaisons help veterans and their families make the transition from one level of care to either inpatient or outpatient rehabilitation treatment (Amdur et al., 2011).

Given the number of complex and unique rehabilitation needs of veterans, the VA established in 2005 the Polytrauma System of Care (VA, 2011b), a multilevel system intended to meet the unique rehabilitation needs of each veteran with polytrauma injuries (Sigford, 2008). The Polytrauma System of Care was instrumental in meeting the acute and long-term care needs of Roberto Gomez and Tyler Jones. The initial step in establishing this system was the designation of four inpatient VA rehabilitation sites, now called "Polytrauma Rehabilitation Centers" or PRCs, in four geographically dispersed regions of the country, including Tampa, Florida; Richmond, Virginia; Minneapolis, Minnesota; and Palo Alto, California (a fifth center in San Antonio, Texas was added later; Amdur et al., 2011; Sigford, 2008). Before this designation, these centers had been working closely with the Department of Defense through a collaboration called the Defense and Veterans Brain Injury Centers (DVBIC) that included a TBI registry and evaluation program (MacLennan et al., 2008).

Charged with meeting the complex and unique rehabilitation needs of those injured in OEF/OIF, especially those with moderate to severe war-related TBI, by providing comprehensive, multidisciplinary, team-based inpatient care for those with polytrauma, PRCs made explicit efforts to adopt a family-centered approach to care by incorporating processes of care that include interactions with families throughout the course of care. The model used in the PRCs requires providers across different disciplines, such as rehabilitation counselors, physiatrists, neuropsychologists, physical therapists, and blind rehabilitation specialists, to work together to develop treatment plans and deliver services (VA, 2011a). In keeping with their family-centered care model, these teams developed Family Care Map (FCM), a web-based clinical practice tool (Griffin et al., 2009; Hall, Sigford, & Sayer, 2010), to guide their practice. Using a consensus method, the FCM was developed by team members across sites and clinical disciplines, allowing sites and staff to have consistent approaches and vocabulary in preparing families for each phase of rehabilitation in the PRC. The tool provides information on the phase of care to patients, families, and provider; optimizes family involvement in care and decision making; and promotes effective information transfer between the family and PRC clinical team, in preparation for family life after leaving the PRC.

The second step in developing the Polytrauma System of Care was establishing a network of outpatient clinics for patients with less severe polytrauma. Twenty-three sites across the country were designated as polytrauma network sites (PNS) and were charged with creating an interdisciplinary team to provide specialized postacute, outpatient rehabilitation, focusing on the coordination of lifelong VA and non-VA services for the veteran needs, including health care and case management for current conditions as well as developing conditions (Lew et al., 2007). Network sites can be the first entry point into the Polytrauma System of Care for patients with a mild to moderate level of TBI and their families and/or the next level of care for those discharged from inpatient PRC care. More recently, 88 Polytrauma Support Clinic Teams (PSCT) have been established, groups of rehabilitation providers who deliver either follow-up services provided by the PRCs or provide services for mild, yet complex, polytraumatic injuries. The PSCTs are focused on community reintegration (Amdur et al., 2011) and are dispersed across both urban and rural locations. The last level of care is Polytrauma Points of Contact (VA, 2011b). The 39 Polytrauma Points of Contacts are often social workers employed at smaller VA clinics and are responsible for making direct linkages for veterans to local resources and services (Sigford, 2008). Points of Contact are also responsible for making referrals for veterans and their families that require the assistance of services within the Polytrauma System of Care (Amdur et al., 2011). Locally based services, for example, could involve activity programs, home-based primary care, and homemaker home health services (Sigford, 2008). Despite the extensive polytrauma rehabilitation services available through the VA, access remains a concern as not all families utilize available supports. The reasons that available services are not utilized vary. In some cases, individuals like Tyler Jones may choose to refrain from using available services. The underutilization of available supports may also be due to geographical barriers; individuals like Roberto Gomez may live too far away from the services to access them. Using innovative communication technologies, such as instant messaging or video conferencing, can allow families and patients to work in real time with care teams for couples or family counseling and crisis intervention. They may also be used for managing symptoms, such as medication and appointment reminders, and effectively reducing veteran dependency on families' support.

Throughout the Polytrauma System of Care, there is a strong focus on effective case management and a focus on the individualized needs of veterans with polytrauma and their families (Amdur et al., 2011; Sigford, 2008). Every veteran with polytrauma injuries is assigned a case manager, called "the lead case manager," who serves as a central source of communication among the other case managers and professionals involved in the veteran's care within the Polytrauma System of Care. The lead case manager maintains regular contact with the veteran and family to ensure all necessary services are received (Amdur et al., 2011). The VA's approach to providing health care in its Polytrauma System of Care and other systems of support has been noted as a model of effective patient-centered care due in part to its use of integrated health care (Kuehn, 2012). It should be noted, however, that the VA has been criticized because of its long delays in processing veteran disability claims. As of August 2013, the VA had approximately 780,000 pending disability claims, with about 500,000 of these in pending status for more than 125 days (Hennessey, 2013). While the VA has faced significant challenges in serving veterans and their families, it also has been at the forefront of efforts to treat TBI, PTSD, and other polytrauma injuries (Friedemann-Sánchez, Sayer, & Pickett, 2008).

STRESSORS FACED BY FAMILIES OF VETERANS WITH POLYTRAUMA INJURIES

The families of persons affected by polytrauma injuries potentially face multiple stressors related to adjusting to someone much different than he or she was before his or her injuries. Flora Gomez struggles with her employment situation and feels rather impotent in Roberto's recovery. Jessica worked hard to help Tyler recover, but his memory deficits and impulsive behavior affected how the family functioned. In providing services to these families, rehabilitation counselors need to approach their work with an understanding that family stress and adjustment is likely quite different from that experienced in the general population of persons affected by disabilities associated with polytrauma injuries like TBI and PTSD (Degeneffe & LeNoir, 2011; Griffin et al., 2009, 2012). Rehabilitation counselors should be aware that families of veterans with polytrauma injuries may have experienced multiple stressors associated with deployment before the onset of his or her injuries.

Irrespective of a polytrauma injury, families of veterans commonly struggle with the challenges of successfully reintegrating into civilian life. During deployment, families struggle with long absences and chronic worries about the health and safety of their military family members. Deployments to Iraq and Afghanistan averaged 12 months, and before this date, deployments were as long as 15 months (Brown, 2008). Children lose the nurturing care of their deployed parent and can be fearful about their physical safety. A child's adjustment difficulty can be expressed through poor school performance, acting out, or inappropriate behavior (McFarlane, 2009). Spouses of deployed military personnel have been found to experience significant mental health challenges and difficulties effectively coping with stress (e.g., Eaton et al., 2008).

Family Experience of Acute Polytrauma Care

Following a polytrauma injury, families will often go to the hospital where the injured veteran was medically evacuated following the polytrauma event in Iraq or Afghanistan. The military does not follow a standardized system of informing families about an injury event, and this notification can sometimes come from the injured person him- or herself (Cozza, Chun, & Polo, 2005), resulting in incomplete or inaccurate information. The medical evacuation hospitals can be located overseas or in the continental United States in such locations as the San Diego Navy Medical Center, Brooke Army Medical Center in Fort Sam Houston, Texas, or the National Naval Medical Center in Bethesda, Maryland. Although families may have considered the possibility that their family member could be seriously harmed or killed, facing the reality of such a situation is incredibly stressful and traumatic. Families are immediately propelled into a complex and confusing system of hospitals, medical personnel, rehabilitation centers, and other individuals and systems associated with treatment of polytrauma.

Following medical stabilization, the next phase of rehabilitation may differ on the basis of the severity of polytrauma injuries. Initially, they may be supported by a Polytrauma Rehabilitation Center or a Polytrauma Network Site (described previously). Those with more severe injuries are sent to Polytrauma Rehabilitation Centers (Sigford, 2008). Those with less severe injuries are supported by a Polytrauma Network Site on an outpatient basis.

To better understand the rehabilitation process for the patients and families served by the Polytrauma Rehabilitation Centers, Friedemann-Sánchez et al. (2008) conducted a qualitative study utilizing semistructured interviews, observations, and the use of a field liaison with 56 purposefully selected Polytrauma Rehabilitation Centers providers and providers from consulting services. Providers at these centers indicated that families are often overwhelmed during this initial period of polytrauma rehabilitation and frequently stay at the bedsides of the injured family members day and night. Providers believed that families of veterans with polytrauma injuries face greater distress than do families of those without multiple injuries. Beyond dealing with feelings of loss and grief, participants also conveyed that families sometimes face significant family stress due to extended work absences or an eventual loss of employment. In the case of Roberto Gomez, his mother's absences from work began at this point, setting into motion a set of circumstances that would ultimately result in his mother losing her job. At each step in this beginning process of treatment and rehabilitation, families are often intensely involved, which sometimes affects the relationship with the treatment team:

> The family is intimately involved with the team. Families are pretty much at the patient's side a lot of the day. Families are very involved in the care; at times obstructive in the care, depending on the level of stress, the support they have, or their premorbid personality or coping. They can displace that anger and stress toward the team. It happens quite frequently where the anger and stress are put on the team, on nursing and physicians, occasionally therapists as well. (Friedemann-Sánchez et al., 2008, p. 175)

Cozza and associates (2005) stressed that the experience of families visiting hospitals is unsettling, especially for children, because their schedules and relationships with family are taken outside of a normal rhythm. Families also struggle with how to discuss the veteran parent's injuries when information is sometimes not developmentally appropriate or provided with too much or too little detail.

Research by Schaaf and associates (2013) provides a preliminary understanding of family needs at the acute phase of rehabilitation. They administered the Family Needs Questionnaire (FNQ; Kreutzer, 1988) to 44 family caregivers of patients admitted to the Polytrauma Rehabilitation Center in Richmond, Virginia. Patients included both veterans and active-duty military personnel, and 45% were injured in either OEF or OIF operations. The FNQ is a 40-item measure that assesses both the importance and the extent to which postinjury family needs have been met following brain injury for six-factor analytically derived scales labeled Health Information, Emotional Support, Instrumental Support, Professional Support, Community Support Network, and Involvement with Care. In this early stage of the rehabilitation process, the area rated as most important was for Health Information (e.g., "To be assured that the best possible medical care is being given to the patient"). Health Information needs were also rated as being most often met. Interestingly, meeting needs for Emotional Support and Instrumental Support were the least often rated as important and were also the least met. In the case of Roberto Gomez, significant improvements in his observable physical injuries were evident. Consistent with the findings from Schaaf and associates, during this phase it is therefore likely that Roberto's mother would feel that her health information needs were being met.

Returning Home

Once the OEF, OIF, or OND veteran with polytrauma returns home, families are often tasked with meeting their injured family members' long-term care needs. Little research exists, however, that documents the specific ways these families are affected and their specific needs in the rehabilitation process (Griffin et al., 2009, 2012; Schaaf et al., 2013).

When an OEF, OIF, or OND veteran returns home, the family can experience a range of new stressor events. Adjusting to a family life that has continued and progressed since deployment can be difficult for everyone involved. The literature has shown these adjustments occur across all types of relationships. In their literature review, Worthen, Moos, and Ahern (2012) noted that spouses can encounter a process of reestablishing intimacy, reaching a shared understanding of the deployment experience, redefining family roles, and overall adapting to a new sense of normalcy. In a different study that included 45 male Army soldiers returning from deployment, the veteran and his or her spouse reported less relationship satisfaction the more the veterans expressed PTSD-related symptoms such as sleep disturbances, dissociation, and sexual problems (Goff, Crow, Reisbig, & Hamilton, 2007). Children of veterans, for example, can experience emotional problems during the time of deployment and can suffer from a higher rate of mental health diagnoses after deployment. Worthen and associates provided further insights on how parents of veterans adjusted after the veterans returned home. Using in-depth interviews with 24 OEF and OIF veterans living in California, they found that veterans and their parents held different views on expected family roles, with parents, at times, treating their sons or daughters the same as they did before deployment and not recognizing their postdeployment level of maturity and development. They describe how parents were sometimes overprotective of their veteran family members, especially in cases in which women veterans had been sexually victimized during their military service. In other cases, however, parents who did recognize how their son or daughter matured since deployment seemed to place excessive amounts of expectation and responsibility on the veteran after returning from deployment.

Longer term needs have been examined in the FACES study (Griffin et al., 2012; VA, 2010). This study provides information on how and how much families of veterans with polytrauma provide caregiving support. As previously noted, the FACES study involved surveying 564 family members and friends of veterans treated between 2001 and 2009 at any one of four inpatient VA Polytrauma Rehabilitation Centers. Participants were most often women (79%), and either parents (62%) or spouses (32%). The injured family members incurred polytrauma injuries either in the United States (45%) or overseas in war zones (48%). At the time of survey completion, the care recipient had been injured a median of 4 years. Nearly half (45%) of the veterans injured incurred their injuries from 4 to 6 years previous to study participation. To be eligible for FACES, the injured veteran had to have been discharged from a Polytrauma Rehabilitation Center for at least 3 months. This study demonstrated the extensive assistance provided by families and the difficulties in meeting other role demands and maintaining their physical and mental health. A total of 124 (22%) of the care recipients had high intensity needs (i.e., needing assistance with one or more activities of daily living), and among this group, 61 participants (49%) provided 80 or more hours per week of care. Nearly a third of caregivers reported they were the only caregiver among the care recipient's family and friends ($n = 41$, 33%). Many had additional demands on their time, including 48 (41%) who were employed or attended school, and 39 (31%) who provided unpaid care to children younger than 18 years in addition to the care they provided to the care recipient. It is likely the long-term effects of this extensive caregiver role lead to deleterious outcomes for families, but researchers have not yet examined these outcomes.

One of the implications of the FACES study is that family caregiving for those with polytrauma injuries varies considerably from family to family depending on the nature of the individual's polytrauma injuries. Flora was confronted with extensive instrumental support responsibilities and demands that exerted a pervasive influence on all aspects of her life. The consequences for Flora included poor diet, reliance on alcohol to cope with stress, and job loss. It is also likely she was socially isolated due to the caregiving demands. In the case of Tyler Jones, the type of caregiving and the consequences of providing care were clearly distinct from the experiences of

Roberto Gomez and his mother. The caregiving demands faced by his wife Jessica were primarily affective in nature, where she helped manage his moods and his relationships with others, such as his ex-wife.

While the FACES study details the extensive demands encountered by families of those injured in Iraq or Afghanistan, these families have access to financial resources that are not available to the families of civilians who experience polytrauma resulting in the same types of injuries. The Omnibus Health Services Act (Caregivers and Veterans Omnibus Health Services Act, 2009) makes available a range of new services for families of injured OEF/OIF/OND veterans that are not available to the civilian population. Through the OHA, the U.S. federal government has mandated the VA to provide an array of services and financial assistance to eligible family caregivers of injured OEF/OIF/OND veterans who require assistance or continuous supervision. The financial assistance is stipends directly paid to caregivers and intended to be equivalent to what "commercial caregivers" would earn to give a similar level of care in the geographic region where the veteran lives. Eligible family members receive training on how to provide care and can receive mental health counseling, free health insurance, and be periodically relieved of their caregiving responsibilities through the provision of paid respite care. The families of both Roberto Gomez and Tyler Jones would likely benefit considerably from the financial support and other supports provided through this Act given the variety of stressors the families experienced.

CONCLUSIONS

Veterans with polytrauma injuries represent a significant and growing population for rehabilitation counseling practice. The innovations employed by the Department of Defense and the VA, in many ways, present a model approach for effectively using interdisciplinary teams to promote collaborations among patients, families, and practitioners. This approach could influence future work of rehabilitation counselors outside of the military and veteran communities. Although the U.S. federal government's commitment to meeting the instrumental support, mental health, and financial assistance needs of caregivers of OEF/OIF/OND veterans with polytrauma injuries is commendable, these same benefits are lacking in the general population, providing rehabilitation counselors an opportunity to advocate for needed legislation and funding. Here, we have described what polytrauma is, the formal system of care set up to meet and study the needs of polytrauma patients, and then illustrated common stressors faced by veterans and their families, especially as they learn to manage the persistent consequences of their injuries.

Rehabilitation counselors have an important role to play in assisting families of injured veterans. However, rehabilitation counseling educators have not sufficiently prepared those in the profession to do this important work. This is a shortcoming.

The profession needs to make a commitment to respond and to work with families who have made and will continue to make sacrifices for injured veterans. Sigford (2008) aptly reminds practitioners of the admonition given by President Abraham Lincoln during the Civil War when he stated, "To care for him who shall have borne the battle and for his widow and his orphan" (p. 160).

Toward meeting this objective of fully addressing the needs of injured veterans and their family caregivers, Frain and associates (2010) stressed the need for rehabilitation counselors to possess the following areas of understanding:

1. be prepared to screen for and identify non-visible disabilities;
2. be made aware of the treatments, psychological and psychosocial sequelae, and symptoms of commonly experienced disabilities; and
3. have an understanding of the military, medical, psychological, and rehabilitation systems that veterans are likely to be involved in (frequently this involves multiple systems concurrently). (p. 16)

Because of their expertise with employment and disability, Frain and associates further recommended that rehabilitation counselors understand specific techniques in working with veterans and prospective employers to advance employment participation among veterans, especially those with polytrauma and other types of disabilities. Burke and associates (2009) encourage rehabilitation counselors to engage in research that furthers the understanding of employment outcomes, family adjustment, and treatment interventions for veterans affected by the combined effects of TBI and PTSD. Degeneffe and LeNoir (2011) have argued about the importance of knowing how veteran-related services and funding contribute to differences between the experiences of family caregivers of veterans and family caregivers of civilians. Informed rehabilitation practitioners, knowledgeable of the needs of veterans and their families, the systems of services available to them, and the barriers to accessing these services, embody the potential to enhance recognition of the rehabilitation counseling profession in service of greater objective; assisting families of veterans with disabilities to address the lasting challenges posed by exposure to trauma and to help maximize the veteran's reintegration into family, community, and vocational aspects of life.

Altogether, these recommendations point to an unfinished research and practice agenda for rehabilitation counselors. To improve veteran and family outcomes, rehabilitation counselors should advocate to reduce bureaucratic inefficiencies in obtaining needed services and work to change current criminal justice procedures and protocols that prevent veterans from being eligible to receive VA services. Their research and training should include how to better train families in providing long-term care, how to communicate more effectively, and how to adequately support families as they move through the rehabilitation process, and help to establish successful approaches for families to adjust to long-term caring for someone with polytrauma injuries (Griffin et al., 2009).

REFERENCES

Amdur, D., Batres, A., Beslisle, J., Brown, J. H., Cornis-Pop, M., Mathewson-Chapman, M., . . . Washam, T. (2011). VA integrated post-combat care: A systems approach to caring for returning combat veterans. *Social Work in Health Care, 50*, 564–575.

Bagalman, E. (2013). *Mental disorders among OEF/OIF veterans using VA health care: Facts and figures* (Report No. R41921). Washington, DC: Congressional Research Service.

Brown, F. W., III. (2008, April 10). Bush announces shorter deployment lengths. American Forces Press Service. Retrieved from http://www.defense.gov/news/newsarticle.aspx?id=49530

Burke, H., Degeneffe, C. E., & Olney, M. (2009). A new disability for rehabilitation counselors: Iraq War veterans with traumatic brain injury and post-traumatic stress disorder. *Journal of Rehabilitation, 75*(3), 5–14.

Caregivers and Veterans Omnibus Health Services Act of 2010, S. 1963, 111th Cong. (2009).

Council on Rehabilitation Education. (2013). *Accreditation manual for masters level rehabilitation counselor education programs*. Schaumburg, IL: Author.

Cozza, S. J., Chun, R. S., & Polo, J. A. (2005). Military families and children during operation Iraqi freedom. *Psychiatric Quarterly, 76*, 371–378.

Degeneffe, C. E., Boot, D., Kuehne, J., Kuraishi, A., Maristela, F., Noyes, J., . . . Will, H. (2008). Community-based interventions for persons with traumatic brain injury: A primer for rehabilitation counselors. *Journal of Applied Rehabilitation Counseling, 39*(1), 42–52.

Degeneffe, C. E., & LeNoir, J. (2011). Understanding families of veterans with traumatic brain injury: The Pearlin Stress Process Model. *VEWAA Journal, 38*, 9–17.

Eaton, K. M., Hoge, C. W., Messer, S. C., Whitt, A. A., Cabrera, O. A., McGurk, D., . . . Castro, C. A. (2008). Prevalence of mental health problems, treatment need, and barriers to care among primary care-seeking spouses of military service members involved in Iraq and Afghanistan deployments. *Military Medicine, 173*, 1051–1056.

Fischer, H. (2012). *U.S. military casualty statistics: Operation new dawn, operation Iraqi freedom, and operation enduring freedom* (Report No. RS22452). Washington, DC: Congressional Research Service.

Frain, M., Bishop, M., & Bethel, M. (2010). A roadmap for rehabilitation to serve military veterans with disabilities. *Journal of Rehabilitation, 76*, 13–21.

Friedemann-Sánchez, G., Sayer, N., & Pickett, T. (2008). Provider perspectives on rehabilitation of patients with polytrauma. *Archives of Physical Medicine and Rehabilitation, 84*, 171–178.

Goff, N., Crow, J., Reisbig, A., & Hamilton, S. (2007). The impact of individual trauma symptoms of deployed soldiers on relationship satisfaction. *Journal of Family Psychology, 21*, 344–353.

Griffin, J. M., Friedemann-Sánchez, G., Hall, C., Phelan, S., & van Ryn, M. (2009). Families of patients with polytrauma: Understanding the evidence and charting a new research agenda. *Journal of Rehabilitation Research and Development, 46*, 879–892.

Griffin, J. M., Friedemann-Sánchez, G., Jensen, A. C., Taylor, B. C., Gravely, A., Clothier, B., . . . van Ryn, M. (2012). The invisible side of war: Families caring for US service members with traumatic brain injuries and polytrauma. *Journal of Head Trauma Rehabilitation, 27*(1), 3–13. doi:10.1097/HTR.0b013e3182274260

Hall, C., Sigford, B., & Sayer, N. A. (2010). Practice changes associated with the Department of Veterans Affairs' Family Care Collaborative. *Journal of General Internal Medicine, 25*, 18–26.

Hennessey, K. (2013, August 10). *Before vacation, Obama seeks to reassure veterans on healthcare.* Retrieved from http://articles.latimes.com/2013/aug/10/nation/la-na-obama-vets-20130811

Ilgen, M., McCarthy, J. F., Ignacio, R. V., Bohnert, B., Valenstein, M., Blow, F. C., & Katz, I. R. (2012). Psychopathology, Iraq and Afghanistan service, and suicide among Veterans Health Administration patients. *Journal of Consulting and Clinical Psychology, 80,* 323–330.

Jenkins, W. M., Patterson, J. B., & Szymanski, E. M. (1998). Philosophical, historical, and legislative aspects of the rehabilitation counseling profession. In R. M. Parker & E. M. Szymanski (Eds.), *Rehabilitation counseling: Basics and beyond* (3rd ed., pp. 1–40). Austin, TX: Pro-ed.

Kreutzer, J. S. (1988). *Family needs questionnaire.* Richmond, VA: Rehabilitation Research and Training Center on Severe Traumatic Brain Injury, Medical College of Virginia.

Kuehn, B. M. (2012). Veterans health system cited by experts as a model for patient-centered care. *JAMA: The Journal of the American Medical Association, 307*(5), 442–443.

Lew, H. L., Poole, J. H., Vanderploeg, R. D., Goodrich, G. L., Dekelboum, S., Guillory, S. B., . . . Cifu, D. X. (2007). Program development and defining characteristics of returning military in a VA Polytrauma Network site. *Journal of Rehabilitation Research and Development, 44,* 1027–1034.

MacLennan, D., Clausen, S., Pagel, N., Avery, J. D., Sigford, B., MacLennan, D., & Mahowald, R. (2008). Developing a polytrauma rehabilitation center: A pioneer experience in building, staffing, and training. *Rehabilitation Nursing, 33,* 198–213.

Mathewson, J. (2011). In support of military women and families: Challenges facing community therapists. In R. B. Everson & C. R. Figley (Eds.), *Families under fire: Systemic therapy with military families* (pp. 215–235). New York, NY: Routledge.

McFarlane, A. (2009). Military deployment: The impact on children and family adjustment and the need for care. *Current Opinion in Psychiatry, 22,* 369.

Meis, L. A., Griffin, J. M., Greer, N., Jensen, A. C., Macdonald, R., Carlyle, M., . . . Wilt, T. J. (2013). Couple and family involvement in adult mental health treatment: A systematic review. *Clinical Psychology Review, 33*(2), 275–286.

Meyers, R. J., Miller, W. R., Smith, J. E., & Tonigan, J. S. (2002). A randomized trial of two methods for engaging treatment-refusing drug users through concerned significant others. *Journal of Consulting and Clinical Psychology, 70*(5), 1182–1185.

Miller, W. R., Meyers, R. J., & Tonigan, J. S. (1999). Engaging the unmotivated in treatment for alcohol problems: A comparison of three strategies for intervention through family members. *Journal of Consulting and Clinical Psychology, 67*(5), 688–697.

Ramasamy, A., Hill, A. M., Hepper, A. E., Bull, A. M., & Clasper, J. C. (2009). Blast mines: Physics, injury mechanisms and vehicle protection. *Journal of the Royal Army Medical Corps, 156*(4), 258–264.

Schaaf, K. P. W., Kreutzer, J. S., Danish, S. J., Pickett, T. C., Rybarczyk, B. D., & Nichols, M. G. (2013). Evaluating the needs of military and veterans' families in a polytrauma setting. *Rehabilitation Psychology, 58,* 106–110.

Sigford, B. J. (2008). "To care for him who shall have borne the battle and for his widow and his Orphan" (Abraham Lincoln): The Department of Veterans Affairs Polytrauma System of Care. *Archives of Physical Medicine and Rehabilitation, 89,* 160–162.

True Cost of War Act, H.R. 1238, 113th Cong. (2013).

United States Department of Defense. (2012). *2011 Demographics: Profile of the military community.* Retrieved from http://www.militaryonesource.mil/12038/MOS/Reports/2011_Demographics_Report.pdf

United States Department of Defense. (2013). *Casualty statistics.* Retrieved from http:// www .defense.gov / news / casualty.pdf

United States Department of Labor, Bureau of Labor Statistics. (2013). *Employment situation of veterans summary.* Retrieved from http://www.bls.gov/news.release/vet.nr0.htm

United States Department of Veterans Affairs. (2010). *Family and caregiver experience survey.* Retrieved from http://www.hsrd.minneapolis.med.va.gov/FACES/

United States Department of Veterans Affairs. (2011a). *Polytrauma rehabilitation centers.* Retrieved from http://www.polytrauma.va.gov/system-of-care/care-facilities/poly-trauma-rehabilitation-centers.asp

United States Department of Veterans Affairs. (2011b). *Polytrauma system of care.* Retrieved from http://www.polytrauma.va.gov/system-of-care/

World Health Organization. (2011). *International classification of functioning, disability and health: ICF.* Geneva, Switzerland: Author. Retrieved from http://www.who.int/classification/icf

Worthen, M., Moos, R., & Ahern, J. (2012). Iraq and Afghanistan veterans' experiences living with their parents after separation from the military. *Contemporary Family Therapy, 34*(3), 362–375.

CHAPTER 12

Cultural Perspectives on Family Attitudes Toward Disability

Michael J. Millington

A community-based approach to rehabilitation counseling requires that the counselor enter the family's worldview to understand and engage its beliefs and goals in regard to its loved one with a disability. The working alliance depends on it. In an increasingly diverse cultural milieu, it is incumbent on the professional to broaden his or her understanding of the phenomenon of disability across the cultural landscape and to consider how best to respond on behalf of the client and the profession in any family context.

This is, however, a daunting proposition. We are chained, in a sense, to our own worldview. We can imagine other perspectives, but we cannot live them. The potential variations on cultural and ethnic themes that construct the lives of people with disabilities are infinite in the specifics, and access to the details is not for outsiders. We do our best to become conversant in the larger themes of culture and open to the unique differences that present themselves in dialog of lived experience with our clients and their families.

In this chapter, we explore cultural perspectives on disability and their relationships to family from the vantage point of four established collective identities: Hispanic Americans, African Americans, Asian Americans, and Native Americans. Within each, we find the family and describe it in the context of its communities. Within the family, we look closer at the experience of disability, its broad cultural implications, and the family response. Along the way, we touch upon some of the more salient historical and cultural aspects that inform the disability experience.

We use the idea of attitudes as an organizing concept for investigating the changeable meaning of disability across these social identities and the potential for change within them. Attitudes are affectively charged cognitions, predisposing a class of stereotypical behaviors toward a referent in social situations (Triandis, 1971), and a cultural artifact of social learning (Livneh, 1988). We are primarily concerned with attitudes toward people with disabilities because they are historically charged with negative biases (Wright, 1988) that can ultimately influence the efficacy of service and inclusion of people with disabilities (Marinelli & Dell Orto, 1999) at all levels of community.

HISPANIC FAMILY ROOTS

Family is the center of Hispanic American life. It is more important than either the individual or the larger community. Hispanic families are traditionally extended generationally with well-defined roles within. The elders (grandparents) hold a place of honor and respect. Often they are sought for advice. In Cuban families, family elders retain ownership of the family's most valuable possessions (e.g., the business, the boat, the tractor, the land). Elders contribute as stewards of familial wealth rather than through physical labor. The head of household is the adult male (father) who is the primary wage earner and around whom family supports revolve. The family's task is to maximize the earning potential of the head of household. The adult female (mother) is responsible for the home and the raising of the children. The oldest male child is recognized as the future head of household and groomed accordingly. The oldest female child is expected to share in the task of raising younger siblings. Children grow up in a highly protective and supervised home, remaining more deeply dependent on the family hierarchy for a much longer period of time than their cohorts in the dominant culture. Dominican children do not leave the familial home until they are married, and if they do not marry, they are not likely to leave at all (Lopez-De Fede & Haeussler-Fiore, 2002).

Machismo is an unavoidable term in the discussion of family roles, but it is poorly defined and even more poorly understood. The term itself has a very recent 20th-century etymology and no stable core. At the center is the concept of an idealized masculine worldview and deportment. To some it is the patriarchic duty of protecting the family, instilling and enforcing the right values in the home and the education of the young. To others it is the rejection of all feminine values, and baser interpretations of what it means to be a man (aggression, sexual promiscuity, etc.). What they have in common is the strong expectation of a narrowly defined identity for the male (husband, father, colleague) and the potential for shame and conflict if the role is compromised (Lopez-De Fede & Haeussler-Fiore, 2002).

Women are similarly idealized in role and value. Women are the stewards of the family and home. In a Catholic world, the primacy of Saint Mary holds the mother of Christ in reverence and through the Virgin of Guadalupe a strong symbol of the ideal. The values projected on this ideal of the feminine tend to be quiet, dutiful submission to the male, and chaste piety. Failure to live up to the ideal can result in public and private (DePaul, Lagana, & Gonzalez-Ramirez, 1996) sanction and shame.

Disability in the Family and Community

There is a general lack of research into Hispanic American attitudes and beliefs concerning disabilities. What has been done is largely dated, potentially biased (see Ruiz & Padilla, 1977), and does not taken the heterogeneity of the population into consideration (Graf, Blankenship, Sanchez, & Carlson, 2007). Hispanic Americans understand and accept the premise of western medicine, but understanding is couched in a religious worldview. Health, either good or bad, is a dispensation from God. And so disability is often construed as punishment, a test, or simply "God's will." The implication being that you somehow deserve your lot in life or that it was your destiny (Alvarez & Ruiz, 2001).

Psychological states (worry, anger, fear), environmental conditions (bad air, germs, bad food, imbalance of cold and hot, etc.), and supernatural agents (Lafitte, 1983) conspire to cause illness and disability. Mothers are often held responsible for the congenital disabilities of their offspring, as it is assumed that they violated a taboo (e.g., eating the wrong food, witnessed a horrific event, or encountered a disfigured person) while pregnant (Brice, 2002). Psychiatric disabilities are the most prone to supernatural explanation, usually attributable to evil spirits or witchcraft (Molina, Zambrana, & Aguirre-Molina, 1994).

Response

The family is responsible for care giving. Each member of the family has a role to play (Trevino & Szymanski, 1996). Family members provide all of the support, if possible, including nurturance, home remedies, and spiritual petitions for relief. Seeking help outside of the family is a sign of weakness and incompetence (Hanline & Daley, 1992). Families tend to draw inward, to protect the family member, especially children to the point of overprotection (Rivera, 1983). Sheltering and isolation is seen as a way to protect the family members (and the family) from a world that they believe will stigmatize them, shame them, and offer them nothing of value (Lopez-De Fede & Haeussler-Fiore, 2002).

Religious coping involves drawing strength directly from one's faith. The observation of ceremony and ritual add to the psychological well-being of the individual and the family (Abraido-Lanza, Vasquez, & Echeverria, 2004). Religiosity increases the perception of control over something that it ultimately the will of God. Because God intervenes directly in the lives of people, the family believes in the potential for miraculous cures and devotion as a means to the miracle (Weisman, 2000).

There are folk healers in the Mexican tradition (Glover & Blankenship, 2007) who holistically treat problems in body, mind, and spirit. They are considered to be divinely inspired to provide natural and supernatural remedies. Herbs and medicinal plants may be ingested or topically applied in combination with massage and ceremonial intervention in the spirit world. Folk healers are most commonly used when conventional medicine and prayer have failed to produce the desired result (Zavaleta, 2000).

Hispanic American women play the central role in care giving, are most informed about service, and most likely to seek it. Help is sought from the family outward. Case in point, mental health is enmeshed in the interrelationships of the family (Vera & Conner, 2007). Mental health is "taught" parent to child in terms of harmony and interdependence. Promoting mental health moves outward into the community. Mental health is provided through local community resources (e.g., day care, parks with programs). Mental health is operationally defined by having jobs nearby and knowing that you are providing for your family and they are safe. Outside of the family, Hispanic Americans prefer to turn to trusted individuals, family friends, clergy, or peers in the community. Hispanic women will willingly try everything but mental health services (Vega, Kolody, & Aguilar-Gaxiola, 2001) as they are highly stigmatizing to the individual and the family. However, the more familiar she is with mental health services (through the experiences of friends) and the less attributable the mental illness is to supernatural causes and moral failing, the more likely mental health services will be engaged (Alvidrez, 1999).

AFRICAN AMERICAN FAMILY ROOTS

The extended family is the center of life with an emphasis on group survival. Family members are protective of their own and tend to define problems in terms of external threat rather than internal fault or conflict (Boyd-Franklin, 2003). The identity of the individual is negotiated in the context of interdependence and his or her contribution to the family (Lee, Blando, Mizelle, & Orozco, 2007). Multigenerational households are common, with grandparents acting as heads of household. Traditional gender roles are followed in that women are responsible for taking care of the family, but women are often the heads of household, by economic necessity or matriarchic tradition. Aunts and uncles living in close proximity will serve as surrogate parents, providing emotional and financial support, and receive the same level of respect as biological parents (Miller, 2002). Kinship bonds often extend informally to friends and neighbors (Jacobson, 2003).

Within this collectivist theme, class influences family structure. In Haiti, class is sharply delineated by language and economics. The French-speaking ruling class retained the lion's share of public resources within the urban centers and segregated its education system accordingly. The Creole-speaking people of Haiti are rural and left with few resources and little opportunity for education and advancement. In Jamaica, the upper and the middle classes are also concentrated in the urban centers and delineated by church affiliation. The Anglican Church provides an organizing center for the community of the wealthy; the Baptist church serves the same function for the poor. Each holds the other in some level of contempt (Miller, 2002). The wealthy tend to cleave to a more European standard of traditional marriage, proscribed spousal partnership, and nuclear families. Cohabitation is more common among the poor. Children may continue to live in the family home well into adulthood, out of economic necessity (Jacobson, 2003).

Disability in the Family and Community

As we investigate the attitudes of African Americans toward people with disabilities, it is important to look at the special circumstances that the history of an enslaved people in America created around this issue. The American version of slavery was particularly dehumanizing: "African Americans were thought to have good mental health if they were subservient (being controlled and docile), whereas protesters were categorized as deranged and mentally ill" (Wilson, 2005, p. 157). The psychology of the time pathologized the African American experience to justify the oppression of African Americans first through slavery and later through every social outlet including education, health, and employment (Wilson, 2005).

Mental illness carries stigma exacerbated by that history. In a qualitative study (Matthews, Corrigan, Smith, & Aranda, 2006), African Americans identified good mental health as being stable, in touch, positive attitude, resilient, and in good spiritual health. Stress and trauma were reported as the primary reason for mental health problems in general, but religious leaders attribute mental illness, at least in part, on spiritual intercession (e.g., demons). Overall, mental illness was seen as unresponsive to treatment. Appraisals of life with mental illness were consistently negative. Positive appraisals, when they occurred, were usually attributable to spiritual intervention. The stigma of mental illness is socially contagious, capable of diminishing the standing of those who associate with people with mental illness. Compassion carries the risk of sharing in the consequences of stigma.

Jamaican perception of disability depends on the cause of the disability and the worldview of the perceiver. Because God punishes the wicked and rewards the good, disability is often seen as the consequence of sin. Disability thus attributed becomes a public shame for both the person with a disability and the family. Disabilities acquired by observable means under circumstance beyond the control of the person generate the most compassion; disabilities acquired through negligence generate the least compassion. Illnesses that cannot be explained otherwise may be construed as the work of evil spirits or witchcraft (Leavitt, 1992). Mental illness is often thought to be a vengeful act of an enemy who attached a ghost to the person's spirit.

Haiti perspectives on disability are similarly defined in terms of shame and further charged with the propensity for community rejection and abuse. What may be considered a disability in the United States is often attributed to personal failing in Haiti. Public response to personal failing is actively negative and exclusionary. Children with developmental disabilities are seen as especially devastating to the family's hopes for the future because of Haitians' high expectations that education is the solution to current economic hardship. Disabilities, developmental or acquired, are mysterious and dangerous and not readily discussed. If a woman bears a child with a disability, the man may impregnate another woman to demonstrate that the disability is attributable to the mother and not to him. Often, the mother of the child with a disability is abandoned (Jacobson, 2003). A spirit curse, punishment of a Christian god, or spell cast by an enemy, disability is often thought to be supernatural in origin. Many Haitians are afraid of people with disabilities, as if they are contagious, whether the disability is mental or physical (Jacobson, 2003).

Response

Turner and Alston (1994) identified four basic strengths that support the African American family's response to physical disability, namely, strong kinship bonds, role flexibility, religious orientation, and education/work ethic. Where extended families are intact, the family member with a disability is supported from within. Family roles are flexible and adaptable to need. New tasks are taken on easily within the role or shared as a community task. Grandparents, spouse, uncles and aunts may all take on the duties as head of household should the need arise. Neighbors supervise the young in public settings. The extended family tends to be active in family affairs whether it is in close proximity or living at a distance. Active participation in church spirituality is pursued as a way of coping individually and collectively with the consequences of mental illness. The church provides a social gathering place and a resource for supportive pastoral counseling, community outreach, and charitable giving. It is the hub of the social support network where extended families connect and share. Education/work ethic links hard work and education instrumentally to the attainment of a good life and families come together to support the achievements of their members (Turner & Alston, 1994). The strong family focus dictates that problems associated with disability are resolved as close to home as possible. This support strategy facilitates inclusion for people with physical disabilities and challenges for people with mental illness. The African American community expects self-reliance and stoic silence about mental health problems. Seeking help is embarrassing and stigmatizing (Matthews et al., 2006). Mental health services are only appropriate in cases of extreme need and seen as ineffective and unresponsive. Avoidance is fueled by expectations of loss and ill treatment within the system. Psychotropic medication is mistrusted and hospitalization is feared. Once labeled, the person is thought labeled for life. The label portends reduced opportunities and a bleak economic outlook. Medication and its side effects are thought to be a permanent burden that carries the risk of addiction (Cooper et al., 2003). It is clear why parents will fight the labeling process to the point of avoiding service. The resistance to outside intervention can be ameliorated somewhat with the inclusion of familiar and trusted figures, especially church officials and spiritual counselors (Snowden, 2001). Depending on racial identity and attitudes toward Whites, some clients are more comfortable with counselors with a similar ethnic background (Ferguson, Leach, Levy, Nicholson, & Johnson, 2008).

Jamaican families tend to resolve their familial issues in the home before they seek help in their community, and they seek help in their community before they seek help in the form of government services (Miller, 2002). Family interventions may include reading bible passages, use of talismans and animistic ritual to ward off the evil ghosts. Children with congenital disabilities are closeted away from public view, to protect them from abuse and to avoid shaming the family. They may maintain a passive "sick role" all of their lives. Deep conflict arises where demand for chronic care exceeds the family's ability to provide. Institutionalization for any family member is a failure of the family obligation and a public humiliation, to the point that abandonment is a possible and preferable option. Little is expected from people with mental illness, care is meager, and abuse is historically common. When help is sought, it is the women's task to find it. They tend not to trust the experts, will challenge their conclusions, demand to be heard, and will confront anything they feel is unjust (Miller, 2002).

Haitian families hold a similar hierarchy of responses. The family as a group makes decisions, and, where possible, it uses family support systems to provide for the family member. Children with disabilities are loved but considered worthless in the family's economic struggle, which takes precedence over other concerns. When outside help is needed, the family turns to religion and, in contrast to the Jamaican response, public institutions. However, Haitians turn to state-sponsored support looking for a cure rather than an extended rehabilitation process with limited outcomes (Jacobson, 2003).

ASIAN FAMILY ROOTS

Family is the basic social unit, transcending the individual in many traditions (Liu, 2001). With the group's well-being at the center, harmony and balance are the measures of wellness. Harmony in the home leads to harmony in the community, which in turn leads to harmony in the nation. Harmony is sustained through well-established roles for husband, wife, daughter, son, grandparents, and so forth, and these roles are defined by subordination to authority and interdependence (Kim-Rupnow, 2001). There is hierarchy in the roles, but the hierarchy tends to serve the family unit rather than the head of household. Parents sacrifice for their children, particularly in education. Children, in turn, are obligated to support their aging parents (Kim-Rupnow, 2001). Roles are gender and age based. Father takes the lead. Mother follows. Older siblings are responsible for helping in raising their younger siblings (De Torres, 2002) who in turn are taught to show respect and obedience. Assertiveness, particular among the young, is rude. Frank expression of emotions or needs is discouraged especially for men (Kim-Rupnow, 2001). Sacrifice and sublimating one's own ego for the sake of the family is the rule. Improper behavior of the individual shames the person and the family (Hunt, 2002). Family is extended multigenerationally (Liu, 2001). There is a reverence for age. Family concept moves outward from the extended family to the community and obligations and benefits go with it. Community is a tightly knit group that will help members find work, support, education, and housing. Being faithful to the family and the local community that supports the person is a source of pride.

Compared with other Asian groups, the traditional Filipino family is perhaps less reserved and formal in its interrelations and more democratic in its approach to dealing with family decisions. Filipino families engage in complex social relationships with extended family networks of both blood and affiliation (e.g., godparents) through which favors are traded and obligations are served. Social obligations and family grudges can be passed down generationally and revisited in family gatherings (De Torres, 2002). Pinoys (individual Filipinos) living alone are rare. Core families stay together until married off, even longer if economically necessary. Elder siblings support younger siblings once they have employment, avoiding marriage until younger siblings are through with their education. The youngest daughter takes care of the parents (De Torres, 2002).

The collectivist Indian family may be contrasted against other Asian groups by the extent of the patriarchal emphasis. Family property is held in common, but the male head of household is the sole decision maker on matters of property and family. Beyond the patriarch, males of all ages are to be respected and obeyed. Women tend to join their husband's family and inherit subservient positions (Pinto & Sahu, 2001). The relationship of the family to the community at large is still influenced by an ancient caste system that sets the social and economic parameters of appropriate behavior and association. Castes are a formalized class system that reserve the best schools, homes, jobs, and ultimately wealth and influence for the upper castes and relegates the lower castes to powerlessness, poverty, and exclusion (Pinto & Sahu, 2001).

Disability in the Family and Community

Disability is seen as disharmony, which is a threat to the natural Confucian order of things. Stigma is often high in Chinese communities (Lam, Tsang, Chan, & Corrigan, 2006); indeed, the common Chinese term for disability translates as "useless" or "sick" (Liu, 2001). Lay theories abound as to the cause of disability, from retribution for sins of a past life (Liu, 2001) to eating lamb while pregnant (Lam et al., 2006). While any disability of any kind is stigmatizing, the most severe response has historically been reserved for people with mental illness. Mental illness is attributed to weak moral character, and so the afflicted's behavior brings shame to the family.

In India, disability is punishment for misdeeds in past lives (karma). Congenital disability is accepted as karmic fate, although little help is forthcoming. Indians see their children as an investment in the future, especially the male children. A child with developmental disability isn't seen as a good investment of time, money, or effort. He or she is loved, but no effort is made to make him or her independent. Acquired disabilities are more sympathetic, particularly if there is hope that former productivity can be regained. Disability is a family affair, and the women shoulder the burden. Empowerment is selfishness. Indians live for the family, especially the females (Pinto & Sahu, 2001).

In Korea (Kim-Rupnow, 2001) and Vietnam, disability is caused by supernatural agents, such as punishment from God, curse from evil forces, or punishment for the sins of one's ancestors. Oftentimes, it would be divined that the mother did something wrong during pregnancy, failing to eat right, or breaking a taboo. Educated Koreans are more likely to believe in genetic and biologic causes. Koreans tend to see developmental disabilities as karmic retribution, bringing shame to the person and family. As a sign of retribution for sins, the family member with a disability is often isolated from the public. Acquired disabilities may be seen in a positive light if they are seen as sacrifice for the common good, and others seek to regain their role (Kim-Rupnow, 2001). In Vietnam, the congenitally blind are thought to have spiritual vision, special powers to see into the future and the past. They are often employed as psychics at the temple or in the marketplace. Vietnamese attitudes toward disabilities have been especially shaped by our war. Following the war and in the aftermath of landmines, people with all nature of physical disability were very common and without stigma. Agent Orange created both congenital and acquired disabilities and a new generation of "victims of the war." These are also held faultless and without shame.

Asian Americans are generally more accepting of acquired disabilities than congenital physical or mental illness (Wang, Chan, Thomas, Lin, & Larson, 1997). Mental illness is associated with weak character or blamed on evil spirits or punishment of the gods. Mental illness is shameful and worse, reflects badly on the family and ancestors (Ho, 1984). It is not generally discussed in the family.

Response

Those with a scientific background seek solutions. Those with a spiritual background seek healing. Many pursue both. Noting the coping strategies of Chinese families, Lam et al. (2006) observed,

> The prime source of coping relies on oneself, including facing the problem and devising a solution; enduring and persevering; striving; and having confidence. It is generally believe [sic] that if one has the willpower; one should be able to overcome the problem. The second major source of coping is help from one's family and social network. The third source is from shamanism and folk religions. The final coping strategy is doing nothing and letting nature take its course, an approach which is greatly influenced by Taoist philosophy. (p. 276)

Believing strongly in the mind–body connection (Hampton, Yeung, & Nguyen, 2007), they will often integrate medical care with spiritual healing. People with mental illness often prefer Chinese spiritual healers to physicians (Lam et al., 2006). Institutionalization is an agreeable and often preferred treatment of people with mental illness, and group homes for people with developmental disabilities are disliked by many Chinese Americans. Where services are available, they may be underutilized because, as a group, Asian Americans have a higher tolerance for psychological discomfort of stress and anxiety (Zhang, Snowden, & Sue, 1998).

Help seeking is mitigated or encouraged by community pressure (Christopher, Skillman, Kirkhart, & D'Souza, 2006) as well as support. Chinese Americans and Korean Americans seek medical treatment for mental illness. Koreans offer religious ritual along with Western medicines. Korean systems recognize disabilities as those stemming from the human body, mind, and environment. Filipinos dealing with developmental disabilities turn to the church for support with little expectation. Others go to folk healers looking for compassion when nothing else works (DeTorres, 2002).

NATIVE AMERICAN FAMILY ROOTS

The traditional definition of family among Native Americans differs qualitatively from Western models and is even rather unique compared with other ethnic expressions of extended family systems (Light & Martin, 1996). Family includes biological (blood) kinship, both nuclear and extended, and social kinship (nonblood) in the home, clan, tribe, and beyond (Lomay & Hinkebein, 2006). Kinship bonds create massive social networks that provide economic, social, and logistical support to family members (Rowley & Rehfeldt, 2002).

Bonds between the individual and family, and family and tribe are forged in an often-complex web of ceremonial relationships. Family systems are matriarchal in some tribes (Thomason, 2000) and more patriarchal in others, but the overarching values are interdependence (Red Horse, 1983) and egalitarian, with all roles taking a place of honor in the tribe. Native American women's traditional role is based in the care and nurturance of others (Gilligan, 1993) and the stewards of culture and tradition (Allen, 1986). They are in charge of child rearing, domestic tasks, and the overall concerns of the family (John, 1988) and wield great power in the home and through the network of family relationships. The role for Native American men is primarily outside of the home as provider for the family and in leadership roles in the clan or tribe such as medicine man or representative in tribal council. Elders hold a special place of honor in the family and the community. With age come wisdom and the collection of oral history, language, songs, dances, ceremonies, and the personal virtues of patience and generosity. Elders often hold healing positions and other positions of authority earned through their years of experience. Children are the focus of the family, and their care and education is largely a communal activity. Aunts and uncles (blood and nonblood) discipline the children. Elders will provide cultural knowledge. Grandfathers teach the young men. Grandmothers teach the young women. Roles are taught by observation, modeling, and practice. History is taught through stories. Children are allowed freedom, and discipline tends to be light so as not to break their spirit. Everything is learned against the backdrop of community and spirituality. While traditional roles are clearly defined, role shift has been common and not stigmatizing.

Disability in the Family and Community

The Western concept of disability does not translate well into the Native American worldview. There is often no word equivalent. Its closest interpretation would describe a person who has a limited social network and dysfunctional interpersonal relationships in the community (Locust, 1994) or a person who exhibits moral weakness (Rowley & Rehfeldt, 2002). Many conditions that Western thought perceives as disabling are simply functional descriptors. For example, a person diagnosed with Down syndrome simply "thinks slowly." The tribe is more concerned that the person be supported according to his or her needs and give to the community according to his or her abilities. Where the concept of disability in Western thought immediately focuses on the difference implied by the characteristics of impairment, Native American thought does not. As Locust (1994) points out, "[tribal] life was like a flowing stream, and the disabilities of tribal members merely stones which the water encountered. The water flowed around and over the stones, perhaps rippling a bit here and there, but incorporating the stones within itself and continuing on as before. A stone—or many stones—did not make the running water less a stream" (p. 3).

Wellness is harmony in body, spirit, mind, and community. Unwellness is disharmony in the same. Natural unwellness results from the breaking of taboos. Unnatural unwellness is the consequence of malicious manipulation of supernatural forces, that is, sorcery (Locust, 1985). Unwellness can be brought on by bad dreams, gambling, sexual activity, ignoring ceremonies, contact with the dead, or the transgression of ancestors (Rowley & Rehfeldt, 2002). Talking about an illness or disability may cause it or make it worse (Rowley & Rehfeldt, 2002). Mental illness can be caused by the desecration of holy objects. Epilepsy is caused by incest. Mental wellness, posits Gone (2008), is tied to the land, often the reservation, and the constellation of relationships that move on it. The reservation is part of the person in body and spirit. Leaving the reservation is a struggle with identity (Anderson & Ellis, 1995). Living in two worlds is an existential challenge (Rayle, Chee, & Sand, 2006) that can lead to spiritual unwellness.

Breaking taboos is not necessarily an intentional act; one may be totally unaware of having done so, particularly in the case of congenital disabilities. Pregnant women are admonished to respect a great many taboos such as stepping over a snake (Hopi), contact with bear scat (Apache), sitting under a tree that has been hit by lightning, witnessing an eclipse, and so on, all of which are thought to cause birth defects (Joe & Miller, 1987). For the child born with a congenital disability, the body is compromised, not the spirit. There is a lack of stigma associated with congenital disabilities.

The person born with such a disability is due respect, inasmuch as the spirit had its reasons for choosing to enter the world in this form.

Response

Native American healing is concerned with the "why" of an illness or impairment rather than the "what" (Joe & Miller, 1987). The visionary healer seeks the cause, that is, the broken taboo and the offended spirit behind the illness (Locust, 1994). The purpose is to restore balance in body, mind, and spirit. The instrument of healing is the canon of intricate rituals and ceremonies acquired over a lifetime of study (Lomay & Hinkebein, 2006). Native American medicine's priority is not to cure, but to heal. The Western cure assumes a fix that will return one to a previous state. Native American medicine seeks to reestablish balance and harmony under the current circumstances. This results in a different interpretation of the relationship between person and disability. It is possible that behavior judged symptomatic of mental illness in Western medicine may be construed as signs of a vocational (shamanic) calling in Native American medicine (Schacht, 2001). Many who would be labeled with a disability by Western services are absorbed by the Native American culture and never seen. The tribal community takes care of its own in the name of harmony. People with obvious, visible, and severe disabilities are often fully engaged and included in all aspects of community life (Schacht, 2001). For members with severe disabilities, the family finds meaningful work within the community that is within the person's ability. Whatever work is found is enough to provide dignity and a place of honor in the tribe (Joe & Miller, 1987). Invisible disabilities such as learning disabilities are greeted with skepticism and distrust. Family often sees the diagnoses of a learning disability as a problem in the school, not in the person or the family (Joe & Miller, 1987). Trepidation in dealing with government service is based in history. Services can become taboo in and of themselves.

The interface between Western and Native American medicines requires special attention. While it is easy for them to fall into conflict, it has been shown that they can also be integrated into effective service. Traditional healers need to be consulted. Accommodations must be made for the healing ceremonies. In acute care, tribal healers must consider the spiritual ramifications of assistive devices and treatment. Foreign objects have their own energy and spirit. They can disrupt Native American healing rituals or be disrupted by them. Organ donations, transplants, and other surgical interventions that alter the body can be problematic. The spirit is obliged to return the body as complete as possible to the creator at the end of life. Self-destructive behaviors such as alcohol abuse are an affront to this obligation. Heroic life-saving efforts are not a priority in Native American healing. Healing is about balance. Respecting the spirit's choice to leave this world is the balanced response; the body dies, but the spirit lives on. "Dying with dignity" trumps "life at any cost."

Integration in rehabilitation and recovery is just as important. There is a chasm of distrust that must be recognized and confronted. Counseling and other "helping" organizations have consistently been in the service of assimilation into White culture and interpreting the needs of clients through the prism of Western values. "I'm from the government and I am here to help" is an especially hollow introduction on the reservation. Family members are reticent to approach service providers in issues with children and mental health because the historical consequence was often the removal of the person from the social network, creating disharmony in the person and tribe (Gone, 2008). For those who do come forward, there is an expectation for expert advice, but advice that is informed of the cultural and abides by it. Uncles, aunts, and elders may be actively engaged and may expect to be consulted (Garrett & Carroll, 2000). Healing is collaborative and decision making is deliberative. Words have power. Speaking about the person with a disability from a deficit perspective is counterproductive. Words are chosen carefully to match intent. Unkept promises of any kind are bad medicine. Thus, planning is a slow process punctuated by silent contemplative intervals.

The most effective interventions are those that arise from the identity movement and empower the community (Archambault, 2001). For example, substance abuse has been a plague on the reservation since it was introduced by the West. The 12-step program, with its emphasis on a "higher power" has been effectively adapted to Native American culture (Garrett & Carroll, 2000). This required interpretation of principles, the editing of a few steps, and a Native American view on alcoholism and its treatment. Native Americans prefer native healers' approach to mental illness with or without Western medicine (Marabella, Harris, Diehr, Ignace, & Ignace, 1998).

Cultural competence is important to psychosocial rehabilitation counseling in a multicultural society (Lomay & Hinkebein, 2006). Native American vocational rehabilitation (VR) is served through tribal VR programs and is a family-centered affair, linked as they are to the extended family and more distant kinship bonds (Clark & Kelley, 2001). Embracing the customs and history of the tribe, understanding and living within your role, and becoming accepted within the community facilitates service delivery and communication with the tribe. Communication is key. Conflict can come in the simple pace of conversation or the imposition of Western values that derive status and identity out of accomplishment, rather than being valued for your own sake. Respect in communication requires spending time together, rather than being a task to be completed (Marshall, Johnson, & Lonetree, 2001). Problems are best approached indirectly and after appropriate social amenities. Humor is a subtle value and means of communicating among Native Americans; it provides an indirect path to subject matter, teaches through storytelling, and distances people from problems. Certain humorous exchanges are part of the role played by extended family members and a sign of closeness played out in the community (Garrett, Garrett, Torres-Rivera, Wilbur, & Roberts-Wilbur, 2005). Rehabilitation efforts focus on the family to identify and marshal resources on behalf of the client (Sanderson, 2001).

FAMILY THEMES AND CONSIDERATIONS

The social construction of disability is displayed in bold relief in its cross-cultural comparisons. The culture in which the person is embedded creates the meaning of disability, the identity of the individual, and in very real ways, directs what is possible in terms of adjustment and adaptation. The meaning of and response to disability varies widely across cultures, but themes do arise.

Resistance to Oppression

The history of each of these groups is rooted in generations of oppression and struggle for identity in the United States (see Millington, 2012). Waves of Hispanic and Asian immigrants fleeing war and deprivation formed an underclass of migrant workers, exploited for their cheap labor and as scapegoats for societal ills. Africans arrived as slaves and property, not immigrants, and their struggle and value to the ruling class were essentially the same, only with heavier chains. The indigenous peoples of this country faced a holocaust that dwarfs any other in numbers of nations destroyed, the span of time dedicated to the task, and the complicity of generations.

The history of oppression and resistance that creates minority experience does not go away; it folds into the next generation. Furthermore, we would be naïve to think that the struggle has ended for anyone. Struggle is woven into identity, and it is a matter of pride. We are reminded that the social justice movement that begat the disability movement started with these peoples. Rehabilitation counseling is redeemed in the social model. We would like to think of ourselves as part of the struggle for community inclusion, but upon entering a home that shares these histories one must be aware that the family inside has seen your kind before.

Family and the Social Support Network

The hub of all culture is the family unit. Families are the core context in which the meaning of disability is coined. Although the operational definition of family changes across cultures, what families represent does not. The family is the first support network, from nuclear to extended. A strong support network is a bulwark against life stressors and a resource for the individual. Family is the frame for identity development in terms of the individual and the individual's relationship to the network.

Collectivism and the Extended Family

We find that extended families and a collectivist worldview are common among immigrant groups. It is important to understand that the difference in these orientations, contrasted with the nuclear family and individualistic trend in Middle America, have deep psychological and sociological implications. Collectivist self-esteem and identity are derived from one's worthiness to the family, as the family's identity is derived from its worth to the community (Crocker, Luhtanen, Blaine, & Broadnax, 1994)—where we have called family the first community. In a collectivist sense, it is also the first identity. All meanings shift in such a profoundly different worldview. Professional language of counseling does not translate well across the value borders.

Extended families are the natural expression of well-being in a collective culture. They are not necessarily bound by blood, but are bound by tradition and obligation. A social identity is a complex thing; it is defined, or triangulated, by its relationship to every other person in the group. The counselor enters such a family often ignorant of the number, character, and depth of these connections. This is at once the amazing untapped resource we are looking for, and the invisible wall that protects the family from outsiders.

Spirituality

We are unified across cultures in our need for organizing principles that bring order to the world. Religion and ritual are artifacts of fundamental spiritual beliefs that tell us who we are, what is required of us, and what shall become of us in the end. Religion interprets disability in the community according to its values and creates its own response. Where disability is God's will, the response is forbearance. Where disability is punishment for past sin, the response is atonement. Where disability is a gift, the response is celebration. Where disability disappears, the response is simply to live. Religious practices are the means by which individuals are included in community. The religious space is sanctifying and unifying. Out of faith comes teaching and sharing of values. Service to the community includes charity, support groups, and pastoral counseling or visionary healing.

History and Change

The only constant in the human condition is change. Tradition is the current interpretation of a history to which new events accrue every day. As much as we try to preserve, everything evolves. At one point in time, Korea did not have a written language. Feeling the need, one was created, and a new tradition emerged. Trade among Native American tribes spanned the continent for thousands of years before the European invasion, and with trade came confluence. The recent economic boom in China has brought Westernized ideas and urbanization to the family structure. As a result, there is no longer a "typical" Chinese family, even in China (Lee, 1996).

The cultural roots we reviewed in this chapter exist in communion with one another and with the dominant U.S. culture. On the one hand, we can think of this change in terms of acculturation and enculturation. Acculturation is the adaptation of indigenous culture patterns to the norms of the dominant culture. Enculturation is the process by which people learn and maintain their indigenous culture (Cokely & Helm, 2007) within the framework of the dominant culture (Kim & Abreu, 2001). Thinking of these as dimensions of adjustment, we can imagine four developmental directions: (a) assimilation (high acculturation, low enculturation) is complete identification with the dominant culture to the exclusion of the indigenous; (b) integration (high acculturation, high enculturation) is the ability to "walk in two worlds" (Diemer, 2007) comfortably, to find a way to maintain the indigenous identity and values while often living in the other; (c) separation (low acculturation, high enculturation) is an active rejection of the dominant, often by physically sequestering in enclaves and reservations; and (d) marginalization (low acculturation, low enculturation) is the loss of the traditional and failure to assimilate (Berry, 1980; Rudmin, 2003).

On the other hand, we can accept that the "dominant culture" is itself in flux and indeed an increasingly flimsy construct in a melting pot of multicultural influences. How a person experiences disability in his or her life and how disability interfaces with the family and community depends on the quality of the community response to these social dynamics. The issues of disability identity are different for Native Americans than they are for African Americans, Hispanics, or Asian Americans, and as we have shown they are different within groups as well. They are also different across generations even within immigrant families as they continue to adapt. The challenge for the rehabilitation counseling in such a fluid cultural environment is, as we said, a daunting proposition. The best advice perhaps is to become a student of every culture you wish to serve, to immerse yourself in it, and learn all that is possible to learn. And then, when you enter the home of a family, forget it all: Be quiet, be humble, and listen.

REFERENCES

Abraido-Lanza, A. F., Vasquez, E., & Echeverria, S. E. (2004). En las manos de Dios [in God's hands]: Religious and other forms of coping among Latinos with arthritis. *Journal of Consulting and Clinical Psychology, 72,* 91–102.

Allen, P. G. (1986). *The sacred hoop.* Boston, MA: Beacon Press.

Alvidrez, J. (1999). Ethnic variations in mental health attitudes and service use among low-income African American, Latina, and European American young women. *Community Mental Health Journal, 35,* 515–530.

Alvarez, L. R., & Ruiz, P. (2001). Substance abuse in the Mexican American population. In S. L. A. Straussner (Ed.), *Ethnocultural factors in substance abuse treatment* (pp. 111–139). New York, NY: Guilford.

Anderson, M. J., & Ellis, R. (1995). On the reservation. In N. A. Vace, S. B. DeVaney, & J. Wittmer (Eds.), *Experiencing and counseling multicultural and diverse populations* (3rd ed., pp. 179–198). Bristol, PA: Accelerated Development.

Archambault, J. (2001). Sun dance. In R. DeMallie (Ed.), *Handbook of North American Indians* (Vol. 13, pp. 983–995). Washington, DC: Smithsonian Institution.

Berry, J. W. (1980). Acculturation as varieties of adaptation. In A. Padilla (Ed.), *Acculturation: Theory, models, and some new findings* (pp. 9–25). Boulder, CO: Westview.

Boyd-Franklin, N. (2003). *Black families in therapy: Understanding the African-American experience.* New York, NY: Guilford.

Brice, A. (2002). *An introduction to Cuban culture for rehabilitation service providers* [Monograph]. Buffalo, NY: Center for International Rehabilitation Research Information & Exchange.

Christopher, M. S., Skillman, G. D., Kirkhart, M. W., & D'Souza, J. B. (2006). The effect of normative and behavioral persuasion on help seeking in Thai and American college students. *Journal of Multicultural Counseling and Development, 34,* 80–93.

Clark, S., & Kelley, S. D. M. (2001). Traditional Native American values: Conflict or concordance in rehabilitation? *Journal of Rehabilitation, 58*(2), 23–27.

Cokely, K., & Helm, K. (2007). The relationship between African American enculturation and racial identity. *Journal of Multicultural Counseling and Development, 35,* 142–153.

Cooper, L. A., Gonzales, J. J., Gallo, J. J., Rost, K. M., Meredith, L. S., Rubenstein, L. V., & Ford, D. (2003). The acceptability of treatment for depression among African-American, Latino and White primary care physicians. *Medical Care, 41,* 479–489.

Crocker, J., Luhtanen, R., Blaine, B., & Broadnax, S. (1994). Collective self-esteem and psychological among White, Black, and Asian college students. *Personality and Social Psychology Bulletin, 20,* 503–513.

DePaul, T., Lagana, K., Gonzalez-Ramirez, L. (1996). Mexican Americans. In J. G. Lipson, S. L. Dibble, P. A. Minarik (Ed.), *Culture and nursing care* (pp. 203–221). San Francisco, CA: UCSF Nursing Press.

De Torres, S. (2002). *Understanding persons of Philippine origins: A primer for rehabilitation service providers* [Monograph]. Buffalo, NY: Center for International Rehabilitation Research Information & Exchange.

Diemer, M. A. (2007). Two worlds: African American men's negotiation of predominatly White educational and occupational worlds. *Journal of Multicultural Counseling and Development, 35,* 2–14.

Ferguson, T. M., Leach, M. M., Levy, J. J., Nicholson, B. C., & Johnson, J. D. (2008). Influences on counselors race preferences: Distinguishing Black racial attitudes from Black racial identity. *Journal of Multicultural Counseling and Development, 36,* 66–76.

Garrett, M. T., & Carroll, J. J. (2000). Mending the broken circle: Treatment of substance dependency among Native Americans. *Journal of Counseling & Development, 78,* 379–388.

Garrett, M. T., Garrett, J. T., Torres-Rivera, E., Wilbur, M., & Roberts-Wilbur, J. (2005). Laughing it up: Native American humor as spiritual tradition. *Journal of Multicultural Counseling and Development, 33,* 194–204.

Gilligan, C. (1993). *In a different voice.* Cambridge, MA: Harvard University Press.

Glover, N. M., & Blankenship, C. J. (2007). Mexican and Mexican Americans' beliefs about God in relation to disability. *Journal of Rehabilitation, 73*(4), 41–50.

Gone, J. P. (2008). "So I can be like a whiteman": The cultural psychology of space and place in American Indian mental health. *Culture Psychology, 14,* 369–399.

Graf, N. M., Blankenship, C. J., Sanchez, G., & Carlson, R. (2007). Living on the line: Mexican and Mexican American attitudes towards disability. *Rehabilitation Counseling Bulletin, 50,* 153–165.

Hampton, N. Z., Yeung, T., & Nguyen, C. H. (2007). Perceptions of mental illness and rehabilitation services in Chinese and Vietnamese Americans. *Journal of Applied Rehabilitation Counseling, 38*(2), 14–23.

Hanline, M. F., & Daley, S. E. (1992). Family coping strategies and strengths in Hispanic, African-American, and Caucasian families of young children. *Topics in Early Childhood Special Education, 12,* 351–366.

Ho, M. K. (1984). Social group work with Asian/Pacific Americans. *Ethnicity in Group Work Practice, 7,* 49–61.

Hunt, P. C. (2002). *An introduction to Vietnamese culture for rehabilitation service providers in the U.S.* [Monograph]. Buffalo, NY: Center for International Rehabilitation Research Information & Exchange.

Jacobson, E. (2003). *An introduction to Haitian culture for rehabilitation service providers* [Monograph]. Buffalo, NY: Center for International Rehabilitation Research Information & Exchange.

Joe, R. E., & Miller, D. (Eds.). (1987). *American Indian cultural perspectives on disability* (pp. 3–23). Tucson: University of Arizona, Native American Research and Training Center.

John, R. (1988). The Native American family. In C. Mindel, R. Habenstein, & R. Wright, Jr. (Eds.), *Ethnic families in America: Patterns and variations* (pp. 325–363). Englewood Cliffs, NJ: Prentice-Hall.

Kim, B. S. K., & Abreu, J. M. (2001). Acculturation measurement: Theory, current instruments, and future directions. In J. G. Ponterotto, J. M. Casas, L. A. Suzuki, & C. M. Alexander (Eds.), *Handbook of multicultural counseling* (2nd ed., 394–424). Thousand Oaks, CA: SAGE.

Kim-Rupnow, W. S. (2001). *An introduction to Korean culture for rehabilitation service providers* [Monograph]. Buffalo, NY: Center for International Rehabilitation Research Information & Exchange.

Lam, C. S., Tsang, H., Chan, F., & Corrigan, P. W. (2006). Chinese and American perspectives on stigma. *Rehabilitation Education, 20*(4), 269–279.

Lafitte, I. (1983). Counseling and the rehabilitation process. In *The special rehabilitation and research needs of disabled Hispanic persons* (pp. 51–58). Edinburg, TX: National Institute of Handicapped Research and President's Committee on Employment of the Handicapped.

Leavitt, R. L. (1992). *Disability and rehabilitation in rural Jamaica*. London, England: Associated University Press.

Lee, E. (1996). Chinese families. In M. McGoldrick, J. Giordano, & J. Pearce (Eds.), *Ethnicity family therapy* (2nd ed., pp. 248–267). New York, NY: Guilford.

Lee, W. M. L., Blando, J. A., Mizelle, N. D., & Orozco, G. L. (Eds.). (2007). *Introduction to multicultural counseling for helping professionals* (2nd ed.). New York, NY: Routledge.

Light, H. K., & Martin, R. E. (1996). American Indian families. *Journal of American Indian Education, 26*(1). Retrieved from http://jaie.asu.edu/v26/V26S1ame.htm

Liu, G. Z. (2001). *Chinese culture and disability: Information for U. S. service providers* [Monograph]. Buffalo, NY: Center for International Rehabilitation Research Information & Exchange.

Livneh, H. (1988). A dimensional perspective on the origin of negative attitudes towards persons with disabilities. In H. E. Yuker (Ed.), *Attitudes towards persons with disabilities* (pp. 35–46). New York, NY: Springer.

Locust, C. S. (1985). *American Indian concepts concerning health and unwellness* (Monograph Series: Native American Research and Training Center, g00830094). Washington, DC: NIDRR, USDOE.

Locust, C. S. (1994). *The piki maker: Disabled American Indians, cultural beliefs, and traditional behaviors* (Monograph Series: Native American Research and Training Center, h133B30058). Washington, DC: NIDRR, USDOE.

Lomay, V. T., & Hinkebein, J. H. (2006). Cultural considerations when providing rehabilitation services to American Indians. *Rehabilitation Psychology, 51*(1), 36–42.

Lopez-De Fede, A., & Haeussler-Fiore, D. (2002). *An introduction to the culture of the Dominican Republic for rehabilitation service providers* [Monograph]. Buffalo, NY: Center for International Rehabilitation Research Information & Exchange.

Marabella, A. M., Harris, M. C., Diehr, S., Ignace, G., & Ignace G. (1998). The use of Native American healers among Native American patients in an urban Native American health center. *Archive of Family Medicine, 7,* 182–185.

Marinelli, R. P., & Dell Orto, A. E. (1999). *The psychological and social impact of disability.* New York, NY: Springer.

Marshall, C. A., Johnson, S., & Lonetree, G. (2001). Acknowledging our diversity: Vocational rehabilitation and American Indians. In C. A. Marshall (Ed.), *Rehabilitation and American Indians with disabilities: A handbook for administrators, practitioners, and researchers* (pp. 85–99). Athens, GA: Elliot & Fitzpatrick.

Matthews, A. K., Corrigan, P. W., Smith, B. M., & Aranda, F. (2006). A qualitative exploration of African-Americans' attitudes toward mental illness and mental illness treatment seeking. *Rehabilitation Education, 20*(4), 253–268.

Miller, D. (2002). *An introduction to Jamaican culture for rehabilitation service providers* [Monograph]. Buffalo, NY: Center for International Rehabilitation Research Information & Exchange.

Millington, M. J. (2012). Culturally different issues and attitudes toward disability. In I. Marini, N. M. Glover, & M. J. Millington (Eds.), *Psychosocial aspects of disability: Insider perspectives and counseling strategies* (pp. 61–95). New York, NY: Springer.

Molina, C., Zambrana, R., & Aguirre-Molina, M. (1994). The influence of culture, class and environment on health care. In C. Molina & M. Aguirre-Molina (Eds.), *Latino health in the US: A growing challenge* (pp. 23–43). Washington, DC: American Public Health Association.

Pinto, P. E., & Sahu, N. (2001). *Working with persons with disabilities: An Indian perspective* [Monograph]. Buffalo, NY: Center for International Rehabilitation Research Information & Exchange.

Rayle, A. D., Chee, C., & Sand, J. K. (2006): Honoring their way: Counseling American Indian women. *Journal of Multicultural Counseling and Development, 34,* 66–79.

Red Horse, J. (1983). Indian family values and experiences. In G. J. Powell (Ed.), *The psychosocial development of minority group children* (pp. 258–271). New York, NY: Brunner/Mazel.

Rivera, O. A. (1983). Vocational rehabilitation process and Hispanic culture. In *The special rehabilitation and research needs of disabled Hispanic persons* (pp. 39–41). Edinburg, TX: National Institute of Handicapped Research and President's Committee on Employment of the Handicapped.

Rowley, D., & Rehfeldt, R. A. (2002). Delivering human services to Native Americans with disabilities: Cultural variables & service recommendations. *North American Journal of Psychology, 4*(2), 309–316.

Rudmin, F. W. (2003). Critical history of the acculturation psychology of assimilation, separation, integration, and marginalization. *Review of General Psychology, 7,* 3–37.

Ruiz, R. A., & Padilla, A. M. (1977). Counseling Latinos. *The Personnel and Guidance Journal, 55,* 401–408.

Sanderson, P. L. (2001). American Indians: An overview of factors influencing health care, disability, and service delivery. In C. A. Marshall (Ed.), *Rehabilitation and American Indians with disabilities: A handbook for administrators, practitioners, and researchers* (pp. 27–41). Athens, GA: Elliot & Fitzpatrick.

Schacht, R. M. (2001). Engaging anthropology in disability studies: American Indian issues. *Disability Studies Quarterly, 21*(3), 17–36.

Snowden, L. R. (2001). Barriers to effective mental health services for African Americans. *Mental Health Services Research, 3*(4), 181–187.

Thomason, T. C. (2000). Counseling American Indians: An introduction for non-American Indian counselors. *Journal of Counseling & Development, 69,* 321–327.

Trevino, B., & Szymanski, E. M. (1996). A qualitative study of the career development of Hispanics with disabilities. *Journal of Rehabilitation, 62*(3), 5–13.

Triandis, H. C. (1971). *Attitude and attitude change.* New York, NY: John Wiley.

Turner, W. L., & Alston, R. J. (1994). The role of the family in psychosocial adaptation to physical disabilities for African Americans. *Journal of the National Medical Association, 86*(12), 915–921.

Vega, W. A., Kolody, B., & Aguilar-Gaxiola, S. (2001). Help seeking for mental health problems among Mexican Americans. *Journal of Immigrant Health, 3,* 133–140.

Vera, E. M., & Conner, W. (2007). Latina mothers' perceptions of mental health and mental health promotion. *Journal of Multicultural Counseling and Development, 35,* 230–242.

Wang, M. H., Chan, F., Thomas, K. R., Lin, S. H., & Larson, P. (1997). Coping style and personal responsibility as factors in the perception of individuals with physical disabilities by Chinese international students. *Rehabilitation Psychology, 42*(4), 302–316.

Weisman, A. G. (2000). Religion: A mediator of Anglo-American and Mexican attributional differences towards symptoms of schizophrenia? *Journal of Nervous & Mental Disease, 188,* 616–621.

Wilson, K. B. (2005). Cultural characteristics of the African American community. In D. A. Harley & J. M. Dillard (Eds.), *Contemporary mental health issues among African Americans* (pp. 32–52). Alexandria, VA: American Counseling Association.

Wright, B. (1988). Attitudes and the fundamental negative bias: Conditions and corrections. In H. E. Yuker (Ed.), *Attitudes toward persons with disabilities* (pp. 3–21). New York, NY: Springer.

Zavaleta, A. N. (2000). *Do cultural factors affect Hispanic health status?* Retrieved from http://vpea.utb.edu/elnino/researcharticles/doculturalfactorsaffect.html

Zhang, A. Y., Snowden, L. R., & Sue, S. (1998). Differences between Asian- and White-Americans' help-seeking and utilization patterns in the Los Angeles area. *Journal of Community Psychology, 26,* 317–326.

CHAPTER 13

Family Assessments in Rehabilitation Service Provision

ELIAS MPOFU, LISA LOPEZ LEVERS, KUMBIRAI MPOFU, PHILOMENA TANUI, AND ZAKIA S. HOSSAIN

The rehabilitation field is dedicated to optimizing functionality and health for persons with disabilities and their families. The field promotes specialized care to improve, maintain, or restore physical strength, cognition, and functioning with optimum results (Mpofu & Oakland, 2010a, 2010b). According to Mpofu and Oakland (2010a, 2010b) and Ryan and Keitner (in press), an increase in professional interest in assessing family functioning has emerged. This interest extends to the ways in which family functioning relates to and connects with a person with a disability's activity restrictions and participation limitations as part of rehabilitative interventions to restore, maintain, and enhance functioning. This interest also extends to those who provide care, as needed, to persons with disabilities. Carers are mostly family members, friends, relatives, significant others, or disability support workers (Hui, Elliott, Shewchuk, & Rivera, 2007) and are included as an important part of the assessment picture. Family assessments are typically guided by a systems orientation and driven by person-/family-centered and culturally competent practices.

The World Health Organization's (WHO, 2001) International Classification of Functioning (ICF) framework proposes a holistic view of assessment for rehabilitation intervention, taking into account the reciprocal relationship between the individual and his or her sociocultural context, of which the family is such a context. One purpose for assessing the entire family is to identify and weigh the familial factors that may have an impact on the person with a disability and especially his or her rehabilitation process. In general, comprehensive family assessment can provide a foundation for assisting families at critical points, including treatment decisions, appropriateness of interventions, need for support, safety issues, new challenges with which the family is presented, service efficacy, and resource acquisition (U.S. Department of Health and Human Services, n.d.). Family assessments in a rehabilitation context may include any of the following foci: identification of and screening for the needs of the person with a disability, and understanding of social safety nets and mechanisms for acquiring fiduciary assistance, safety and risk evaluation, and family strengths and needs, including cultural issues (Skinner, Steinhauer, & Santa-Barbara, 1983; Zubrick, Williams, Silburn, & Vimpani, 2000). These aggregate to three resource domains for social and family functioning relevant to health and well-being outcomes for which assessment data are needed: information, social support and coping, and resilience resources.

Family involvement in assessment encourages engagement by enhancing communication between the rehabilitation agency and the family about what has to change, considering services needed, and laying expectations and responsibilities of accomplishing tasks that promote well-being. Assessments may be observational and inquiry oriented or may rely on formal psychometric instruments; however, in either case, such assessments can yield rich information concerning family structure and function in their influence on rehabilitation health outcomes.

Cook and Ferritor (1985) found that family services were provided in less than 2% of closed cases for rehabilitation services. Interest in family systems theory has grown over the decades since family theory first became prominent in the 1950s. While the theoretical- and practice-based literatures have expanded, the literature regarding family assessment, and particularly assessment of family functioning, is not as robust. Only one review of related assessment literature (from 1978 to 1997) was located. In this review, the authors identified nine family assessment tools that were used in a variety of clinical settings (Neabel et al., 2000), several of which are briefly described in the following. Although interest has been expressed throughout the relevant literature regarding the importance of the role of the family in various medical and psychiatric disorders and conditions (e.g., Kabacoff, Miller, Bishop, Epstein, & Keitner, 1990; Maundeni, Levers, & Jacques, 2008; Millington, Jenkins, & Cottone, in press), the focus on comprehensive family assessments to inform rehabilitation interventions is of relatively recent times (Erosa, Elliott, Berry, & Grant, 2010). This is despite the fact that assessments aimed to inform interventions to support health and well-being of carers are rare and the fact that quality of life, when living with a chronic illness or disability, is intricately dependent on the carer providing health and well-being support (Gamas, Kelly, Daharsh, & Vogel, 2011).

Rehabilitation professionals are aware that families with a member with a disability typically assume responsibility for varying aspects of his or her care. Yet many families know little about the caregiving function until they are faced with the illness or disabling condition of one of the family members. Family rehabilitative assessments must consider the important role of family as context for the lived experience with disability.

The family is a contextual or environmental influence on health and well-being at several levels: instrumental support and access, and long-term rehabilitation success or positive living with disability. First, the family constellation is a microenvironment in how it supports or nourishes health and well-being among the members. It is also a resource by which members access external resources for health and well-being. Family members who serve as informal carers provide an estimated 1.32 billion hours of care each year in Australia, for example, and using cost replacement methodology, the value of informal care provided is $40.9 billion or 3.2% of Australia's gross domestic product (Access Economics, 2010). Second, families are the context for comprehensive rehabilitation service provision, and an assessment of the family unit itself, along with the systems it interfaces for healthy living with disability, are important for long-term or successful rehabilitation service outcomes. Rehabilitation service providers have in family both an agent and resource for positive living with disability. The instrumental functions and mechanisms, as well as the resourcing of family for successful living with disability, need accurate assessment to translate into efficacious rehabilitation services.

In this chapter, we address the types of family assessments that are needed to determine quality rehabilitation services for the family member with disability, including social support, information, and advocacy. Rather than focusing on specific measures or psychometric properties of particular family functioning instruments (see Mpofu & Oakland, 2010b; Thomlison, 2010), the chapter explicates the various domains of family assessment and how these are likely to lead to successful rehabilitation outcomes. This chapter addresses the types of family assessments that are needed to determine quality rehabilitation services for the family member with disability, including social support, information, and advocacy. Specifically, we explore and examine the various domains of family assessment most likely to lead to successful rehabilitation outcomes, family carer health and well-being, information support assessments, advocacy support assessments, and assessment of family resilience. A holistic approach to family function, based on individual and collective roles and participation of the family members in healthy family functioning, is the ideal (Georgiades, Boyle, Jenkins, Sanford, & Lipman, 2008).

FAMILY ROLE, CARER HEALTH, AND WELL-BEING

The family is typically a provider of care to a member or members with disability. It might also be with disability experience–related needs for which assessment intervention is needed. The influence is reciprocal, so family assessments need to take into account the relational dynamics from changed or evolving family life participation of the person with disability as much as the emergent needs of the family unit itself from living with a disability of a member. Two domains of assessment are apparent from this: role-positioning-type assessments and those on the health and well-being of the family from the care provisioning.

Role-Focused Assessments

The dynamics associated with the family carer role, and for which assessment may be needed, are well known and briefly considered here for context setting. For instance, chronic illness or disability (CID) might disrupt the individual's life as well as the lives of those who live around them (Ramkumar & Elliott, 2010). Family members typically take on new supportive roles to living well with disability, and these can include provisioning and resourcing, while taking into account the individual needs of a family member with disability; such person's needs also extend into the family as system. Family members may need to reevaluate and assess what really matters in life, reassigning priorities, and drawing strength from the new challenges resulting from the caregiving role (Ott, Sanders, & Kelber, 2007). Family members who serve as primary care providers have to adjust to the reality of the ongoing support needs of a member with disability, often including daily activity planning, feeding, dressing, and personal hygiene (Matousova-Done & Gates, 2006; Norup, Snipes, et al., 2013). The family may define or dictate access to the use and availability of assistive tools and technology, as well as to environmental adaptation and its accessibility (Chan, Cardoso, & Chronister, 2009).

Family assessments need to take into account their perceptions of role repositioning (with acquired disability) and role development (with developmental or chronic disability). Specific areas of focus include perceived role marginalization, dependency, and enmeshment in living with disability in a member (Norup, Snipes, et al., 2013; Raffael, 2014). For instance, if a member with disability perceived family to not recognize or acknowledge him or her (being marginalized), the person might bring along a secondary health condition (such as depression), adding to the family subjective loading as a carer agent. If there is a lack of role clarity for family members, including the member with disability (role enmeshment), this might disable the family in its effectiveness in providing care and support. It might also create unwanted dependency in a member with disability, which would compromise the family's coping with the disability experience. Assessments are needed on family members' availability to give care, but decision-making conferences may help in delegating duties and providing emotional support in terms of phone calls, financial responsibilities, medical care and supplies, and time-tabling issues of availability to take on assigned duties periodically (Cohen & Eisdorfer, 2001).

Assessment of disability-related family lifestyle changes is important relative to potential rehabilitation intervention aimed at preventing family carer compassion fatigue or burnout. Other carers, however, may discover personal growth and may become more caring and connected to others as they take on roles of caregiving and leadership. Indeed, most families may discover closeness as they work together to care for someone they love (Cohen & Eisdorfer, 2001). Family assessment data are often needed for initiating and supporting rehabilitation interventions for full community inclusion. Specific areas for assessment to address role-positioning effects include family perceptions on accountability, duty of care, and decision making with the person with disability. Additionally, disability-related family lifestyle changes may bring disagreements within the family as they become overwhelmed or discouraged or experience anger, isolation, or depression.

The Family Assessment Measure-III (FAM-III; Skinner, Steinhauer, & Santa-Barbara, 1983, 2009) is an assessment of family functioning with three self-report subscales that concern overall family health, family relationships, and a self-rating scale for each family member. The FAM-III was derived from the Family Categories Schema based on a construct validation that involved the interplay of the specification of the theory model of family functioning and the construction of a measurement instrument that has three scales: (a) a general scale that views the family from a systems perspectives; (b) a dyadic relationship scale that assesses the family from a relationship perspective between pairs within the family, with each dyad being rated and providing an overall rating of the family function; and (c) a self-rating scale, which is an individual's perspective of his or her functioning within the family (Skinner, Steinhauer, & Sitarenios, 2000). This assessment process provides a quantitative measure of the family strengths and weaknesses on the basis of seven basic concepts or dimensions: task accomplishment, affective expression, communication, role performance, involvement, control, and values and norms (Skinner et al., 1983).

Health- and Well-Being–Focused Assessments

Family health is known be an important factor in a family member's recovery (Neabel, Fothergill-Bourbonnais, & Dunning, 2000). Health and well-being of informal carers of people living with chronic illness and disability are influenced by the demands on them from caregiving and the support and resources to which they have access (Kreutzer, 2010). Family carers' physical health is often much worse than the rest of the population (Pinquart & Sörensen, 2003a; Population Research and Outcome Studies Unit, 2007). For example, carers may experience verbal, emotional, and physical abuse by their charges (Erosa et al., 2010), and the effects on care quality may not be assessed. Reactive stressors related to the carer function, if not assessed and addressed, may exacerbate preexisting health conditions in family members or result in new symptoms (Navaie-Waliser et al., 2002). For instance, the carer family member can experience adverse mental health outcomes such as depression, chronic stress, and anxiety (Cochrane, Goering, & Rogers, 1997; Pinquart & Sörensen, 2003a, 2003b; Population Research and Outcome Studies Unit, 2007). Female carers often experience more distress from caregiving than do male caregivers from their involvement in providing close physical support needs compared with males (Losada et al., 2010; Pinquart & Sörensen, 2005), and assessments need to take into account the gendered aspects of disability care by family (Morriss, Wright, Smith, Roser, & Kendall, 2013).

The Family Assessment Device (FAD; Epstein, Baldwin, & Bishop, n.d.) screens family functioning on seven dimensions, distinguishing between healthy and unhealthy families. The FAD is a self-report questionnaire and assesses specific aspects of family functioning as problem solving, behavior control, communication roles, affective responsiveness, and affective involvement. The FAD was designed as a screening instrument to identify family problem areas that needed intervention and required follow-up by a professional in a clinical setting (Bihum, Wamboldt, Gavin, & Wamboldt, 2002). The measure was developed using family systems theories and also influenced by a global General Functioning Scale aimed at assessing overall family functioning of a given subject within a specified period on a continuum (Bihum et al., 2002). Use of the FAD enhances the chances of early identification and intervention for relevant family health issues (Akister & Stevenson-Hinde, 1991). The FAD is still in need of validation with culturally diverse families (Aarons, McDonald, Connelly, & Newton, 2007).

The Family Systems Stressor-Strength Inventory (FS³I; Berkey & Hanson, 1991; Mischke & Hanson, n.d.) is an instrument that can identify stressors or stressful situations occurring in families along with the mechanisms instituted by the families in coping with these stressors to be able to stay as a healthy functioning family (Hanson & Mischke, 2005). The FS³I provides for rating family perception scores and the professional's perception scores. The tool collects information that applies to the family in general, that is specific to an individual family member, and finally that pertains to strengths that can aid the family system in coping. Data from use of the instrument are helpful for the design of a family care plan for more adaptive living (Hanson & Mischke, 2005). However, challenges arise in the use of the tool. Family members may not be willing to divulge in-depth information, as historically family matters have been perceived to be private. This is especially true for issues considered to violate social norms such as child abuse, spousal violence, and personally held deep secrets that the holder considers a violation of privacy (McDonald & Jouriles, 2001; Skinner et al., 2000). In this regard, a comprehensive family assessment can incorporate information collected through other assessments, particularly protective and health risk assessments.

FAMILY RESOURCING

A comprehensive assessment requires a continued ongoing commitment to recognizing and identifying current, continuing, and emerging issues concerning a health condition, with a view to addressing the related needs with appropriate service. These are family resource assessments, and their goal is to equip the family unit to manage disability in a member as well as to enhance responsiveness to living with disability. Family resourcing assessments address four aspects: information, social support, advocacy, and resilience (Sung et al., 2013).

Family assessments may address the extent to which members have information on the availability, adequacy, and accessibility of services to the family, including coordination of services provided through other agencies. Understanding the status of a family can lead to providing information and assisting entry into a broader range of support services available outside the health system; such services may in turn aid families with current pressing health and well-being issues to identify their needs and be motivated to change. The family also may need to understand the historical or intergenerational genesis of a CID to learn how the family may have coped in similar conditions in the past. Two types of information-oriented assessments are implied here: (a) genealogical and (b) health care access and treatment usage. These are discussed briefly in the following.

Genealogical Assessments

Genograms can be used to identify family members and relationships, significant dates, family illnesses, and inheritance patterns. The genogram has become a practical tool for mapping family patterns, as it records information on family members and relationships for up to three generations (McGoldrick, Gerson, & Petry, 2008). The information is recorded graphically, thus lending a visual pattern or configuration that can help rehabilitation professionals to rapidly assess for historical aspects influencing current health needs by family. For instance, the patterns so configured provide a way of making predictions that point to current dysfunctions. A rehabilitation professional is able to access information on genetic history that can facilitate genetic counseling if referrals need to be made (McGoldrick et al., 2008). As a tool in family therapy, genograms aid rehabilitation counselors in developing goals for therapy and facilitating decision making in intervention measures to be instituted (Shellenberger, 2007). For instance, historically recurring secondary conditions from disability can be identified and proactively addressed, breaking the psychosocial cycle that fuels their reemergence. Genograms are primary organizing tools that help a rehabilitation professional to discover clues about family functioning that lead to resolving disabling patterns of behavior and enabling a healthier functioning of the family (McGoldrick et al., 2008; Shellenberger, 2007).

Health Care Access and Treatment Support Assessments

Understanding needs of a family member through in-depth assessment can lead to access to the appropriate rehabilitation care services. For example, disability-specific information support can enable mother carers to acquire special services such as home and vehicle modifications, aids, and equipment (Ostensjo, Eva-Brogren, & Vollestad, 2003).

Family information supports can assist in building the capacity of the family system to cope with accompanying challenges, especially as these regard psychological education therapy, medical equipment and assistive devices suppliers, home health care, centers for independent living, client assistance programs, supported employment, psychopharmacological therapy, managing illness and recovery, and group counseling (Chan et al., 2009). Three types of information supports are critical to families in their carer roles, and these supports concern information about the disability condition, support services, and advocacy skills (Berry, 1995; Burton-Smith, McVilly, Yazbeck, Parmenter, & Tsutsui, 2009; Wehmeyer et al., 2008). If information support needs are identified and addressed, families will be more effective in carer roles, which, in turn, will reduce their disability-related stress. This will contribute to the family well-being and that of the individual with disability (Langford, Bowsher, Maloney, & Lillis, 1997; Shearn & Todd, 2000).

The Critical Care Family Needs Inventory (CCFNI; Molter & Leske, 1983) assesses the informational and psychosocial needs of families with a critically ill member. This inventory consists of a list of need items, and the respondents indicate the level of importance for each given item, on a 4-point Likert scale (1 = *not important*; 4 = *very important*). The families of critically ill patients have been known to require honest and ongoing information on the treatment, progress, and changes in the condition of their critically ill member (Burr, 1998). A situation may be perceived by family as irrelevant, benign, or stressful. Since family members often act as substitute decision makers, their understanding is crucial (Rukholm, Bailey, Coutu-Wakulczyk, & Bailey, 1991). The tool assesses the needs of adults with functional disabilities to remove barriers to timely and appropriate health care.

The focus of the Disability-Competent Care Self-Assessment Tool is to generate sufficient data or information that are then used to engage care and supports for maximum function of the individual with disability (Centers for Medicare & Medicaid Services, 2013). The tool is person centered and is provided and administered through an interdisciplinary team (IDT); the tool is intended as a roadmap for wellness and care in the environment in which the affected person lives. The family rehabilitation counselor is part of the IDT; as a behavioral health practitioner who is versed in the needs of the person with disability, the counselor has specific knowledge about the client and thus is able to tailor the intervention plan to suit the needs of the client and family. The tool targets information about demographics, behavioral long-term services, transitional measures, vendors and comprehensive long-term services, and supports. The health service–related information support need assessments are critical because they underpin the needs arising from having a member who is critically ill (Burr, 1998).

Typical information needs of family relate to enhancing the participation of the member with disability and family in preferred or normative community life for social inclusion. For instance, the Common Functional Assessment (CFA; MacDermott, 2004) is an example of a tool that yields data to support decision making concerned with selecting from a broad range of services: physical, psychosocial, and community access (MacDermott, Muhajarine, Waygood, Duczek, & Soiseth, 2004; Matson & Minshawi, 2007). Disability-Competent Care Self-Assessment Tool (Centers for Medicare & Medicaid Services, 2013) assessments may tend to be informal and life-task oriented for the purpose of lifestyle design (Mpofu, 2013).

Information support assessment needs may be comparatively more acute among indigenous families as well as among those who are culturally and linguistically diverse (CALD). There is evidence to suggest that families of a member with disability experience significant difficulties gaining access to supports and services (Brolan, Taylor Gomez, Lennox, & Ware, 2013). The reason may be due to limited English communication language skills or to disability support service providers who do not use interpreters as supports when working with families with first languages other than English (Carlson & van Kooten Prasad, 2000). Families with a member with disability may need information published in their own languages, which will enable them to identify organizations that provide supports and services, the availability and benefits of the supports and services, and the policies regarding accessing the supports and services. CALD families providing care for their member with disability may be reluctant to use supports and services that they need due to unpleasant past experiences with service providers (Carlson & van Kooten Prasad, 2000). On the basis of timely and appropriate information support services, families are better prepared to determine their eligibility to acquire needed supports and services (Berry, 1995; Burton-Smith et al., 2009).

Family Social Support

Families of people with disability will likely be more successful when supported in their carer roles (Griffith et al., 2011; Stainton & Besser, 1998). The family members find that they have to establish new ways of coping. They even may plan to establish family conferences or meetings to manage the logistics of caring for their member, with or without their presence. Assessment data are often needed on familiy awareness of the availability of disability support services and their knowledge about having access to the appropriate supports and services (Brolan et al., 2013; Carlson & van Kooten Prasad, 2000). For instance, family assessments can provide information on their capacity to assist with rehabilitation service access, activities of daily living, and community living needs. Data are often needed on family functioning to support family members with disability and to network on their behalf concerning appropriate services for their needs.

Providing care and support for people with disability at home is both a positive and challenging experience for family carers (Nankervis, Rosewarne, & Vassos, 2011). It can be challenging in the resource demands for appropriate support (Tucker & Degeneffe, 2013), as much as it can be rewarding in strengthening family bonding from sharing carer roles (de Arroyabe, Calvete, Hayas, & Zubizarreta, 2013). Support received from the family is critical, as it provides a secure network and connects people to extended friendship networks, the broader community, and society (Meadan, Halle, & Ebata, 2010; Wei et al., 2012).

Four types of social supports for which assessment data may be needed include emotional, affiliation, instrumental, and informational supports (Cobb, 1976; Langford et al., 1997; Norup, Siert, & Mortensen, 2013). Emotional support refers to the feeling of being loved, cared for, and esteemed by others (Langford et al., 1997; Norup, Kristensen, Poulsen, Nielsen, & Mortensen, 2013). Emotional support is provided by social networks, health care providers, family members and other relatives, and friends. Affiliation support relates to the feeling of belonging to a group, with shared interests and participation in social activities including sports, leisure, arts, and culture (Cobb, 1976; Langford et al., 1997). Adult children may also find themselves bringing an aging parent to live with them or moving away from their present locations to take on new roles and responsibilities to take care of an aging parent whose health or mobility is declining. Instrumental support involves providing assistance with tasks, money, housing, food, respite services, and so forth (Langford et al., 1997). Information support provides advice, suggestions, directives, and education about advocacy, supports, and services as well as policies regarding supports and services (Berry, 1995; Wehmeyer et al., 2008).

Families may be required to provide instrumental support in different aspects of their daily living such as mobility and modifications of the environment in order to improve safety and accessibility for people with disability (Ostensjo et al., 2003). However, in their carer roles, families living with a member with disability may lack the knowledge of supports and services to which they potentially could have access for quality care (Biddle et al., 2012). For instance, troubleshooting such gaps requires assessment data to facilitate families in their carer roles for long-term or sustained recovery (Griffith et al., 2011; Jones, McLafferty, Walley, Toland, & Melson, 2008; Redmond & Richardson, 2003; Stainton & Besser, 1998). Health and well-being of the family and person with disability is premised on assessment data on the need for emotional, affiliational, and instrumental supports by family as carers (Burton-Smith et al., 2009; Shearn & Todd, 2000; Sung et al., 2013; Wei et al., 2012). Comparatively, the informational supports for assisting families in their caring roles are relatively understudied compared with the disability-specific service needs of the person with disability (Burton-Smith et al., 2009; Wei et al., 2012).

In regard to disability care, orientations have been associated with the subjective cultural values of individualism and collectivism (Higgins, Mpofu, Hawkins, Brock, & Cant, 2011). Individualism largely views caregiving as a burden placed on the caregiver as a result of the condition of the individual family member, an attitude mostly associated with Western values; conversely, a more family-oriented collectivism emphasizes family responsibility. For instance, expectations with disability may be different so that those with an individualist culture may place more demands on the individual with disability for coping with the disability experience (Tucker & Degeneffe, 2013). With collectivist culture, disability experience may be perceived to be a family experience and one in which the person with disability works with others complementarily to address family needs, some of which may be from having a disability (Sung et al., 2013). Family assessment data for rehabilitation services need to take into account the influences of subjective culture on prospects for long-term rehabilitation services provisioning.

Advocacy Support Assessments

Families with a member with disability often need information or education and guidance to develop advocacy skills so that they can advocate for themselves as carers of a member with disability (Berry, 1995; Wehmeyer et al., 2008). Specifically, family assessment data may be needed on how to gain access to advocacy groups or organizations that assist, support, and represent persons with disability and their families (Berry, 1995; Wehmeyer et al., 2008). Family advocacy resource assessments can help families acquire knowledge about government laws, policies and practices, and developing advocacy skills, including rights, equality, and justice (Berry, 1995; Wehmeyer et al., 2008). Data on family advocacy skills are critical for interventions to empower families to seek services proactively in order to provide adequate support and services to meet the needs of family carers of a member with disability (Berry, 1995; Wehmeyer et al., 2008). When the family can self-advocate obtaining professional rehabilitation services, care acquires a new meaning.

Resilience Assessment

To live well with chronic illness and disability, families need to be resilient to the associated challenges (Herman, 2002). With regard to chronic illness and disability management, resilience can be defined as the ability to "bounce back" to healthy functioning when faced with significant stress or adversity due to disability (Atkinson, Martin, & Rankin, 2009; McCubbin & McCubbin, 1988; Walsh, 1996, 2003). Family resilience and coping consists of a number of factors such as stress management, emotion regulation, collaborative goal setting, and problem solving. Interventions to support or augment family resilience are on the increase (Masten & Obradović, 2006; Walsh, 2006). Their implementation presumes valid measures for assessing expected effects. For instance, Benzies (2009) focused on measuring the attributes of resilient families that are important for rehabilitation intervention.

CONCLUSION

Interest in family assessment as an important aspect of rehabilitation intervention is gaining momentum, especially from the increasing realization of the systemic effects of the disability experience, as it necessitates adaptive adjustment by the member with disability and the family unit. Family assessments are critically important to the design and implementation of comprehensive rehabilitative interventions for living well with disability. The main function of comprehensive assessment in this regard is to develop a service plan or a strategy for rehabilitation intervention.

Three classes of family assessment domains are apparent and have been discussed in this chapter: instrumental carer support focus, family health and wellbeing, and family resourcing. These are useful in generating the evidence needed for comprehensive family-oriented rehabilitation interventions. While the need for family assessments in rehabilitation service provision is vast, professional understandings about the functioning of a particular family and the role of a family-member carer have been limited. We have emphasized in this chapter that it behooves helping professionals to understand the level of caregiving knowledge possessed by the family as well as the family's level of functioning.

REFERENCES

Aarons, G. A., McDonald, E. J., Connelly, C. D., & Newton, R. R. (2007). Assessment of family functioning in Caucasian and Hispanic Americans: Reliability, validity, and factor structure of the family assessment device. *Family Process, 46*(4), 557–569.

Access Economics. (2010). *The economic value of informal care in 2010* (Report for Carers Australia). Canberra, Australia: Author.

Akister, J., & Stevenson-Hinde, J. (1991). Identifying families at risk: Exploring the potential of the McMaster family assessment device. *Journal of Family Therapy, 13*(4), 411–421.

Atkinson, P. A., Martin, C. R., & Rankin, J. (2009). Resilience revisited. *Journal of Psychiatric and Mental Health Nursing, 16*(2), 137–145. doi:10.1111/j.1365-2850.2008.01341

Benzies, K. (2009). Fostering family resiliency: A review of the key protective factors. *Child & Family Social Work, 14*, 103–114.

Berkey, K. M., & Hanson, S. M. (1991). *Pocket guide to family assessment and intervention.* St. Louis, MO: Mosby.

Berry, J. (1995). Families and deinstitutionalization: An application of Bronfenbrenner's Social Ecology Model. *Journal of Counseling & Development, 73*(4), 379–383. doi:10.1002/j.1556-6676.1995.tb01768.x

Biddle, N., Al-Yaman, F., Gourley, M., Gray, M., Bray, J. R., Brady, B., & Montaigne, M. (2012). *Indigenous Australians and the National Disability Insurance Scheme: The extent and nature of disability, measurement issues and service delivery models.* Barton, Australia: Commonwealth of Australia.

Bihum, J. T., Wamboldt, M. Z., Gavin, L. A., & Wamboldt, F. S. (2002). Can the Family Assessment Device (FAD) be used with school aged children? *Family Process, 41*(4), 723–731.

Brolan, C. E., Taylor Gomez, M., Lennox, N. G., & Ware, R. S. (2013). Australians from a non-English speaking background with intellectual disability: The importance of research. *Journal of Intellectual and Developmental Disability, 38*(1), 70–73.

Burr, G. (1998). Contextualizing critical care family needs through triangulation: An Australian study. *Intensive and Critical Care Nursing, 14*(4), 161–169.

Burton-Smith, R., McVilly, K., Yazbeck, M., Parmenter, T., & Tsutsui, T. (2009). Service and support needs of Australian carers supporting a family member with disability at home. *Journal of Intellectual and Developmental Disability, 34*(3), 239–247. doi:10.1080/13668250903103668

Carlson, G., & van Kooten Prasad, M. (2000). Services for people with intellectual disability of culturally and linguistically diverse backgrounds. *International Journal of Practical Approaches to Disability, 25*(1), 3–14.

Centers for Medicare & Medicaid Services. (2013). *Disability-Competent Care Self-Assessment Tool.* Retrieved from http://www.cms.gov/Medicare-Medicaid-Coordination/Medicare-and-Medicaid-Coordination/Medicare-Medicaid-Coordination-Office/Downloads/DCCAssessmentTool.pdf

Chan, F., Cardoso, E. D. S., & Chronister, J. A. (2009). *Understanding psychosocial adjustment to chronic illness and disability: A handbook for evidence-based practitioners in rehabilitation.* New York, NY: Springer.

Cobb, S. (1976). Social support as a moderator of life stress. *Psychosomatic Medicine, 38*, 300–314.

Cochrane, J. J., Goering, P. N., & Rogers, J. M. (1997). The mental health informal caregivers epidemiological survey. *American Journal of Public Health, 87*, 2002–2007.

Cohen, D., & Eisdorfer, C. (2001). *The loss of self: A family resource for the care of Alzheimer's disease and related disorders.* New York, NY: W.W. Norton.

Cook, D., & Ferritor, D. (1985). The family: A potential resource in the provision of rehabilitation services. *Journal of Applied Rehabilitation Counseling, 16*(2), 52–53.

De Arroyabe, E. L., Calvete, E., Hayas, C. L., & Zubizarreta, A. (2013). Distress of the caregiver in acquired brain injury: Positive aspects of care to moderate the effects of psychological problems. *Australian Journal of Rehabilitation Counselling, 20*(1), 84–99.

Epstein, N. B., Baldwin, L. M., & Bishop, D. S. (n.d.). *Family assessment device*. Retrieved from http://web.up.ac.za/UserFiles/FAD.pdf

Erosa, N., Elliott, T., Berry, J., & Grant, J. (2010). Verbal and physical abuse experienced by family caregivers of adults with severe disabilities. *Italian Journal of Public Health, 7*(2), 76–84.

Gamas, S. I., Kelly, E. H., Daharsh, E. Z., & Vogel, L. C. (2011). Health-related quality of life after pediatric spinal cord injury. *Journal of Pediatric Psychology, 36*(2), 226–236.

Georgiades, K., Boyle, M. H., Jenkins, J. M., Sanford, M., & Lipman, E. (2008). A multilevel analysis of whole family functioning using the McMaster family assessment device. *Journal of Family Psychology, 22*(3), 344.

Griffith, G. M., Hastings, R. P., Nash, S., Petalas, M., Oliver, C., Howlin, P., & Tunnicliffe, P. (2011). "You have to sit and explain it all, and explain yourself." Mothers' experiences of support services for their offspring with a rare genetic intellectual disability syndrome. *Journal of Genetic Counseling, 20*(2), 165–177.

Hanson, S. M. H., & Mischke, K. B. (2005). Family Systems Stressor-Strength Inventory (FS^{3}I). *Family Health Care Nursing Theory, Practice, and Research*, 535.

Herman, T. (2002). Parents' of children with disabilities: Resilience, coping and future expectations. *Journal of Developmental and Physical Disability, 14*(2), 159–171.

Higgins, A., Mpofu, E., Hawkins, T., Brock, K., & Cant, R. (2011). Access to child care services by Filipino-Australian families with children with intellectual disabilities. *Ethnographia Journal on Culture and Disability, 1*(1), 44–45.

Hui, S.-K. A., Elliott, T. R., Shewchuk, R., & Rivera, P. (2007). Communal behaviors and psychological adjustment of family caregivers and persons with spinal cord injury. *Rehabilitation Psychology, 52*(1), 113–119.

Jones, M. C., McLafferty, E., Walley, R., Toland, J., & Melson, N. (2008). Inclusion in primary care for people with intellectual disabilities: Gaining the perspective of service user and supporting social care staff. *Journal of Intellectual Disabilities, 12*(2), 93–109.

Kabacoff, R. I., Miller, I. W., Bishop, D. S., Epstein, N. B., & Keitner, G. I. (1990). A psychometric study of the McMaster Family Assessment Device in psychiatric, medical, and nonclinical samples. *Journal of Family Psychology, 3*(4), 431–439.

Kreutzer, J. (2010). Family needs and psychosocial functioning of caregivers of individuals with spinal cord injury from Columbia, South America. *NeuroRehabilitation, 27*(1), 83–93.

Langford, C. P. H., Bowsher, J., Maloney, J. P., & Lillis, P. P. (1997). Social support: A conceptual analysis. *Journal of Advanced Nursing, 25*(1), 95–100. doi:10.1046/j.1365-2648.1997. 1997025095.x

Losada, A., Márquez-González, M., Knight, B. G., Yanguas, J., Sayegh, P., & Romero-Moreno, R. (2010). Psychosocial factors and caregivers' distress: Effects of familism and dysfunctional thoughts. *Aging & Mental Health, 14*(2), 193–202.

MacDermott, W. (2004). *Common functional assessment and disability-related agencies and departments in Saskatoon*. Saskatoon, Saskatchewan: Community-University Institute for Social Research and the University of Saskatchewan. Retrieved from http://www.usask.ca/cuisr/sites/default/files/MacDCFA.pdf

MacDermott, W. E., Muhajarine, N., Waygood, K., Duczek, L., & Soiseth, N. (2004). *Common functional assessment and disability-related agencies and departments in Saskatoon*. Saskatoon,

Saskatchewan: Community-University Institute for Social Research, University of Saskatchewan, Canada Printing Services.

Masten, A. S., & Obradović, J. (2006). Competence and resilience in development. *Annals of the New York Academy of Sciences, 1094*(1), 13–27.

Matousova-Done, Z., & Gates, B. (2006). *The nature of care planning and delivery in intellectual disability nursing.* Boston, MA: Blackwell.

Matson, J. L., & Minshawi, N. F. (2007). Functional assessment of challenging behavior: Toward a strategy for applied settings. *Research in Developmental Disabilities, 28*(4), 353–361.

Maundeni, T., Levers, L. L., & Jacques, G. (Eds.). (2008). *Changing family systems: A global perspective.* Gaborone, Botswana: Bay.

McCubbin, H. I., & McCubbin, M. A. (1988). Typologies of resilient families: Emerging roles of social class and ethnicity. *Family Relations,* 247–254.

McDonald, R., & Jouriles, E. N. (2001). Measuring family problems. *Handbook of Family Measurement Techniques, 2,* 259.

McGoldrick, M., Gerson, R., & Petry, S. S. (2008). *Genograms: Assessment and intervention.* New York, NY: W.W. Norton.

Meadan, H., Halle, J. W., & Ebata, A. T. (2010). Families with children who have autism spectrum disorders: Stress and support. *Exceptional Children, 77*(1), 7–36.

Millington, M. J., Jenkins, B., & Cottone, R. R. (in press). Finding the family in rehabilitation counseling. In M. Millington & I. Marini (Eds.), *The family in rehabilitation counseling: A community-based approach.* New York, NY: Springer.

Mischke, K. B., & Hanson, S. M. H. (n.d.). *Family Systems Stressor-Strength Inventory (FS³I).* Retrieved from http://faculty.mwsu.edu/nursing/marty.gibson/pdf/familysystems-stressors.pdf

Molter, N. C., & Leske, J. S. (1983). *Handbook of family measurement techniques* (Vol. 3). Thousand Oaks, CA: SAGE.

Morriss, E., Wright, S., Smith, S., Roser, J., & Kendall, M. (2013). Parenting challenges and needs for fathers following acquired brain injury (ABI) in Queensland, Australia: A preliminary model. *Australian Journal of Rehabilitation Counselling, 20*(1), 135–141.

(2010a). *Assessment in rehabilitation and health.* Upper Saddle River, NJ: Merrill/Pearson.

Mpofu, E. (2013). Qualities of life design measures with chronic illness or disability. *Disability & Rehabilitation, 35,* 1055–1058.

Mpofu, E., & Oakland, T. (Eds.). (2010b). *Rehabilitation and health assessment: Applying ICF guidelines.* New York, NY: Springer.

Nankervis, K., Rosewarne, A., & Vassos, M. (2011). Why do families relinquish care? An investigation of the factors that lead to relinquishment into out-of-home respite care. *Journal of Intellectual Disability Research, 55*(4), 422–433.

Navaie-Waliser, M., Feldman, P. H., Gould, D. A., Levine, C., Kuerbis, A. N., & Donelan, K. (2002). When the caregiver needs care: The plight of vulnerable caregivers. *American Journal of Public Health, 92,* 409–413.

Neabel, B., Fothergill-Bourbonnais, F., & Dunning, J. (2000). Family assessment tools: A review of the literature from 1978–1997. *Heart & Lung, 29,* 196–209.

Norup, A., Kristensen, K. S., Poulsen, I., Nielsen, C. L., & Mortensen, E. L. (2013). Clinical significant changes in the emotional condition of relatives of patients with severe traumatic brain injury during sub-acute rehabilitation. *Journal of Rehabilitation Medicine, 45*(8), 820–826.

Norup, A., Siert, L., & Mortensen, E. L. (2013). Coping strategies, emotional distress and quality of life in relatives of patients with severe brain injury in Denmark: One year after injury. *Australian Journal of Rehabilitation Counselling, 20*(1), 142–154.

Norup, A., Snipes, D. J., Siert, L., Mortensen, E. K., Perrin, P. B., & Arango-Lasprilla, J. C. (2013). Longitudinal trajectories of health related quality of life in Danish family members of individuals with severe brain injury. *Australian Journal of Rehabilitation Counselling, 20*(1), 71–83.

Ostensjo, S., Eva-Brogren, C., & Vollestad, N. K. (2003). Everyday functioning in young children with cerebral palsy: Functional skills, caregiver assistance, and modifications of the environment. *Developmental Medicine and Child Neurology, 45*(9), 603–612.

Ott, C. H., Sanders, S., & Kelber, S. T. (2007). Grief and personal growth experience of spouses and adult-child caregivers of individuals with Alzheimer's disease and related dementias. *The Gerontologist, 47*(6), 798–809.

Pinquart, M., & Sörensen, S. (2003a). Differences between caregivers and non-caregivers in psychological health and physical health: A meta-analysis. *Psychological Aging, 18*(2), 250–267.

Pinquart, M., & Sörensen, S. (2003b). Associations of stressors and uplifts of caregiving with caregiver burden and depressive mood: A meta-analysis. *Journal of Gerontology, 58*(2), 112–128.

Pinquart, M., & Sörensen, S. (2005). Ethnic differences in stressors, resources, and psychological outcomes of family caregiving: A meta-analysis. *The Gerontologist, 45*, 90–106.

Population Research and Outcome Studies Unit. (2007). *The health and wellbeing of adult family carers in South Australia: An epidemiological analysis 1994–2004.* Adelaide, Australia: Department of Health.

Raffael, M. (2014). Subjective wellbeing in men following neurosurgery for adult onset epileptic seizures. Unpublished doctoral dissertation, University of Sydney.

Ramkumar, N. A., & Elliott, T. R. (2010). Family caregiving of persons following neurotrauma: Issues in research, service and policy. *NeuroRehabiltiation, 27*(1), 105–112.

Redmond, B., & Richardson, V. (2003). Just getting on with it: Exploring the service needs of mothers who care for young children with severe/profound and life-threatening intellectual disability. *Journal of Applied Research in Intellectual Disabilities, 16*(3), 205–218. doi:10.1046/j.1468-3148.2003.00165.x

Rukholm, E., Bailey, P., Coutu-Wakulczyk, G., & Bailey, W. B. (1991). Needs and anxiety levels in relatives of intensive care unit patients. *Journal of Advanced Nursing, 16*(8), 920–928.

Shearn, J., & Todd, S. (2000). Maternal employment and family responsibilities: The perspectives of mothers of children with intellectual disabilities. *Journal of Applied Research in Intellectual Disabilities, 13*(3), 109–131. doi:10.1046/j.1468-3148.2000.00021.x

Shellenberger, S. (2007). Use of the genogram with families for assessment and treatment. In F. Shapiro, F. W. Kaslow, & L. Maxfield (Eds.), *Handbook of EMDR and family therapy processes* (p. 76). Hoboken, NJ: John Wiley & Sons.

Skinner, H. A., Steinhauer, P. D., & Santa-Barbara, J. (1983). The family assessment measure. *Canadian Journal of Community Mental Health (Revue Canadienne De Santé Mentale Communautaire), 2*(2), 91–103.

Skinner, H. A., Steinhauer, P. D., & Santa-Barbara, J. (2009). *Family Assessment Measure-III (FAM-III).* Retrieved from http://www.cebc4cw.org/assessment-tool/family-assessment-measure-iii/

Skinner, H., Steinhauer, P., & Sitarenios, G. (2000). Family assessment measure (FAM) and process model of family functioning. *Journal of Family Therapy, 22*(2), 190–210.

Stainton, T., & Besser, H. (1998). The positive impact of children with an intellectual disability on the family. *Journal of Intellectual & Developmental Disability, 23*(1), 57–70.

Sung, C., Perrin, P. B., Mickens, M., Cabrera, T. V., Jimenez-Maldonado, M., Martinez-Cortes, M. L., & Arango-Lasprilla, J. C. (2013). Influence of TBI impairment and related caregiver stress on family needs in Guadalajara, Mexico. *Australian Journal of Rehabilitation Counselling, 20*(1), 100–118.

Thomlison, B. (2010). *Family assessment handbook: An introductory practice guide to family assessment* (3rd ed.). South Melbourne, Australia: Cengage.

Tucker, M., & Degeneffe, C. E. (2013). Future concerns among families following brain injury in the United States: Views from the Brain Injury Association of America state affiliates. *The Australian Journal of Rehabilitation Counselling, 19*(2), 135–141.

U.S. Department of Health & Human Services. (n.d.). *Comprehensive family assessment*. Retrieved from https://www.childwelfare.gov/systemwide/assessment/family_assess/

Walsh, F. (1996). Family resilience: A concept analysis and its application. *Family Practice, 35*, 261–281.

Walsh, F. (2003). Family resilience: A framework for clinical practice. *Family Process, 42*(1), 1–18.

Walsh, F. (2006) *Strengthening family resilience*. New York, NY: Guilford.

Wehmeyer, M. L., Buntinx, W. H. E., Lachapelle, Y., Luckasson, R. A., Schalock, R. L., Verdugo, M. A., . . . Yeager, M. H. (2008). The intellectual disability construct and its relation to human functioning. *Intellectual and Developmental Disabilities, 46*(4), 311–318.

Wei, Y. S., Chu, H., Chen, C. H., Hsueh, Y. J., Chang, Y. S., Chang, L. I., & Chou, K. R. (2012). Support groups for caregivers of intellectually disabled family members: Effects on physical-psychological health and social support. *Journal of Clinical Nursing, 21*(11–12), 1666–1677.

World Health Organization. (2001). *International classification of functioing, disability and health*. Geneva, Switzerland: Author.

Zubrick, S., Williams, A., Silburn, S. R., & Vimpani, G. (2000). Indicators of social and family functioning. Canberra: Commonwealth of Australia.

CHAPTER 14

Managing the Rehabilitation Environment Around Families

Terri Lewis

A perusal of the case made (see Chapters 1–5) for serving the family in rehabilitation counseling reveals a basic assumption that paradigmatic systems change is possible. Embracing the philosophical mandate and building from ethical first principles to model, theory, and application has great grassroots appeal. But social movement requires management. The value-driven epistemological blind spot that made family service problematic also created the administrative structures and management processes designed to sustain that worldview. Any rational attempt to translate this community-based approach into established practice and a body of evidenced knowledge will require a top-down societal commitment as well. From federal-to-state policy and from executive-to-supervisor leadership, an evolving community-based practice must be supported by community-friendly organizational design.

The vocational rehabilitation (VR) program is the primary federal government program helping individuals with disabilities to prepare for and obtain employment and the primary sponsor of the rehabilitation counseling profession. Initially authorized by Title I of the Rehabilitation Act of 1973, the VR program has historically been administered by the U.S. Department of Education–Rehabilitation Services Administration (USDOE-RSA) in partnership with the states. With the passage of the Workforce Innovation and Opportunity Act or WIOA (H.R. 803, July 22, 2014), the U.S. Department of Education retains authority for administration of the Rehabilitation Services Agency (USDOE-RSA), but transfers some program functions to another agency of the federal government, the U.S. Department of Health and Human Services (HHS). With this reconfiguration comes the accompanying constellation of changes to policy, services, and administrative expectations and relationships. This nascent sea change affords an opportunity for the profession to take a fresh look at the machinery of administration program management. Now is the time to catalog and preserve those characteristics necessary to maintain program functions while navigating the task of incorporating new federal agency stakeholder relationships. This is a fluid moment ripe for intentional organizational change.

Interestingly, the model and the moment for change may coincide. State agencies have had broad latitude to interpret the Rehabilitation Act provisions for VR service delivery resulting in significant variability in agency design, program administration, data management and reporting, performance monitoring, and partnering relationships. These structural differences have obfuscated our understanding of complex interactions of factors that exert influence on outcomes and our interpretation of their impact, including the characteristics of individual consumers served by state agencies and their partners, program characteristics, and community characteristics (GAO-03-672SP; Maag & Wittenburg, 2003; National Council on Disability, 2008; Summit Workgroup, 2010). This inefficient conceptual fragmentation has generated strategic governmental attention and pressure for change. Federal leadership is promoting best use of the synergistic relationship between measures of effective governance, program accountability to communities, mission management, and management of results (USDOE-RSA, 2010; U.S. Government Accountability Office, n.d.)—and they expect progress.

In a season of change, there are important questions to ask: Is the VR mission still adequately reflected in our systems? What are the characteristics of the system in which we operate? How should we view the administrative and management practice of rehabilitation programs on the whole? What is our role as stewards of public system resources? To whom are we accountable? Can we improve on current knowledge translation practices? How shall we measure our impact on communities, families, and individuals? The interests of family practice in VR are subsumed in these larger questions; the programmatic answers to large-scale systemic problems will entail the structures and processes that will make family practice in VR possible.

Thus, professional advocacy directs toward an understanding of the effective mobilization of our resources at the macro level. The answers to these questions become important to the growth of the profession and its emerging family science and practice. To answer these questions, we have to examine the current understandings about program context, configuration, and the variability that exists in the overall design of programs.

DEFINING THE MANAGEMENT CONTEXT

Context establishes expectations for program impact. The Rehabilitation Act of 1973 (revised 1998, 2013) incorporate certain assumptions central to mission design. First, citizens have the right to expect accessible services and supports in order to participate fully in the communities where they live. Periodically planned input from stakeholders (i.e., family, friends, peers, and others) who have specific knowledge about community standards, capacity, and the needs of its citizens reflects this civic right. Second, environment (again with significant input from family and others) figures prominently in planning for successful community integration. Building an active, collaborative network of community resources including employers, medical providers, education services, transportation, assistive technology, housing, and so forth is necessary to ensure long-term program success. Third, support to individuals also means support and training provided to the families, friends, and neighbors or persons of their choosing. Consumers may request formal family inclusion and recognition in plans for service provision, and it is recognized that such inclusion may be crucial for success. Fourth, the role of supporters and advocates chosen by consumers of this public system of service will continue long after the public service system role ends. Plans for long-term, indirect supports by family, friends, peers, or service providers extend the reach of the public program while maximizing opportunities for successful implementation.

Accordingly, our laws have been designed and modified to ensure that systems of community include identification and planning for services in the least restrictive environment, with feedback from providers who can mobilize community resources, and with input from the individual with a disability, family, and others who provide support or advocacy (U.S. Department of Education, 2000). The success of public program impact measures can only be interpreted within a context of community activities, outcomes, and other metrics reflective of active participation from all members of the community rehabilitation team.

Configuration and Design

Federal agencies delegate responsibility for program operations to states through federal state agreements (Government Performance Results Act [GPRA], 1993, 2010). This is referred to as "flow-down" and binds the relationship of subordinate entities to the receipt and pass-through of federal dollars into state and local programs (Financial Stability Board, 2010; USDOE, 2008). When the VR program was initially configured in legislation (1973), each state and territory was afforded wide latitude in the configuration and design of local systems of implementation (National Institute on Disability and Rehabilitation Research [NIDRR], 2010). Individual states and territories designated a single VR agency to administer the VR program—except where state law authorizes a separate agency to administer VR services for blind individuals. In total, there are currently 87 state agencies that deliver VR services through a variety of configurations. Twenty-four states have two separate agencies, one that exclusively serves blind and visually impaired individuals (known as blind agencies) and another that serves individuals who are not blind or visually impaired (known as general agencies). Twenty-six states, the District of Columbia, and five territories have a single combined agency that serves both blind and visually impaired individuals and individuals with other types of impairments (known as combined agencies). Specialized vocational agencies provide services to Native American tribes (Consortia of Administrators for Native American Rehabilitation [CANAR], n.d.; NIDRR, 2010). This aggregate scheme is subject to change as state priorities shift or public monies are periodically reconfigured.

Administrative Practices

State and tribal agencies have significant latitude in the administration of VR programs. Within the framework of legal requirements, public agencies have adopted
different policies and approaches to achieve earnings outcomes for their clients. VR
agencies vary in locations housed within state government and their operations.
Some are housed in state departments of labor or education, whereas others are free-
standing agencies or commissions. The Workforce Innovation and Opportunity Act
(WIOA) of 2013 mandates that all VR agencies are partners in the state workforce
investment system, but agencies vary in the degree to which they coordinate with
other participating programs. Although all state VR agencies are required to have
their VR counselors meet Comprehensive System of Personnel Development (CSPD)
standards, states can adopt the CSPD certification standard on behalf of their VR
counselors. Because policies and practices are dictated by alignment with other state
agencies, multiple pathways are created for unique implementation of VR programs
(NIDRR, 2010; Office of Personnel Management [OPM], n.d.). This also leads to multiple pathways to understanding the conclusions generated by collected data.

Data Reporting

By law, each of the 87 VR agencies submits specific information to the USDOE regarding individuals that apply for, and are eligible to receive, VR services. The required
information includes (a) the types and costs of services the individuals received;
(b) demographic factors, such as impairment type, gender, age, race, and ethnicity; and
(c) income from work at the time of application to the VR program. The USDOE also
collects additional information such as (d) the weekly earnings and hours worked by
employed individuals; (e) public support received; (f) whether individuals sustained
employment for at least 90 days after receiving services; and (g) summary information on agency expenditures in a number of categories from each state VR agency.

Performance Reporting

The measurement targets of federal agencies are bound by federal law, captured
in regulation, and often referred to as *common measures* (U.S. Department of Labor,
n.d.). The use of common measures between programs provides tangible benefits.
They help us to focus on the core purposes of the workforce system; improve communication and break down barriers to integration across programs; resolve questions about data consistency or reliability; and help to reduce confusion about the
meaning of outcomes measures.

Since 2000, the USDOE has used employment and the characteristics of persons served as standards for evaluating performance. The first standard assesses
the agencies' performance in assisting individuals in obtaining, maintaining, or
regaining high-quality employment. The second assesses the agencies' performance

in ensuring that individuals from minority backgrounds have equal access to VR services. Six performance indicators were published for the employment standard, and one was published for the minority service standard. To merit a passing performance, state VR agencies must meet or exceed performance targets in four of the six categories for the first standard and meet or exceed the performance target for the second standard. However, this is a relative benchmark that evaluates current-year performance against prior-year performance. It does not provide for recognition of conditions of state economy, changes in communities, or the characteristics of the workforce or individuals served although attempts are made by federal auditors to account for differences at the time of federal state agency audits.

Partnering

Designated state programs collaborate with a network of vendors, community rehabilitation organizations, and education agencies in order to implement the requirements of the Act. The capability of partner organizations varies widely within regions of the country and is heavily dependent on regional resources and economic differences. In the context of the community setting, the 87 state agencies rely heavily on the social capital of their partner organizations to meet the requirements of their state plans.

Social capital is a relational term that suggests the interactions among persons and groups throughout the system have the strength to enhance and support results. It refers to the specific processes among people and organizations, working collaboratively in an atmosphere of trust, that lead to accomplishing a goal of mutual social benefit. Despite this reliance, there are few measures that reflect whether relationships are actually effective. State organizations have not yet adopted uniform metrics for evaluating the efficacy of these partnerships, even though this is an important feature of performance management systems.

In 2014, RSA made $887,564,893 in 80 grants to states to provide people with disabilities to support a variety of efforts such as job counseling and placement, diagnosis and treatment of impairments, vocational training, and postsecondary education. This funding has systematically trended downward in the environment of federal program sequestration (USDOE-RSA, n.d.-b). The VR program serves about 1.2 million people each year, and over a quarter of those who complete VR are beneficiaries of the Disability Insurance (SSDI) or Supplemental Security Income (SSI) programs administered by the Social Security Administration (SSA). This proportion has increased steadily since 2002.

Understanding Effectiveness

In 2007, the General Accounting Office (GAO) released an analysis of effectiveness for state VR agencies (GAO, 2007). Using data from SSA beneficiaries, the GAO found that state agencies varied widely across different outcome measures for the years under review. From 2001 to 2003, average annual earnings levels among those SSA beneficiaries with earnings during the year after completing VR varied across state agencies from about $1,500 to nearly $17,000. After controlling for a range of factors, the GAO found that organizations vary in the factors that directly affect the management of operations (GAO, 2007; Kreider & Pepper, 2007; NIDRR, 2010). This variance places limits on our understanding of program effectiveness at a number of levels:

- **Community characteristics have a great deal of influence on program outcomes.** Much of the differences in state agency earnings outcomes can be explained by state economic conditions and the characteristics of the agencies' clientele. State unemployment rates and per-capita income levels accounted for roughly one third of the differences between state agencies in the proportion of SSA beneficiaries that had earnings during the year after VR.

- **Organizational characteristics and agency practices exert positive influence on earnings results.** State agencies with a higher proportion of state-certified counselors had more SSA beneficiaries with earnings during the year after completing VR. The productivity of agencies that adopt innovative practices is more sustainable than the productivity of organizations that have not adopted innovative practices.

- **The characteristics of individual consumers served by public organizations and their partners influence interpretation of agency effectiveness.** As our society ages, the number of SSA disability beneficiaries is expected to grow, along with the cost of providing SSA disability benefits, and it will be increasingly important to manage this growth by optimizing the ability of VR programs to help and encourage SSA beneficiaries to participate in the workforce. The demographic profile of SSA clients being served by agencies (e.g., the proportion of women beneficiaries, or persons who have lost their jobs due to plant closures) also accounts for some of the variation in earnings outcomes. Changes that occur over the lifespan of the individual and his or her family have undocumented impact on how we are to understand these numbers from year to year.

Impaired Understandings

Current standards and indicators provide no information for interpreting differences in earnings or job-placement rates for persons across personal characteristics. There is no discernible relationship between the two standards and individual or community impact. This is due in part to the USDOE's data design, which lacks metrics on the important factors that research has linked to work and community outcomes, such as detailed data on the severity of clients' disabilities or characteristics of communities. Although education collects extensive client-level data, some key data are self-reported and are not always verified by state agencies. The current system does not allow for uniform interpretation of data collected between state agencies and their data-collection partners. To address this, it is necessary to reassess the data collected on consumers, evaluate the processes that generate these data, understand the economic factors that influence state agency performance, and identify effective and promising practices. Mastery of the basic factors that allow us to manage for results is paramount. That they remain outside of the profession's control should be a call to action.

The influence of economic and political circumstances has and will continue to exert influence on VR programs and the agenda set by legislation and future revisions to legislation. The public management environment is changing in response to turnover, increased recognition of changing expectations, demand for accountability, and demand for resources. Policy decisions are particularly vulnerable to biases derived from poor or incomplete data processes. Management for results as an approach to systems change refocuses organizational attention on the central issues of (a) changing expectations for the empowered participation of persons with disabilities, (b) client-centered changes to models of service delivery systems, (c) reallocation of customer and partner relationships, and (d) the push to empower stakeholder organizations to contribute to program design.

Management for Results

The singular responsibility of organizations operated by states or community agencies is to link government resources to the service needs of people who live within their geographic service areas. The role of organizational management is to manage the mission, build community coalitions, lead people and processes, drive business activities and account for their results, and provide evidence of effectiveness or impact. Management for results is a strategic approach to orchestrating complex systems that accomplish these desired ends against a backdrop of community and customer needs, political culture, and available resources.

Linking management practices to community results involves linking customer and family needs to community values, culture, and priorities. It also involves understanding the differences between best practices, effective practices, and promising practices.

- *Best management practices* (BMP) are methods, programs, activities, or strategies found to have the highest degree of proven effectiveness supported by objective and comprehensive research and evaluation. Results are superior to those achieved with other means and can be used as a benchmark.
- *Promising management practices* are those programs, activities, or strategies that have worked within one or more organizations, which show promise during their early stages for becoming best practices with long-term sustainable

impact. A promising practice must have some objective basis for claiming effectiveness and must have the potential for replication among other organizations.

▪ *Effective management practice* is the extent to which the objectives of a team or an organization are achieved and stabilized by managerial activities utilizing good governance and stewardship (Fitzpatrick, Sanders, & Worthen, 2004; Flowers, Lewis, Grayson, & Okino, 2010).

Management Functions

Rehabilitation organizations are systems with specific characteristics and management demands common across type and size. There are five major areas of management function common to every rehabilitation organization (Emerson, Wachowicz, & Chun, 2001). Governance and executive management functions focus on advisory and leadership associated with the mission, values, and culture of the organization. The administration function focuses on indirect and direct organizational capacity management functions. The program-management function focuses on knowledge translation, management of direct costs, servicing, and utilizations. The management of financial, social, and community return on investment focuses on the ultimate systems impact of organizational efforts. Each of these system areas are best managed through a comprehensive approach to policy development, a well-defined set of operating procedures, work instructions that ensure consistency of implementation, and change control procedures that provide guidance for daily decisions. Each of these system areas generates specific data unique to its functions, with metrics designed for change control and reporting designed for clarity of interpretation by management.

Leadership for VR Results

Public leadership operates in ensuring public health and safety, delivering essential services, and providing for those in need. In today's environment, government and public organizations are called upon to do more with less, which has the potential to compromise effective leadership in favor of expediency (Carns, Crowell, Flyzik, Poneman, & Wade, 2007, pp. 1–6; GAO 06-15, 2005; Kaplan & Norton, 1992, 1996a, 1996b, 1998). The conflict between what constitutes adequate government and effective government is certain to continue, especially in essential public services. The unresolved battles between constituent political voices will likely linger in our profession for a long time to come. Leaders who understand their ethical responsibility are more likely to find creative solutions and implement innovative strategies that solve the problems that are visited upon them in a changing political environment (Public Leadership Institute, n.d.).

In the field of VR, we talk about the role of VR programs in the placement of persons with disabilities as though VR is entirely responsible for the numbers of persons who find and maintain employment. Realistically, we know that by itself the profession has a limited amount of influence on the numbers of jobs available to persons with disabilities or the characteristics of a community. Major influences are exerted on results on the basis of the characteristics of individuals, their family members, community system resources, and local values and culture. A relationship with a strong social network is associated with improved quality of life for individuals. There is evidence to suggest that social networks positively influence other community outcomes such as participation in groups and utilization of services. When individuals form social ties, their capacity for community social control is increased because they are better able to recognize behavior associated with victimization (Skogan, 1986).

Public rehabilitation leadership is under the aegis of the federal personnel system by the nature of their federal state agreements. The federal personnel system defines the role of executive management as leading people, leading change, and focusing on results with competent business acumen, and a capacity for building coalitions across diverse stakeholders. Customer influence is always core to ethical decision making in leadership, especially in management planning for business risk (Project Management Institute [PMI], 2006, 2008, 2011). Enterprise-wide risk management (ERM) is implemented to help leadership avoid common missteps of less principled organizations such as (a) investing in unnecessary risk; (b) centralized, top-down monitoring of highly complex systems (and the millions of opportunities for things to go wrong); (c) developing unnecessarily complex practices; and (d) conceptualizing measurement as the summative end of a process rather than a continuous and formative practice with the process. Faulty management approaches add unnecessary cost and frustration and ultimately undercut the processes of organization adaptation and change (Niven, 2006, 2008; Preizler, Martin, & Christiansen, 2009; Rohm, 2009). Enterprise risk management is "the discipline by which an organization assesses, controls, exploits, finances, and monitors risks from all sources for the purpose of increasing [its] short- and long-term value to its stakeholders" (Odomirok, McFarlane, Kennedy, Brenden, & Ernst & Young, 2003, p. 8; Kidasa Software, n.d.).

Management has access to a number of essential organizational tools associated with proven best and effective practices. Public leadership training programs are increasingly focused on defining leadership in terms of ethical conduct as an important metric for organizational performance (Public Leadership Institute, n.d.; Code of Federal Regulations, 2011; Slunky & Wheeler, 2007). Where the domains of leadership, ethics, and performance intersect, they provide a framework to guide the development and implementation of public policy. This value-driven leadership paradigm is an appropriate fit for a value-driven profession such as VR as it requires more than budgetary drivers in the pursuit of excellence. The value-driven manager focuses on interpreting policy in terms of doing the "right thing" in selecting courses of action. Moral courage is evinced by proactively anticipating, identifying, and overcoming bureaucratic obstacles to principled action. Leadership demonstrates commitment to values by supporting key change issues from the top level of management while remaining committed to follow-through on the necessary organizational objectives in the present. Leaders accept personal responsibility and expect to be held accountable for all courses of action as a model for all stakeholders in the professional community. By creating an environment of transparency and trust that causes the values of performance ethics to permeate and characterize the activities of the enterprise, the manager establishes the context for a maximally productive work and policy environment.

Best Practice Tools

Tools have evolved that can be employed to ensure that the intersection of ethical performance to organizational behavior is observable, auditable (evidence based), verifiable, and reliable (systematic and repeatable). These tools create the capacity to identify essential metrics, select the appropriate leadership models, design responsive performance management systems, and monitor results. Knowing when and how to employ best practices, effective practices, or promising practices is important for leading people and monitoring results.

Identify the Desired Impact Metrics. What is the organizational mission? Who are the external and internal stakeholders? What are the program requirements? What are stakeholder needs? How will effectiveness be measured? What are the metrics that comprise impact? Do these metrics reflect mission impact and stakeholder impact?

Adopt the Appropriate Leadership Model. Adopt a leadership model that integrates leadership at all levels of the hierarchy and links it back to the executive. What organizational structure is necessary to implement this model? How is this reflected in the organizational chart and the span of control? What responsibilities and authorities shall be deployed to members of the customer servicing team? What is the role of the customer in this set of relationships and what kind of feedback will be incorporated into the overall design?

Establish a Performance Management System. The use of standards establishes a platform on which to manage systemic behavior and risk and provide for continuous improvement practices. Among the most well-known management system standards are the International Organization for Standardization (ISO, n.d.), the Malcolm Baldrige Criteria for Performance Excellence (NIST.org, n.d.), and the Project Management Standards. Of particular interest to governmental entities, the Balanced Scorecard is "a performance management system that can be used in organizations of any size to align vision and mission with customer requirements, while managing the day to day work of controlling the business strategy, monitoring operations, building capacity and communicating progress" (Rohm, 2009, p. 1). Through the adoption of this government-wide strategy, the federal government dismantled its processes associated with centralized risk management and implemented a revised strategy for supplier assumption of and management of all risks associated with the provision of goods and services. From 1993 through 2006, the federal government was rapidly downsized but retained strategic planning and policy making or tactical functions (Kaplan & Norton, 1992, 1996a, 1998). Agreements were struck with states to assume day-to-day management requirements of what were previously federal responsibilities for oversight, monitoring, and measurement.

These criterion-referenced tools provide a model to follow for setting up and operating a management system. Like all standards, this group of tools is the result of international, expert consensus about best management practices. Each of these standards shares the characteristics of clearly stated expectations for focusing results in the management performance areas of processes, customer management, workforce, leadership and governance, finance, and markets. By implementing a management system standard, organizations benefit from both global management experience and consensus about best practices. Each of these standards can be applied to any organization, public or private, regardless of its sector of activity.

Monitor Results. Criteria lend themselves to clarity of measures, auditability and traceability, transparency, and continuous improvement. Policies should be focused on the notion that organizational resilience and adaptability are important functional approaches to assuring stakeholders that the organization is focused on results. Utilizing an effective management system has many benefits for organizational leadership including making efficient use of resources, improved risk management, and increased stakeholder and customer satisfaction as service providers more consistently deliver what they promise. An organization assesses its current situation, fixes objectives, develops policy, implements actions to meet these objectives, and then measures the results. All management system standards are based on the principle of continual improvement. Results are reliable, verifiable, systematic, and repeatable. With this information, the effectiveness of the policy and the actions taken to achieve it can be continually reviewed and improved.

Effective Practices

Increasingly, the public rehabilitation organization conducts its work in partnership with others. This serves to extend the capability of the state agency, increases the availability of services, and provides consumers with broader choices. The effectiveness of emerging systemic management practices have resulted from the implementation of new technologies and interstate collaborations. With the growth of contracting to the not-for-profit social sector, new tools have helped contracting partners to manage business risk and have become an evaluation factor for procurement program participation (OPM, 2006; Renn, 1993; Sheridan, 1971).

Risk-Management Practices. Community rehabilitation organizations now find themselves operating and competing for work within this competitive management environment. The pressure to develop lean operations that can still support the social mission are the cause of significant consternation and provoke competition for making decisions about shrinking economic resources. Agencies are being held to account for providing evidence that risk-control mechanisms are deployed throughout their organizations and that personnel, suppliers, customers, and other key stakeholders are held to a shared standard of risk accountability and quality outcomes (Bazeley, 2006; Niven, 2006, 2008).

Distance Technologies. At every level, distance technologies have been embraced for counseling, human resources training, marketing to consumers, and collaboration in data sharing. The use of these tools requires new understandings of IT security, data design and management, and confidentiality of consumer information. Rapid improvements in deployment of inexpensive technology tools have made a great deal of impact in overcoming aversion to the use of digital technology both from public organizational and consumer perspectives. Technology standards are now in place that address consumer confidentiality, certification of digital platforms, and integration with local community Internet platforms. Digital tools have great impact in reducing disparities and increase access to services (NIDRR, 2010).

Use of Dashboard Tools. Monitoring key performance indicators through the use of dashboard tools allows all members of the organization to have access to the same information and derived meanings. Business intelligence (BI) is a way of organizing and structuring data in a way that they become easily accessible and readily available. These tools help to direct and focus performance over reward and punishment. Dashboards should create dialogue among the users. Transparency is essential; these are shared knowledge resources that facilitate the deployment of information and allow staff to make timely decisions (NIDRR, 2010).

Promising Practices

Can we identify emergent practices that lend themselves for use across rehabilitation organizations? In 2010, NIDRR surveyed four state agencies to illuminate and quantify trends and emergent promising practices. Using open-ended survey methodology, a number of trends were identified in the areas of customer service, management of organizational behaviors, service delivery practices, and innovative practices (NIDRR, 2010).

Customer Service Practices. Developing ethical, effective business relationships means providing effective customer services and supports to the employer community as well as consumers and their families. This is translated as providing excellent service, to every customer, every time within a values- and culture-based response framework. Aligning the business goals of state agencies with community can be effectively represented through effective contracting practices that are focused on rapid response, internal service delivery, and innovation. Stakeholder-focused management practices are represented through relationship management focused on delivery of excellent, inclusive customer service. Specialized case managers ensure that the needs of unique populations are managed by persons with unique expertise. Consumers are encouraged to select a range of partners to the process. Input from families, spouses, or friends is valued, supported, and reflected in processes. Impact measures are reflective of sustainable community outcomes that will be visible long after VR exits as the supplier of services.

Management of Organizational Performance. Agencies that are focused on culture management routinely rely on the right data to establish goals and monitor their organizational performance. At all levels of the organization, counselors, managers, and leaders are held accountable for achieving organizational objectives and are supported by the development of specialized units to foster, incubate, and measure effectiveness of practices. Furthermore, an investment in the clinical and organization skills of employees are perceived as an important organizational asset.

Change management and adaptability are essential skill sets for the public organization. Leading change and innovation is bound within the cultural boundaries of the operating system. The ability to utilize innovative decision practices is reflected in leadership that embraces the mission-driven organizational model, which emphasizes culture, values, and effectiveness. Effecting adaptation is the key to ensuring service quality and customer outcomes. It relies on and values critical thinking; transformative, continuous improvement agendas; and employee engagement. Here the focus is always on the mission, the message, and the goals. Monitoring is based on the recognition of practices that require efficiency and effectiveness while creating opportunities for regular stakeholder input at all levels.

Service Delivery Practices. Outsourcing some functions to external experts may in fact allow organizations to improve administrative functions and reduce loss, waste, and errors. Asking partners to certify to quality standards improves reliability, validity, and interpretability of results. Improved use of digital technologies and communication tools opens the door to improved communication and reduces variability in processes. Continuous and embedded employee "training in place" practices improve efforts to manage business practices and customer servicing operations using just-in-time transfer of training technologies. Intragovernmental partnerships improve multiple state agency functions and invest other divisions of government in the outcomes of the state vocational organization. Offering training to families and supporting their needs throughout periods of transition extends the capability of the VR program and transfers control back to individuals and families through a planned series of exchanges that reflect the wishes and desires of the family unit.

Unique constituent groups have important information for state agency leadership. Typically, they are closely aligned with the stated needs of families and communities. These groups know what the community needs are and what works, and they are directly influenced by both gaps in services and potential solutions. Beyond advising, community groups should have input into design of impact measures because they are the most immediately affected by results or the lack of results. Furthermore, community groups have an accumulated wisdom that complement the work of public organizations.

IMPLICATIONS FOR ADMINISTRATORS

The management and administration of public rehabilitation programs has not been well enough defined by practitioners. Within public service organizations, there is a tendency to give little thought to grooming leadership for the specific tasks and responsibilities of thought leadership around the management of context, program configuration and design, effective practices, and community impact. Within public rehabilitation programs, specific program-management responsibilities have included oversight of public policy and legislative implementation, oversight of the state rehabilitation and independent living councils and implementation of the state plans for supported employment and independent living, monitoring for program results, fiscal management, and deployment of technical assistance (USDOE-RSA, n.d.-a). Importantly, accountability to the community system in which consumers live and receive services is the primary mission of the VR system, with impact measures that reflect effective individual participation, well-operating consumer-selected systems of supports (including family), and the circulation of community resources through a reciprocal partnership.

Organizations must groom specific skills in the areas of ethical conduct, community engagement, strengthening of social capital, leading of coalitions and people, and leading results through program monitoring and fiscal management. Community engagement means having accurate data about community characteristics, individual consumer and family needs, available resources, and priorities for the deployment of transformative practices that improve the overall well-being of the community and the families served. Empowerment is an important by-product of the rehabilitation process, as we have the unique opportunity not only to affect individual change but also to position future community leaders through the use of transformative practices. Community impact measures provide us with indirect metrics to assess how well our skills are being utilized, the adequacy of our data and management decisions, and information that helps us to conclude whether our processes are truly transformative.

Leading results requires clarity of organizational mission, programmatic vision, and community impact measures. Adoption of effective leadership models, while establishing a performance management system with decision indicators and change management strategies is an essential part of practice management. It requires that we have a plan to groom the skills of employees and customers, develop the capacity of organizations and families, and manage knowledge assets while deploying and translating knowledge throughout the system. Finally, we have an ethical obligation to translate what we learn from these processes through the essential research and scholarship practices that inform meaningful public policy.

One of the important insights into family empowerment in a community-based rehabilitation approach to rehabilitation counseling is the role of empowerment in shaping service. Empowerment requires a resilient, fortified, networked, and informed family to self-advocate, but empowerment is also dependent on a responsive environment. This is generally directed at the world beyond the counselor's working alliance with the client and family as the team continuously seeks solutions to life issues within established systems of care. Here, we see that part of the empowerment dynamic involves the relationship between the working alliance and the system of care itself. We are, after all, obliged by the fundamental mission of full community inclusion to make the most effective use of limited resources and model community inclusion in the process. The space for family service continues to evolve in the grassroots work of community advocacy, the discourse of emerging service models, and the systems challenge of change management.

REFERENCES

Bazeley, P. (2006). The contribution of computer software to integrating qualitative and quantitative data and analyses. *Research in the Schools, 13*(1), 64–74.

Carns, P. C., Crowell, W. P., Flyzik, J. J., Poneman, L. A., & Wade, A. (2007). *A CEO's guide: 10 steps for managing enterprise risk* (White paper). Unisys, Security Leadership Institute.

Code of Federal Regulations. (2011). *5 CFR Part 2635—Standards of ethical conduct for employees of the executive branch, Title 5—Administrative Personnel. Chapter XVI—Office of government ethics, Subchapter B—Government ethics.* Retrieved from http://www.gpo.gov/fdsys/pkg/CFR-2011-title5-vol3/xml/CFR-2011-title5-vol3-part2635.xml

Consortia of Administrators for Native American Rehabilitation. (n.d.). Retrieved from http://www.canar.org/

Emerson, J., Wachowicz, J., & Chun, S. (2001). *Social return on investment (SROI): Exploring aspects of value creation* (Harvard Business School Working Knowledge for Business Leaders). Retrieved from http://hbswk.hbs.edu/archive/1957.html

Financial Stability Board. (2010). *What are standards?* (Federal Acquisition Regulations, Parts 1, 15). Basel, Switzerland: International Monetary Fund. Retrieved from http://www.financialstabilityboard.org/about/overview.htm

Fitzpatrick, J. L., Sanders, J. R., & Worthen, B. R. (2004). *Program evaluation: Alternative approaches and practical guidelines* (3rd ed.). Boston, MA: Pearson.

Flowers, C., Lewis, T., Grayson, L., & Okino, T. (2010, October 15). *Essential functions of rehabilitation leadership.* Paper presented at the Professional Conference of the National Rehabilitation Association, New Orleans, LA.

General Accounting Office. (2003). *Forum on key national indicators: Assessing the nation's position and progress* (GAO-03-672SP). Washington, DC: Government Printing Office.

General Accounting Office. (2005, October). *Results-oriented government: Practices that can help enhance and sustain collaboration among federal agencies* (GAO-06-15). Washington, DC: Government Printing Office.

General Accounting Office. (2007). *A call for stewardship: Enhancing the federal government's ability to address key fiscal and other 21st-century challenges* (GAO-08-93SP). Washington, DC: Government Printing Office.

General Accounting Office. (2009, January). VA vocational rehabilitation and employment: Better incentives, workforce planning, and performance reporting could improve program (GAO-09-34). Washington, DC: Government Printing Office.

General Accounting Office, U.S. Government Accountability Office. (n.d.). *Improving and modernizing federal disability programs.* Retrieved from http://www.gao.gov/highrisk/risks/insurance/federal_disability.php#needs

Government Performance and Results Act, U. S. Code, §20 (1993, 2010). Retrieved from http://www.whitehouse.gov/OMB/rewrite/mgmt-gpra/gplaw2m.html#h1

H.R. 803–113th Congress: Workforce Innovation and Opportunity Act. (2013). Retrieved from http://www.GovTrack.us

International Organization for Standardization. (n.d.). *Management system standards.* Retrieved from http://www.iso.org/iso/home/standards/management-standards/iso_9000.htm

Kaplan, R. S., & Norton, D. P. (1992, January–February). The balanced scorecard: Measures that drive performance. *Harvard Business Review*, 71–79.

Kaplan, R. S., & Norton, D. P. (1996a, January–February). Using the balanced scorecard as a strategic management system. *Harvard Business Review*, 75–85.

Kaplan, R. S., & Norton, D. P. (1996b). *The balanced scorecard: Translating strategy into action.* Boston, MA: Harvard Business School Press.

Kaplan, R. S., & Norton, D. P. (1998). *Balanced scorecard.* Whittier, CA: Global Institute for Management.

Kidasa Software. (n.d.). *Earned value management: What did we get for the money we spent?* Retrieved from http://www.earnedvaluemanagement.com/

Kreider, B., & Pepper, J. V. (2007). Disability and employment. *Journal of the American Statistical Association, 102,* 432–441. doi:10.1198/016214506000000997

Maag, E., & Wittenburg, D. C. (2003). *Real trends or measurement problems? Disability and employment trends from the survey of income and program participation* (Grant No. H133B980038). Washington, DC: Rehabilitation Research & Training Center Cornell University, in collaboration with The Urban Institute, U.S. Department of Education, National Institute on Disability and Rehabilitation Research. Retrieved from http://www.disabilitystatistics.org

National Council on Disability. (2008). *Keeping track: National disability status and program performance indicators.* Washington, DC: National Council on Disability. Retrieved from http://www.ncd.gov/publications/2008/April212008

National Institute on Disability and Rehabilitation Research. (2010). *Multiple case studies on effective vocational rehabilitation service delivery practices: Executive summary.* Washington, DC: Government Printing Office.

NIST.org. (n.d.). *Malcolm Baldrige criteria for performance excellence.* Retrieved from http://www.nist.gov/baldrige/enter/nonprofit.cfm

Niven, P. R. (2006). *Balanced scorecard step-by-step: Maximizing performance and maintaining results.* Hoboken, NJ: John Wiley.

Niven, P. R. (2008). *Balanced scorecard step-by-step for government and nonprofit agencies.* Hoboken, NJ: John Wiley.

Odomirok, K. C., McFarlane, L. M., Kennedy, G., Brenden, J. J., & Ernst & Young. (2003). *Financial reporting through the lens of a property/casualty actuary.* Arlington, VA: Casualty Actuarial Society. Retrieved from http://www.casact.org/library/studynotes/Odomirok-etal_Financial-Reportingv2.pdf

Office of Personnel Management. (2006, October). *Guide to senior executive service qualifications.* Washington, DC: Government Printing Office.

Office of Personnel Management. (n.d.). *Comprehensive System of Personnel Development (CSPD) standards.* Retrieved from http://www2.ed.gov/students/college/aid/rehab/cspdintro.html

Oriel Statamatrix. (2009). *The team handbook* (3rd ed.). Edison, NJ: Author.

Project Management Institute. (2006). *Work breakdown structures.* Newtown Square, PA: Author.

Project Management Institute. (2008). *A guide to the project management body of knowledge* (*PMBOK Guide*, ANSI/PMI 99-001-2008) (4th ed.). Newtown Square, PA: Author.

Project Management Institute. (2011). *PMI PSF-EVM-2011 earned value management.* Newtown Square, PA: Author.

Public Leadership Institute. (n.d.). Retrieved from http://www.csm-pli.org

Renn, O. (1993). Public participation in decision making: A three-step procedure. *Policy Sciences, 26*(3), 189–214.

Rohm, H. (2009). A balancing act: Developing and using balanced scorecard performance systems. *Performance Measurement in Action*, 1–5.

Sheridan, T. B. (1971, January). Citizen feedback: New technology for social choice. *M.I.T. Technology Review, 73*, 47–51.

Skogan, W. (1986). Fear of crime and neighborhood change. In A. J. Reiss & M. Tonry (Eds.), *Communities and crime* (pp. 203–230). Chicago, IL: University of Chicago Press.

Slunky, L., & Wheeler, M. C. (Eds.). (2007). *Principles for good governance and ethical practice: A guide for charities and foundations* (Ref. ed.). Washington, DC: Panel on the Nonprofit Sector.

Summit Workgroup. (2010). *Total performance management: National task force draft document.* Unpublished manuscript.

U.S. Department of Education. (2000, June 5). Final regulations: Amendments to State vocational Rehabilitation Services Programs (34 CFR Part 361, RIN 1820–AB14). *Federal Register, 65*(108), 367592–367593.

U.S. Department of Education. (2008, December). General Administrative Regulations 34 CFR Parts 74–99. Washington, DC: United States Department of Education.

U.S. Department of Education–Rehabilitation Services Administration. (2010, September 17). *Research & statistics, evaluation of programs, standards and reports.* Retrieved from http://www2.ed.gov/rschstat/eval/rehab/standards.html

U.S. Department of Education–Rehabilitation Services Administration. (n.d.-a). *Orientation & technical assistance guide for state vocational rehabilitation directors.* Retrieved from https://rsa.ed.gov/display.cfm?pageid=404

U.S. Department of Education–Rehabilitation Services Administration. (n.d.-b). *US total awards to RSA grantees.* Retrieved from https://rsa.ed.gov/programs.cfm?pc=basic-vr

U.S. Department of Labor. (n.d.). *Common measures—Attachment A.* Retrieved from http://wdr.doleta.gov/directives/attach/TEGL17-05_AttachA.pdf

U.S. Government Accountability Office. (n.d.). *Management challenges across the government.* Retrieved from http://www.gao.gov/highrisk/challenges/

Workforce Investment Act of 1998 (WIA, Pub.L. 105–220, 112 Stat. 936, 29 U.S.C. § 2801, et seq.)

CHAPTER 15

Reflection on the Field

Irmo Marini and Michael J. Millington

REFLECTIONS ON FAMILIES IN COMMUNITY-BASED REHABILITATION COUNSELING

"Families in community-based rehabilitation counseling" is a work in progress. The rationale is strong for its development. It has resonance with the great trends of the social movement. It appears to reflect the aspirations of policy, and intuitively it just feels right to stand with, rather than over, our clients. Yet, the approach outlined in the introductory chapters does not reflect current practice. It is admittedly an armchair social construct that has emerged from a conversation among experts. The rehabilitation counseling practice reflected in family experience does not amount to a unified family theory. All we have accomplished in this inaugural work is to make the shortcomings in the current science and practice of family service painfully clear and the gap between the two a space to ponder. But if our philosophical argument is sound, this accomplishment is enough. Indeed, the community-based approach was never meant to be the resolution of professional family practice, just the remit for the bridge-building work ahead.

It is far too early for concluding pronouncements, and so to bring this book to a softer end, we thought it appropriate to resolve in a conversation between the editors who lead the process. In a very poetic way, this book was akin to a piece of grounded theory research. Millington came to Marini with a contract, an idea, and a problem. He needed someone of Irmo's talent and experience, as an editor in the former, and as both a seasoned professional and a person with a disability in the latter. Irmo was familiar with the gist of the work, as it has roots in our previous project (Marini, Glover-Graf, & Millington, 2012), but he was unsure of the details. The problem was that Millington was bereft of details . . . full of process and direction, but no predetermined outcomes. After reading an early draft of Chapter 1, Marini agreed to the partnership, and for the next 9 months they traded in drafts and ideas and became the primary voices in the community of authors who produced the book.

In this chapter, it is fitting to extend a portion of that discussion into a final reflection on our own personal experience and parting thoughts on the major themes of practice and science. What follows is a staged conversation, not one we had in a temporal sense, but one that bespeaks the tone of the partnership.

FAMILY IMPACT ON REHABILITATION COUNSELING IDENTITY AND PRACTICE

Mike: We start this conversation as we did the book, with a fundamental conundrum, that is, the inability of rehabilitation counseling to make progress on family practice beyond generic aspirations. We talk about the reasons from a philosophical point of view, but there are real, human implications for this problem, yes?

Irmo: Rehabilitation counseling has largely failed to include the family in a holistic approach to assisting a loved one with a disability. There has unquestionably been more attention paid to the inclusion of family in medical decisions, schooling decisions, and counseling decisions over the past decade, but the lived experiences of persons with disabilities day-to-day is more "glass half empty" in any perceived sense of being substantively including in the process or in any sense that they are actually benefiting from the little inclusion they do feel. I think this is also part of the medical model problem we face . . . People may be included, but their inclusion has that taint of the expert actually controlling the "what" and "how" of inclusion.

What is worse is that many rehabilitation counselors are proud to espouse the psychomedical model. They are drawn to it for the power, prestige, and recognition it brings. They want to be the expert who knows best and fix the client, much like the physician and the psychologist. We do not wear lab coats, but I suspect that many of us would welcome the opportunity. You can see this subtle trend in the language our students use in the field. Despite the concert of rehabilitation counselor educators to advance person-first language in the classroom, I have noted many graduates slipping into the professional vernacular. Especially out in medical or psychological work environments, they are quick to revert back to calling persons with disabilities "patients" once again. You can see where the medical model still holds sway, where the individual is subtly discounted, and, conversely, where the social model is more influential. I have seen that rehabilitation counselors working at Centers for Independent Living (CIL) and other advocacy agencies call persons with disabilities clients or consumers. You can bet that families are much more influential in those environments. It seems that progress depends on expanding that CIL view of things in practice.

Mike: The expert role is very appealing. Being powerful and doing good like some beneficent superhero allows one to indulge one's self-centered needs for power under the guise of what amounts to charity with strings.

The trouble is this need is antithetical for success with the family in the community model we have constructed. The biggest challenge to the success of family-based services is the fundamental mismatch of underlying models. The community-based rehabilitation counseling model on offer in the first section of this book moves in the contexts of networks, shared power, collaborative work, and innovation based on local difference. It evolves as organic practice based on principles and process. The expert model evolves out of compliance and algorithms.

Unfortunately, the expert role seems entrenched even in the service culture in the state system. Communities of practice just seem alien to the compliance structures of the Rehabilitation Services Administration. Their agents in the field are not prepared to entertain risk; they have no political cover. So in this case, being the expert with the final say is a survival skill for risk avoidance.

For example, I was asked to consult on employment services with a troubled employment agency. In a tight labor market, the traditional job developers had become unproductive despite a redoubling of effort. They were receiving pressure from the state vocational rehabilitation (VR) partner to improve outcomes. I offered a model that engaged family and their social networks in job seeking. Having trained the employment specialists in the model and allowed clients to choose service model options, we began. The families, being networked through the center, came together and asked for a job-club setting where they could come together. The employment specialist adjusted, and the clients were seen when they attended the group. Despite the flurry of activity and positive family response to an empowering approach to job placement, the state VR office shut down the initiative. The reason given was that VR had no mechanism to bill for group work. No discussion, no negotiation, and no challenge to the specious procedural excuse. Families went home. Service stopped. Then the service provider closed its doors.

Irmo: Although I question whether or not there actually was a policy problem here, I can see the counselor's dilemma. Who has time, what with the burdensome case loads and paperwork, to see if an innovative project such as the one you proposed is possible? And who can afford the risk that it wouldn't succeed. Better the devil you know than the one you don't. . . .

Mike: I blame myself for this particular failure. In retrospect, I should have spent considerable time building community with the VR agent, cultivated her connection with central administration (that was well aware of my designs). I believe that significant progress could have been made had I attended more to the principles of community. I could have included the VR agent as a stakeholder in the intervention. Central administration in this state office was always open to innovation. They could, within the confines of compliance, push the boundaries of service toward the family at strategic points. We could have developed a partnership in participatory action research and started the long process from pilot project to evidence-based practice.

Irmo: Perhaps, but the challenges of medical model thinking go deep. Chapter 2 makes a case for the importance of identity in rehabilitation counseling, and I think it holds as true for the counselor as is does for the client. Family's place in that identity, that worldview is preordained. Although the Council on Rehabilitation Education

(CORE) does recognize family collaboration with advocates in community-based rehabilitation, counselors themselves have to become involved with this process, especially where individuals and their families are being discriminated against by the system.

The CORE also requires knowledge of family systems, ethics, and family support interventions using counseling techniques; however, the standards overall can still be viewed as stemming from a medical–psychological model. Specifically, rehabilitation counselors are trained to help individuals adjust to an able-bodied world. The social aspect of our psychosocial model is minimized and the family is marginalized in this worldview. We do not delve into the social source of the problem and try to enact change there. We do not enlist the family to resolve these social issues, nor do we prepare families to adequately advocate for themselves.

We know these things, but find it difficult to change. It's a problem of our professional identity and the processes we use to define it. The role and function studies conducted by the CORE provide the sanction definition of rehabilitation counseling and direct how that identity will be taught (or reinforced). It's an important process with a big flaw. Role and function studies assume that what rehabilitation counselors *do* is what rehabilitation counselors *are*. It's an empirical approach that will standardize whatever it measures, regardless of the quality. We become trapped in a self-reinforcing cycle where rehabilitation counselors do not include families in service because they do not know how to include families, because they were not trained to do so, because research has shown they do not provide services to families, ad infinitum.

Indeed, in reviewing the 136 curriculum standards of CORE, only 7 address any form of family involvement. For example, family is not included in standards involving consumer choice and empowerment, public policies, attitudes and accessibility, and advocacy. In reality, families are often at the forefront of these roles; however, they may go into these roles with little or no training or background because they have not been included in the rehabilitation counseling process. In addition, one would think that families should be included in additional standards addressing: human growth across the lifespan, types of disability benefits, supporting career development (as the families of students with disabilities are included in high school transition), crisis management (the standard recognizes how to assess it among individuals and families; however, it does not address prevention strategies), wellness, group dynamics, and community resources. Families should arguably be included and educated in all these standards because again the daily lived experience of these individuals and their families involve many of these types of issues (Graf, Marini, & Blankenship, 2009; Li & Moore, 1998; Marini, Bhakta, & Graf, 2009). But they are not . . . and why not? Because the medical model still lingers in our system, covertly directing what we believe, how we think and behave, and what we own as professionals. It's in our individual, social, and collective identity.

Mike: Interesting. As we were writing the empowerment chapter, I was reflecting on a long-held thought. I've always seen rehabilitation counseling education as a slightly neurotic profession. Always it seemed the odd duck in an Allied Health setting as we did not have a body system to claim, or the ancillary specialization in a counseling psychology program. Fact is, it is not us, but the artificial boundaries created by the medical model that underpin these professions. Well, I think the pressure of trying to compete in a world that does not recognize our core values makes us a little neurotic. Rehabilitation counseling is systems counseling, not psychotherapy. When we stand among our medicalized peers and claim family counseling, they do not understand what we mean or accept us as equals. And so we chase affirmation in the wrong space and never find it. The empowerment chapter reveals the social justice side of our identity as rehabilitation counselors that is quite liberating.

Irmo: Rehabilitation counselors rarely become involved in issues of social justice and oppression promulgated by societal attitudes and bureaucratic policies designed to marginalize. Our research in these areas remains sparse at best. To date, the professional take on advocacy and self-advocacy has been "not my job." But how long can we ignore the stats (mortality rate, life expectancies, quality of medical care, poverty, unemployment rate, etc.) that consistently profile the effects of systemic oppression of persons with disabilities?

It is our desire that this book advance the conversation of family inclusion and greater advocacy. I think the most productive conversation lies in the systems change needed to translate current practice into to the community-based rehabilitation (CBR) counseling approach we have outlined. This model expands the role and function of the rehabilitation counselor beyond the counselor × client relationship. The CBR approach suggests a new approach to traditional practice, new services foreign to traditional practice, and contexts for all practice that expand to counselor × family, counselor × community, and counselor × agency. If we really want to empower persons with disabilities and their families, we must educate, counsel, and advocate within this entire network. For too long, rehabilitation counselors have hidden behind the misconception that they may lose their job if they advocate against their agency or the government; however, when done appropriately and when relevant, such complaints are non sequitur. With our standard of practice at least addressing such activities, rehabilitation counselors have support for their actions.

Mike: There was a great deal of background research on the CBR model that inspired the approach that we developed and deserves highlighting here. My coauthor on the identity chapter, Ros Madden, is a recognized expert in community-based rehabilitation and the driving force on a project to develop a program monitoring system for CBR with the Centre for Disability Research and Policy at the University of Sydney. I was engaged as a minor player on one of her projects to facilitate local control over the development of the instrument and its processes. Initially, this work was not directly related to the book. As I participated in a workshop with leaders in community-based rehabilitation projects in Fiji, Papua New Guinea, and Timor Leste, their stories immediately captured my attention. These leaders find the traditional medical model approach of Western rehabilitation ineffective in addressing systemic issues of disability in their communities. The CBR model they employ comes from the World Health Organization and is grounded in the values of the Convention on the Rights of Persons with Disabilities. They orchestrate programs that feature families at the core of all processes, the center of all decisions, and integrate them into all facets of community life. The role of family in rehabilitation was never a question for these professionals.

Their programs had a profound effect on the way I conceptualized "community rehabilitation." By comparison, what we tend to describe is an anemic shadow of empowerment. Families, along with everyone else, own these programs . . . and it shows in the strong negotiating stance they take with formal care providers who fly in and out of their lives. When Ros began integrating the ICF as the framework for the monitoring tool, the potential bridge between this international paradigm and our parochial U.S. models came into focus. This most authentic form of CBR could inform our family practice.

Irmo: I think this is made clear in Chapter 4's exposition of CBR as a community development model. I've never really thought about that assignation for rehabilitation counseling until we worked it through the sense of community filter. I also agree that the roots of our interpretation of CBR bear investigation beyond the scope of this book. It is quite rich. However, we have hit upon a variety of interesting issues in the current work worth discussing.

The nature of family is an important core consideration. The changing family landscape is better navigated within this social approach of community rehabilitation. With only 25% of the traditional household family reported in the Census (mother, father, children), rehabilitation counselors must consider how best to work with the remaining and majority contingent of single parents with children—of which a majority are female and minority (U.S. Census Bureau, 2010); extended families; and nontraditional families of increasingly diverse constellations (e.g., grandparents as head of household; lesbian, gay, bisexual, and transgender [LGBT] parents; multigenerational families; etc.). Single parents are often the most overwhelmed and at risk of living in poverty, particularly if they have no family living nearby.

The CBR counselor will have to be culturally sensitive of this diverse population (Liu, 2011). Relatedly, the mental and physical health implications of internalized oppression of minorities and other marginalized groups have a deleterious effect on these families and their children (David, 2014). Rehabilitation research has paid scant attention to understanding or addressing these issues thus far. Understanding and empathizing with the cognitive schema and worldview of minority families caring for a loved one with a disability are sobering challenges for all professional counselors. Particularly when the family is under extreme stress . . . who is to say what constitutes a healthy response to crisis? When you do not know where your next meal is coming from, or whether your power will be turned off that day, or question whether you can mentally hold it together any longer, your life constricts to survival mode on a daily basis. When this struggling but functional family is contrasted with the dysfunctional ones under similar circumstances, we unfortunately observe substance abuse and dependence, suicide, deteriorating health and obesity, and an essential loss of will to live. The holistic counseling implications for these families and their community can be overwhelming, but can be isolated and dealt with step-by-step with counseling and referral to the appropriate community entities.

The CBR counselor will not only be trained to work with the individual and/ or his or her family, but also be able to work with all the ripples in the water that touch these individuals' lives on a daily basis. As we have observed in this book, the community is a complex network of relationships that the CBR counselor must be knowledgeable about, must monitor and encourage in productive collaborations, and must be ready to advocate against, if necessary, to ensure the rights of their clients and their families. Our changing medical system, aging population, decreases in social program funding, increase in cultural diversity, and statistical reality that traditional families no longer reign behooves us to embrace the CBR model. It indeed "takes a village" to raise everyone in a just world. Our values should be "we are our brothers' and sisters' keepers" both socially and politically, and our interdependence on one another must be recognized and must prevail for the goodness of the many rather than the few.

Mike: These are practical observations. When I review the middle chapters in my mind, I see them played out over and over again. I see them in the family experience of disability as they are served, for better or worse, by formal care systems . . . and rehabilitation counseling finding its way in the mix. I think a minor proof of the community-based approach is the degree to which one can see the reflection of it in these narratives. We have always been grappling as a profession with the fundamental mission of community inclusion, and the work we have done to date is admirable. But we can do more, and finding the family voice leads us to a new conversation on how to proceed.

The approach we have outlined is only a working sketch, a starting point for a public discussion. It is familiar. It acknowledges a space where rehabilitation counseling is, or wants to be. Within that space of grace, the argument challenges our assumptions of what practice must be. I note that it does not change anything fundamentally; it simply aligns our definitions with our values. Or at least that is the attempt. The key is that this is not yet a model or an established practice, but just an invitation for a public conversation.

It is crucial that we engage in the dialog because the paradigm shift is on us. The rehabilitation counseling profession has been swimming in the language of full community inclusion since the beginning of the disability rights movement. If the premise of the community-based rehabilitation counselor stands, it does not stand only for the family. It stands for every expression of rehabilitation counseling. Building a new narrative for the practice and for our professional identity requires that we engage the discussion of community and open our community to the family voice.

RESEARCH ISSUES AND IDEAS

Irmo: A community-based approach to family would require a community-based approach to research and, thankfully, steps toward a more nuanced conceptualization of family models and theory. Unquestionably, if one conducts a literature review using keywords of family caregiving and disability, they will be inundated with the number one topic on the matter: caregiver burden, burnout, and stress. This topic has been the most researched and conceptually dissected family construct by far. Many researchers believe it has been overdone (Marini, 2012; Olkin, 1999; Wright, 1988; Yuker, 1988) and severely tainted by stigmatizing bias and preconceived conclusions. Wright (1988) and Olkin (1999) strongly criticized researchers of bias when studying the topic, and Yuker called for a moratorium on such research almost 25 years ago. Nevertheless, the studies on burden and burnout have continued, with only a handful of researchers studying the benefits of caregiving. Stopping this trend would be, in a very real sense, a CBR researcher's act of advocacy. Further burden research in this vein is beyond useless. It gives undeserved weight to a toxic professional conceit.

The care chapter in this book by Millington and Marini is the most evolved aspect of the CBR approach and offers some exciting new directions to replace traditional burden research. It operationalizes Marini's (2012) balanced analysis of burden and benefit in the care literature. In this multidimensional model, it is possible to identify and quantify care needs by ICF classification, identify carers and their roles individually and in combination, and evaluate the quality of care along three meaningful community dimensions (meaning, power, and capital). This creates the opportunity to explore the complex interactions in the phenomenon of care and opens the door to future evaluation and intervention strategies to improve care strategies.

Mike: The care model is definitely the starting place for research into a CBR counseling approach. The measures of meaning, power, and capital are absent at this incipient stage, suggesting the first research steps. Following this model, the concept of burden is replaced by a focus on system processes, balance, and stability. We can actually consider research questions that approach solutions to system processes rather than articulating misery outcomes from inscrutable systems.

Irmo: Lewin (1936) and his social psychology "field theory" becomes an excellent place to begin discussing individuals, their families, and their surrounding environment. Lewin postulated that our behavior is based on our ongoing interaction with our environment and that the two reciprocally affect one another on the basis of these interactions. Lewin also opined that our worldview is based on this intricate interchange between us and the community or environment. For example, if an individual with a disability and his or her family perceive they are being discriminated in a restaurant, segregated to sit in the back of the theater or similar venues, and ignored in a hospital, their worldview about their community would be one of fear, frustration, and distrust. As Marini and Brown discussed in Chapter 10, when persons with spinal cord injuries and their families experience physically inaccessible or poorly segregated public spaces and are treated poorly or devalued in these environmental exchanges, they typically withdraw socially. In worst-case scenarios, adjustment is more difficult due to diminished self-esteem, and these families report feeling dehumanized, frustrated, and stressed as well as socially isolated from a perceived uncaring community.

There are a number of studies regarding the psychosocial impact of how negative community exchanges affect the individual, but not enough regarding why we still have this problem 24 years after the signing of the Americans with Disabilities Act (ADA, 1990). It is somewhat analogous to those who believe racism was resolved following the 1964 Civil Rights Act. Asking African Americans (insiders) this question versus European Americans (outsiders) often results in diametrically different responses. The same vastly differing sentiments are reported when persons with disabilities are asked about the success of the ADA versus those who do not have a disability. If persons with disabilities are still complaining about the daily frustrations and anger over lack of accessibility and negative attitudes, how far have we really come in 24 years (DiTommasso & Spinner, 1997; Graf et al., 2009; Li & Moore, 1998; Marini et al., 2009)?

One future area of research along these lines needs to focus on family attitudes toward community access or the lack thereof, noting specifically the impact on family thoughts, actions, and emotions. How many give up, socially withdraw, and succumb perceiving they have no control to influence change, versus how many fight for their rights and to what lengths? Is locus of control, quality of life, and life-satisfaction measures significantly different for these two types of families? Do those families who perceive they have little control over implementing change then report any emotional or health-related problems at greater frequency?

A related fruitful area for future research somewhat more difficult to access than persons with disabilities and families regarding community access is to explore the environmental hindrances of full participation and civil rights of persons with disabilities. Why have so many public establishments and employers continued to ignore the ADA, and what is their rationale for doing so? Are they being discriminatory or simply ignorant of the laws, and once being informed, will they then go ahead and make necessary accommodations? Since 1990, there has, and continues to be, more than a thousand ADA complaints filed annually with the Office of Civil Rights. These types of studies begin to tie into the environmental component of Lewin's equation, which remains to be fully explored.

Focusing back on the individual response, there are many studies that explore the emotional component of persons with disabilities. These studies in essence are designed to assess how an individual adapts or responds to a disability while functioning in an able-bodied world. Typical findings include depression, social anxiety, social isolation, reduced desire or ability to access the social environment, and lowered self-esteem. Perhaps what we should be studying is what the impact of contributing environmental factors has on their feelings. So if persons/families with disability had spontaneous transportation, a universally designed (not segregated) environment, the finances to go out and engage in social activities, and the perception of being in control of their environment, would they be any happier or less frustrated? Alternatively, if persons with disabilities lack all of these variables, are they negatively affected by internalized oppression (David, 2014)? And if so, to what extent (e.g., substance abuse, risky behaviors, poor self-care and neglect, suicidal behavior, learned helplessness)? David indicates that the majority culture's relentless messages and microaggressions, as well as very blatant discrimination of all things minority convey a message that we are failures and unworthy or lazy. When turned inward for those who are not White, successful, thin, attractive, and so forth, there are negative mental and emotional repercussions. The study of internalized oppression is a contemporary and fruitful area of research regarding an unfair and unjust playing field socially and politically, both perceived and real. Marini, Fox, and Ysasi (manuscript in review) note an alarmingly high spike in social security applications the last several years with more than 70% of over 500 claimants reporting depression, anxiety, obesity, and chronic pain as their chief complaints. Such statistics support David's hypothesis of internalized oppression.

The final idea, but certainly not last in this new era of CBR-related research, is exploring the differences between those individuals and families that thrive despite having a disability, versus those that struggle to simply get by and are always a day away from a crisis. Researchers studying positive psychology for more than a decade have focused on those factors or traits of individuals who seem to excel and succeed amid great adversity. In most instances, results typically point to a number of internal traits such as subjective well-being, happiness, flow, optimism, resilience, hardiness, hope, faith, self-determination, and life satisfaction and external factors such as family and social support as well as finances. Although largely conducted with individuals, including those with disabilities, future research could focus on family member or primary caregiver traits to see how these results could be applied in practice.

Mike: Your reflections on research topics highlight both the connections to be made to existing literature and the pressing need for an overarching program to prioritize and structure the long-term development of a CBR model. A return to Lewin would indeed be a fortifying strategy. As I kept returning to Lewin to establish the bona fides of the approach, I was reminded of the importance of a periodic return to our seminal roots. Lewin is as vital now as then. His theory may even be more relevant in the new context of social justice. His theories could very well provide the general framework for a unifying research program.

Until, in the fullness of time, our community discourse in CBR evolves into such a program, we are left to point at those aspects of research that interest us. In the interest of brevity, I will consider only one more. The care model is superimposed with the ICF functional definition of disability and its ultimate expression in participation. Participation in the family as with participation in work, school, and social contexts is expressed through social relationships, that is, the same social networks through which care and other family tasks trade. What are the essential characteristics of successful social networks in participation? Starting with care, in the presence of a given level of care needs, what defines the character of a sustainable support network? In the context of work, what defines the character of family networks that effectively facilitate the career mobility of its members? Researching participation in terms of social networks moves the focus of potential intervention squarely onto the relationships between the person and the environment. This I believe to be one of the most unique implications of a CBR model and neo-classic Lewin.

CONSIDERATIONS FOR RESEARCH DESIGN

Irmo: This section does not provide an exhaustive list of research designs and statistics as it is beyond the scope of this book; however, specific to the types of future research ideas described previously, some of the research designs discussed will apply primarily to them. For the most part, a minority of studies in rehabilitation counseling uses true experimental designs with random samples, control group, and one or more experimental or intervention groups. Sometimes we rely on data, mining existing databases such as RSA 911 where all the data variables have previously been collected; however, we are unable to manipulate any of them and must rely on the accuracy of information collected. These chi-squared interaction analysis detector (CHAID) studies can provide valuable information regarding, for example, contributing rehabilitation services for successful closure. The limitation of using generally such large data sets are the confounding variables of not being able to inquire about individual circumstances and accuracy of reporting. Epidemiologists often engage in large data set exploratory studies.

Empirical inquiry that involves quantitative research is one that emphasizes working with numbers, statistics, and statistical analyses. In general, one or more dependent variables are numerical using continuous numbers. Related to the previous discussion, a researcher who is interested in the locus of control (which can also be used as an independent variable), quality of life, and life-satisfaction aspect of family members of those with a disability, there are empirically reliable and valid measures available that will obtain scores on each of these phenomena. In addition to these available measures, researchers will often add a demographic survey querying respondents about their age, race/ethnicity, living circumstances, type of family member disability, socioeconomic status, gender, and so forth. These otherwise nonmanipulative independent variables then are analyzed for their relationships and differences with the dependent measures.

Quantitative study participants then are generally responding to the researcher's preconceived hypotheses regarding what he or she expects to find generally on the basis of previous studies and/or theory. Although this is the most commonly accepted methodology among most social scientists, it is not without its confounding factors. Aside from the usual statistical landmines of avoiding type I and type II errors and so on are the assumptions researchers arrogantly make in believing that it is their preconceived ideas, interests, and hypotheses that are worth exploring (e.g., depression in elder caregivers). It is solely the researcher's idea, and in the end it either confirms or disagrees with previous findings and research hypotheses. Because most researchers attempt to build on previous study ideas, there is often a perceived added piece to the puzzle, but never a complete picture, which ultimately calls for further research. What is largely missing from this model is the ability to separate out individual differences since the studies are comparing group data. In addition, respondents have no avenue to discuss their personal circumstances or, as in the case already presented, even why they are depressed. Research designs allowing for individual circumstances are discussed next under qualitative research design.

Qualitative studies are also often conducted, with the researcher still having some theoretical or preconceived hypotheses about a topic; however, they do not in most cases have closed-item measurements for respondents to answer. Instead, the researcher may conduct interviews, develop surveys, or investigate single case studies. In this type of research, the respondents maintain the ability to convey their particular circumstances and their reasons or rationale for why they think, feel, and behave as they do. As such, qualitative research is excellent for exploratory or descriptive studies regarding a phenomenon that is not well understood. The results of such inquiry sometimes then become quantified for more predictive studies.

Regarding some of the ideas formulated above, qualitative design interviews and surveys could be used to ask family members their perceptions about community access and participation for their loved one with a disability. They could similarly be queried on how access or the lack thereof affects their independence, social mobility, and their overall perception of community support. In addition, how does a perceived friendly community versus an unfriendly one impact on family cognitions, emotions, and behaviors. O'Day and Goldstein (2005) interviewed 16 disability advocacy experts with extensive disability grassroots experience and queried them about the top five issues facing persons with disabilities. The consensus was affordable and accessible health care, long-term care, employment, access to assistive technology, and civil rights enforcement concerning Title II and Title III (public services and public accommodations) of the ADA. If we compare these five issues cited by disability experts almost a decade ago with the amount of research dedicated to these issues thus far today, they have scantly been addressed in the literature.

A more recent study design methodology has been to use both qualitative and quantitative designs in collecting data from respondents. Some researchers will use a combination of standardized instruments (e.g., anxiety scale, depression scale) in addition to surveys or interviews to gain a better understanding as to why participants respond to questions the way they do. As such, researchers are not left with having to draw conclusions solely on the basis of quantitative measures and can instead have a deeper understanding as to the nuanced differences between participant responses. For example, if researchers desire to explore why respondents report feeling discriminated or anxious on a monthly basis on the basis of some quantitative measure, the qualitative written response could be attributed by respondents to feeling devalued by disapproving looks from customers in the grocery store when they attempt to use their food stamp card each month. Mixed-methods research will continue to help take the guesswork out of quantitative results where the researcher must make some assumptions about the obtained findings.

Finally, perhaps the strongest yet least utilized research design methodology involves participatory action research (PAR). In this type of exploratory and descriptive research, the researcher goes into the study with none or few preconceived hypotheses or assumptions about the results he or she will obtain. It involves getting persons with disabilities themselves in on the ground floor of the survey or topic development. This is done using interviews, focus groups, and open-ended surveys to solicit what the important topics of the day, by the population who lives the experience on a daily basis, are. Advocating the merits of PAR, Mmatli (2009) writes, "If disability research were to acknowledge and recognize respondents' lived experiences, viewpoints, and aspirations, then the policies, programs, services, and new approaches resulting from the research would be client informed, and more likely to be meaningful to them" (p. 17). Mmatli opines that PAR and qualitative research provide the researcher with a deeper understanding of the value-laden circumstances of peoples' lives, and the richness of these lived experiences can better point researchers into more applicable directions for their research. Oliver (1992) noted the sense of empowerment for participants with disabilities who perceive their ideas and opinions are heard and utilized. It is the power generated from the perceived sense of control individuals feel in having a voice as discussed earlier. It is also the shared ownership between researcher and participant, who are both of equal status and equally interdependent on one another. This type of research revokes the medical model paradigm.

Overall, much like we have been encouraging the CBR counselor to leave his or her office on a regular basis and become more involved with client community-based rehabilitation networks, so too must rehabilitation research educators and other social scientists. We are often criticized for sitting in our Ivy League towers crunching data and pontificating to anyone who will listen about how the world should ideally work, when we actually obtain greater credibility by going into the world and seeing for ourselves. We admire scientists such as Jane Goodall and Charles Darwin who spent much of their careers out in the field performing detailed naturalistic observations. In our discipline, this involves PAR, it involves face-to-face meetings with families and their loved one with a disability, and it involves letting them guide us into their daily lived experiences that bring them happiness, sadness, anxiety, frustration, and contentment. But true to Lewin's reciprocal impact of the environment, it behooves us to research, advocate, and attempt to correct environmental barriers, social injustice, and the negative impact of oppression.

CONCLUDING OBSERVATIONS

One of the most difficult things we can do is change, and yet we change every day. If there is one fundamental theme that carries over every chapter in this book, it is the constancy of the struggle we have as individuals, families, and collectives to adapt . . . and how community creates the space where that change is possible. And so it is with the profession of rehabilitation counseling. We need to create a safe place to share our stories, and to entertain the idea of change and open up to the possibility.

The conversational tone of this final chapter was adopted to symbolize how we, as the editors of this work, want it to be shared. These are our thoughts, and the thoughts of all who contributed. They are compiled here as a congress of voices looking for reason and a reason to collaborate. You may agree in total or part, or you may have a different point of view. The discussion is just beginning and everyone is welcome to join in.

REFERENCES

David, E. J. R. (2014). *Internalized oppression: The psychology of marginalized groups*. New York, NY: Springer.

DiTommasso, E., & Spinner, B. (1997). Social and emotional loneliness: A re-examination of Weiss' typology of loneliness. *Personality and Individual Differences, 22*, 417–427.

Graf, N. M., Marini, I., & Blankenship, C. (2009). 100 Words about disability. *Journal of Rehabilitation, 75*(2), 25–34.

Lewin, K. (1936). *Principles of topological psychology*. New York, NY: McGraw-Hill.

Li, L., & Moore, D. (1998). Acceptance of disability and its correlates. *Journal of Social Psychology, 138*(1), 13–25.

Liu, W. M. (2011). *Social class and classism in the helping professions: Research, theory, and practice*. Thousand Oaks, CA: SAGE.

Marini, I. (2012). Implications of social support and caregiving for loved ones with the disability. In I. Marini, N. Glover-Graf, & M. J. Millington (Ed.), *Psychosocial aspects of disability: Insider perspectives in counseling strategies* (pp. 287–310). New York, NY: Springer.

Marini, I., Bhakta, M. V., & Graf, N. (2009). A content analysis of common concerns of persons with physical disabilities. *Journal of Applied Rehabilitation Counseling, 40*(1), 44–49.

Marini, I., Fox, D., & Ysasi, N. A. (2014). The contemporary face of Social Security claimants. *The Rehabilitation Professional, 22*(3), 177–188.

Marini, I., Glover-Graf, N. M., & Millington, M. J. (2012). *Psychosocial aspects of disability: Insider perspectives and strategies for counselors*. New York: Springer.

Mmatli, T. O. (2009). Translating disability-related research into evidence-based advocacy: The role of people with disabilities. *Disability and Rehabilitation, 31*(1), 14–22.

O'Day, B., & Goldstein, M. (2005). Advocacy issues and strategies for the 21st century. *Journal of Disability Policy Studies, 15*(4), 240–250.

Oliver, M. (1992). Changing the social relations of research production. *Disability, Handicap & Society, 7*, 101–115.

Olkin, R. (1999). *What psychotherapists should know about disability*. New York, NY: Guilford.

U.S. Census Bureau. (2010). *Census*. Retrieved from http://www.census.gov/2010census/

Wright, B. A. (1988). Attitudes and the fundamental negative bias: Conditions and corrections. In H. E. Yuker (Ed.), *Attitudes toward persons with disabilities* (pp. 3–21). New York, NY: Springer.

Yuker, H. E. (1988). *Attitudes toward persons with disabilities*. New York, NY: Springer.

Index